# THE STATE OF FOOD AND AGRICULTURE 1982

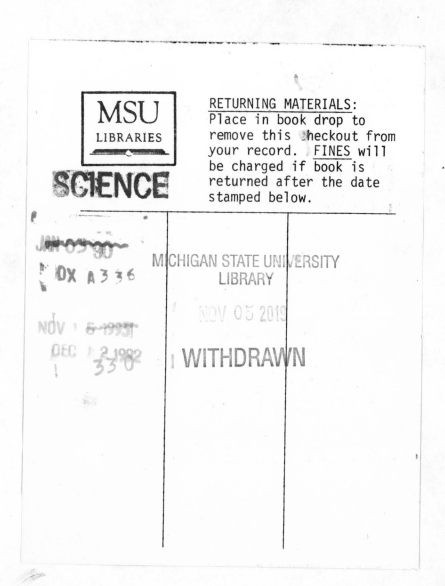

# the state of food and agriculture 1982

WORLD REVIEW
LIVESTOCK PRODUCTION: A WORLD PERSPECTIVE

FOOD AND AGRICULTURE ORGANIZATION OF THE UNITED NATIONS
ROME 1983

*The statistical material in this publication has been prepared from the information available to FAO up to June 1983.*

*The designations employed and the presentation of the material in this publication do not imply the expression of any opinion whatsoever on the part of the Food and Agriculture Organization of the United Nations concerning the legal status of any country, territory, city or area, or of its authorities, or concerning the delimitation of its frontiers or boundaries. In some tables, the designations "developed" and "developing" economies are intended for statistical convenience and do not necessarily express a judgement about the stage reached by a particular country or area in the development process.*

*Chapter 2*, Livestock Production: A World Perspective *was prepared by the Animal Production and Health Division and the Policy Analysis Division of FAO from the work of J. Rendel and B. Nestel, consultants.*

P-00
ISBN 92-5-101341-1

© FAO 1983

*Printed in Italy*

# Foreword

The prolonged economic recession has imposed stress and distress on hundreds of millions of people in agriculture in different parts of the world. It is now over three years that the world economy has been plagued with recession; unemployment; declining demand, investment and income; and rising trade protectionism; accompanied by an alarming rise in the burden of external debt of the developing world, currently estimated at about $700 billion. International assistance programmes, including those of multi-lateral aid agencies, have been curtailed. On the other hand, military expenditures have still steadily grown and are now estimated to be about 4.5% of world GNP.

Although there are now signs of economic recovery, the effects of recession in the poorer nations could hinder their socio-economic progress for some time to come.

The recession has had direct effects on farmers and others who serve agriculture. Declines in industrial country demands have been important factors in the low prices experienced for a long list of export commodities that are mainstays of earnings by developing countries. International monetary and credit problems have made it difficult for many farmers to acquire fertilizer, feed supplements and other inputs needed for increased production. For the first time in 30 years, world fertilizer production and consumption have both declined.

Immediate economic pressures have postponed improvement of farming, marketing and input supply systems. It has been difficult to introduce better natural resource-use practices. Even in the agricultural heartlands of developed nations, income declines and rising debt burdens have put farmers in one of the worst financial squeezes since the Thirties. Many of the people on small farms who have depended on earnings from part-time work have suffered from loss of employment and income.

These economic difficulties have created pressures on governments to protect and subsidize domestic agriculture. The political response has frequently been attuned to the immediate concerns of certain groups within agriculture. Such preoccupations have pre-empted implementation of cohesive, forward-looking policies and development plans related to food, agriculture and rural people. Programmes that help the poor have been among the first to be cut back.

The economic disarray has placed added burdens on many developing countries, particularly those with low incomes, especially in Africa. Since food production increases have often failed to match population growth in these countries, there has been a rising dependence on food imports. Countries facing food shortages and emergencies are disturbingly numerous and their number has increased. Overall agricultural commodity prices have fallen to their lowest real level of the last three decades. It is not, therefore, surprising that many developing countries are facing severe debt servicing and balance of payment problems.

This adverse economic climate has impeded efforts at international levels to strengthen multilateral arrangements related to agricultural trade, food security and development assistance. Nevertheless, FAO has vigorously pursued the objectives of negotiation of international commodity and food security arrangements, as well as food aid flows, to help ensure adequacy of emergency assistance and secure access to food by all people in every country. FAO has energetically sought relaxation of agricultural trade restraints that reduce earnings of poor countries, pleaded strongly for the fulfilment of development assistance targets, and promoted effective programmes for helping the rural poor and the malnourished and for strengthening world agricultural scientific endeavours.

Some progress has been achieved in this past year. And, as borne out in responses to the FAO World Food Day activities, the second of which was on 16 October 1982, many people in the developed nations have demonstrated genuine concern for the plight of the less advantaged. Even so, funds for international development have been among the first victims of budgetary economies in some donor countries.

Until 1981, multilateral aid to agriculture showed considerable resilience. Since then, reductions in donor contributions to important multilateral agencies such as IDA, IFAD and UNDP have caused setbacks in aid and generally in multilateral cooperation, ironically at a time when food-deficit countries are making increased efforts to improve their food production performance.

The World Review Chapter of SOFA 1982 gives considerable attention to the overall economic setting in which agriculture finds itself. Agricultural productivity, access to food and rural wellbeing are closely linked with changes in the economy as a whole. The uncertainties to be faced will include not only the familiar elements of weather, pest outbreaks, prices and political stability, but also new questions about future policies of exporter and importer nations, handling of enormous debts, adequacy of existing monetary systems and attitudes towards investment in and assistance to developing country agriculture.

Along with these broader economic issues, FAO is also concerned about how world economic changes have affected the landless tenant in remote villages or hungry families in urban slums. This concern has been reflected in the reappraisal that I have made of the concept of and approaches to food security. My proposals, which have been welcomed by the Committee on World Food Security and the FAO Council, focus on three pivotal elements - food production, its supply stability and its access by the needy.

The world has emerged from 1982 with a new form of the age-old paradox of hunger persisting in the midst of apparent plenty. Cereal production was abundant and stocks reached new highs - about 21% of apparent consumption - as we entered 1983. But most of these stocks are concentrated in North America and much is in the form of grain normally used for livestock feeding. Despite a fall in dollar prices, the strengthening of the dollar exchange rate meant that many needy nations and people within their borders would not be able to pay for these supplies at times of need.

We did not see in 1982 the continent-wide hunger that attracts world attention. But the FAO Global Information and Early Warning System reported 26 or more countries with abnormal food shortages in early 1983. The haunting reality is that an estimated 450 million people in the world are regularly hungry. There are no indications of a decline in the incidence of hunger.

This would not be so terrible if weather and other elements beyond human control were the only cause of hunger. But, unfortunately, much of it derives also from political disturbance and reluctance to cooperate across national borders.

Moreover, national economic and agricultural policies are sometimes in conflict with the objectives of improved food self-reliance and accessibility. The results of well designed food production undertakings can easily be negated by lack of economic incentives and stability. Hence my decision in November 1982 to initiate a high-priority FAO study of price policies and other incentives conducive to increased food production and improved nutrition in developing countries.

I feel that it is important for people who are concerned about world food and agriculture to view the immediate situation in the longer-run, with a forward-looking perspective. Rapid population changes and urbanization trends in many countries are generating new challenges related to food systems; human services; land, water and forest use; and political balance. The need to find renewable fuel substitutes for petroleum will increasingly be with us. The land clearing and intensive cropping of recent years is already causing new problems of soil erosion, water pollution and eco-logical imbalance that must be addressed. And it seems clear that a 'new generation' of creative and effectively handled scientific research is needed if future food and agriculture needs are to be met.

The food and agricultural development policies for the future must be formulated on the basis of a sound understanding of farming and husbandry systems; the human and ecological setting associated with these systems; and the economic, political and administrative feasibility of the proposed changes.

Policies related to livestock production are one of the areas which, in my view, deserve more cohesive attention. All too often there has been well intended but frag-mented discussion of questions related to the desirability of encouraging livestock production and of using land to grow feed for livestock. This has prompted me to present in this edition of SOFA a special chapter that gives a world perspective to livestock production.

This special chapter brings out that - in many of the world's situations - the production of livestock products does not necessarily have to be at the expense of food crops. Ruminants, especially, can make use of pasture land and by-products that might otherwise not be utilized. The chapter reminds us that livestock are not only a source of protein foods, but also at the very heart of rural family livelihood in many devel-oping country situations as sources of draught power, clothing and materials for cottage industry. It makes the additional point that livestock sectors can be expanded and modernized in a manner that does not make a country heavily dependent on imported feeds, breeding stock and other high-technology inputs.

The renewed concern about the recent outbreaks of rinderpest and other infestations in Africa bears out how important it is for economists, planners and policy makers to have some technical understanding of livestock husbandry and its local settings. Such emergencies demonstrate how critical it is for livestock specialists and programme administrators to employ sound socio-economic judgements when deciding how best to resolve problems and build improved livestock systems in a manner that is in keeping with human needs, capabilities and resource constraints.

The current signs of economic recovery are surrounded by many uncertainties.  But even with these uncertainties, one senses a new mood.  The people who have had to endure unemployment, inflation and low rewards from farming are looking to the future with new hope and this is a challenge to those in positions of leadership to agree on national and international policies that will reach new heights of agricultural development with due regard for the disadvantaged.  To meet this challenge will require, among other things, advances in cooperation in activities related to food, agriculture, and economic development, including trade.  This must surely include reversing the recent decline in multilateralism.  FAO stands ready to play its part in this and to give priority to providing full technical and other support of all initiatives to enable food and agricultural development to play its full part at the centre of economic recovery.


EDOUARD SAOUMA

DIRECTOR-GENERAL

# Contents

## TABLES

TABLES

FIGURES

BOXES

ANNEX TABLES

# Glossary of abbreviations and terms

1. <u>Chapter 1 - World Review</u>

| | | |
|---|---|---|
| ACPE | - | Asian Centrally Planned Economies |
| AT 2000 | - | Agriculture: Toward 2000 (FAO) |
| CCC | - | Commodity Credit Corporation |
| CFA | - | Committee on Food Aid Policies and Programmes |
| CFS | - | Committee on Food Security |
| CILSS | - | Comité Permanent Inter-Etats de Lutte contre la Sécheresse du Sahel |
| ECU | - | European Currency Units |
| EEC | - | European Economic Community |
| EEZ | - | Exclusive Economic Zone |
| FAC | - | Food Aid Convention |
| FFA | - | South Pacific Forum Fisheries Agency |
| FMD | - | Foot-and-Mouth Disease |
| GATT | - | General Agreement on Tariffs and Trade |
| IARC | - | International Agricultural Research Centres |
| IFDC | - | International Fertilizer Development Centre |
| IFS | - | International Fertilizer Supply Scheme (FAO) |
| IMF | - | International Monetary Fund |
| LDCs | - | Least Developed Countries |
| ODA | - | Official Development Assistance |
| OECD | - | Organization for Economic Cooperation and Development |
| OPEC | - | Organization of Petroleum Exporting Countries |
| SADCC | - | South African Development Coordination Conference |
| SELA | - | Sistema Económico Latino Americano |
| SIDP | - | Seed Improvement and Development Programme (FAO) |
| TCP | - | Technical Cooperation Programme (FAO) |
| UNCTAD | - | United Nations Conference on Trade and Development |
| UNFPA | - | United Nations Fund for Population Activities |
| USDA | - | United States Department of Agriculture |
| WFP | - | World Food Programme |
| WHO | - | World Health Organization |

2. <u>Chapter 2 - Livestock Production: A World Perspective</u> (additional to Chapter 1)

| | | |
|---|---|---|
| ACP | - | Africa, Caribbean and Pacific Countries |
| ASF | - | African Swine Fever |
| CBPP | - | Contagious Bovine Pleuropneumonia |
| CLSU | - | Central Luzon State University (Philippines) |
| CRED | - | Centre of Research on Economic Development (University of Michigan) |
| CSF | - | Classical Swine Fever |
| DCS | - | Dairy Cooperative Society |
| ECF | - | East Coast Fever |
| EMASAR | - | Ecological Management of Arid and Semi-Arid Rangelands |

2.  Chapter 2 - Livestock Production: A World Perspective (continued)

    GDP     - Gross Domestic Product
    IAEA    - International Atomic Energy Agency
    IDRC    - International Development Research Centre
    JP 15   - Joint Project 15 (FAO rinderpest project)
    KCC     - Kenya Cooperative Creameries
    KNAIS   - Kenya National Artificial Insemination Service
    ND      - Newcastle Disease
    OIE     - International Office of Epizootics
    SEDES   - Société d'Etudes pour le Développement Economique et Sociale
    UNDP    - United Nations Development Programme
    UNEP    - United Nations Environment Programme
    UNESCO  - United Nations Education, Scientific and Cultural Organization
    USAID   - United States Agency for International Development

3.  Glossary of Terms

    Epidemiology         - Science dealing with the incidence, distribution and con-
                           trol of a disease in a population; the sum of the factors
                           controlling the presence or absence of a disease or pathogen.

    Feed unit            - Equivalent to 1 kg of barley in terms of energy value.

    Herbivore            - A grass or roughage-eating animal

    Polyvalent (vaccine) - Conferring immunity against more than one infectious agent.

    Rumen                - The largest of the four compartments of the stomach of
                           ruminant animals in which food is stored and subsequently
                           returned to the mouth for chewing (rumination).

    Semi-feral           - Domesticated animal reverting to the wild state.

    Transhumance/        - A livestock production system involving the seasonal move-
    transhumant            ment of stock between well-recognized grazing areas, some-
                           times known as semi-nomadism.

    Tsetse challenge     - The degree of risk to infection with trypanosomiasis to
                           which an animal may be liable when exposed to the presence
                           of tsetse.

4.  International Agricultural Research Centres of the Consultative
    Group on International Agricultural Research

    CIAT    - Centro Internacional de Agricultura Tropical
    CIMMYT  - International Maize and Wheat Improvement Centre
    CIP     - International Potato Centre
    IBPGR   - International Board for Plant Genetic Resources
    ICARDA  - International Centre for Agricultural Research in the Dry Areas
    ICRISAT - International Crops Research Institute for the Semi-Arid Tropics
    IFPRI   - International Food Policy Research Institute
    IITA    - International Institute of Tropical Agriculture

4.  <u>International Agricultural Research Centres of the Consultative</u>
    <u>Group on International Agricultural Research</u> (continued)

    ILCA    -  International Livestock Centre for Africa
    ILRAD   -  International Laboratory for Research on Animal Diseases
    IRRI    -  International Rice Research Institute
    ISNAR   -  International Service on National Agricultural Research
    WARDA   -  West Africa Rice Development Association

5.  <u>International Financial Institutions</u>

    | | | |
    |---|---|---|
    | World Bank | - International Bank for Reconstruction and Development | (IBRD) |
    | | International Development Association | (IDA) |
    | Regional Development Banks | - Asian Development Bank | (ASDB) |
    | | African Development Bank | (AFDB) |
    | | African Development Fund | (ADF) |
    | | Inter-American Development Bank | (IDB) |
    | OPEC Multilateral | - Arab Fund for Economic and Social Development | (AFESD) |
    | | Arab Bank for Economic Development in Africa | (ABEDA) |
    | | OPEC Fund for International Development | (OFID) |
    | | Islamic Development Bank | (ISDB) |
    | OPEC Bilateral | - Kuwait Fund for Arab Economic Development | (KFAED) |
    | | Abu Dhabi Fund for Arab Economic Development | (ADFAED) |
    | | Saudi Fund for Development | (SFD) |
    | | Iraqi Fund for Economic Development | (IFED) |
    | Multilateral | - International Fund for Agricultural Development | (IFAD) |
    | Multilateral | - Consultative Group on International Agricultural Research | (CGIAR) |
    | Multilateral | - FAO (Trust Funds/Technical Cooperation Programme) | (FAO(TF/TCP)) |
    | Multilateral | - United Nations Development Programme | (UNDP) |

6.  <u>Organizational Divisions of FAO</u>

    AGL   -  Land and Water Development Division
    AGP   -  Plant Production and Protection Division
    ESC   -  Commodities and Trade Division
    ESP   -  Policy Analysis Division
    ESS   -  Statistics Division

# Explanatory note

The following symbols are used in statistical tables:

- none, or negligible
... not available

"1980/81" signifies a crop, marketing or fiscal year running from one calendar year to the next; "1979-81" signifies the average for three calendar years.

Figures in statistical tables may not add up because of rounding. Annual changes and rates of change and, where applicable, exponential trends have been calculated from un-rounded figures. Unless otherwise indicated, the metric system is used throughout. The dollar sign ($) refers to United States dollars.

PRODUCTION INDEX NUMBERS [1]

In 1978, the FAO index numbers were substantially revised. Since then, with very few exceptions, the production data refer to primary commodities (for example, sugar cane and sugar beet instead of sugar). The base period was updated from 1961-65 to 1969-71 and national average producer prices were used as weights instead of regional wheat-based price relatives (1961-65). The indices for food products exclude tobacco, coffee, tea, inedible oilseeds, animal and vegetable fibres, and rubber. They are based on production data presented on a calendar-year basis.

TRADE INDEX NUMBERS [2]

In 1978, the indices of trade in agricultural products were updated to a new base period (1969-71). They include all the commodities and countries shown in the 1981 issue of the FAO Trade Yearbook. Indices of total food products include those edible products generally classified as "food".

All indices represent the changes in the current values of export (f.o.b.) and imports (c.i.f.), all expressed in US dollars. If some countries report imports valued at f.o.b., these are adjusted to approximate c.i.f. values. This method of estimation shows a discrepancy whenever the trend of insurance and freight diverges from that of the commodity unit values.

Volumes and unit value indices represent the changes in the price-weighted sum of quantities and of the quantity-weighted unit values of products traded between countries. The weights are respectively the price and quantity averages of 1969-71, which is the new base reference period used for all the index number series currently computed by FAO. The Laspeyres formula is used in the construction of the index numbers.

---

[1] For full details, see FAO Production Yearbook 1980, Rome, 1981.
[2] For full details, see FAO Trade Yearbook 1980, Rome, 1981.

REGIONAL COVERAGE

The regional grouping used in this publication follows the "FAO country classification for statistical purposes".  The coverage of the groupings is in most cases self-explanatory. The term "developed countries" is used to cover both the developed market economies and the centrally planned economies of eastern Europe and the USSR, and "developing countries" to cover both the developing market economies and the Asian centrally planned economies. Israel, Japan and South Africa are included in the totals for "developed market economies". Western Europe includes Yugoslavia, and the Near East is defined as extending from Cyprus and Turkey in the northwest to Afghanistan in the east, and including from the African continent Egypt, Libya and the Sudan.  Totals for developed and developing market economies include countries not elsewhere specified by region.

The trade index numbers of a country group are based on the total trade of each country included in the group irrespective of destination, and in consequence generally do not represent the net trade of the group.

# 1. World Review

## INTRODUCTION

The tenacious recession which has plagued the world economy for the past two years provides a sombre background to an assessment of the state of food and agriculture for 1982. It has underlined the inescapable economic interdependence of developed and developing nations and the links between agriculture and the rest of the economy. Fortunately, the prospects for 1983 are for a resumption of economic growth.

The recession - the worst since the Great Depression of the early 1930s - has seriously cut back the pace of development of developing countries. Countries in Latin America, particularly dependent on external trade and exposed to market forces, have been especially set back (regional per caput GNP declined by 2.5% in 1981), as have some middle-income countries in Asia. Africa already had suffered a drop in real per caput growth in 1981: the drop in 1982 is likely to have been still worse. Even the Near East has not been immune to these problems and growth has slowed.

Following a growth of less than 1% in 1981, it is estimated that there will be absolute declines in economic activity in 1982 in member countries of the OECD. Unemployment is also at very high levels in these countries, around 9% of their labour force in 1982. It is undoubtedly worse in many developing countries where employment data are sketchy.

Inflation had reached high levels in the early periods of the recession. It is now coming down in industrialized countries under the impact of tight monetary policies and declining commodity prices. It has left its legacy in the form of high real rates of interest which hamper investment and jeopardize the financial health of the typically capital-intensive agriculture in industrialized countries.

The high rates of interest have created serious difficulties also for several developing countries, particularly those that have incurred large debts to commercial lending institutions. Debt servicing in 1982 represented about 22% of the export proceeds from goods and services of non-oil exporting developing countries.

This situation has been made yet more unstable by exchange rate fluctuations that have been remarkably large, even by the standards of the 1970s. The US dollar has generally strengthened in relation to other currencies. Between the end of 1981 and 1982, according to IMF, the trade weighted value of the US dollar had appreciated by 12%, and over shorter periods by even more.

The widespread worsening in the balance of payment situation, declining real incomes and high unemployment have led to an inevitable contraction in trade in 1982, the first in about 25 years. In terms of US dollars, the decline was nearly 2% compared to the annual rate of increase approaching 20% from 1970 to 1981.

The contraction in demand and its consequent effect on trade was not uniform across all commodities.   Indeed, agricultural trade was relatively unaffected by the deepening recession in 1980, but the 2% decline in value in 1981 matched that of merchandise trade overall.   Raw materials including forest products and commodities such as the tropical beverages were hit hard.   These products are of crucial importance to the export earnings of many non-oil exporting developing countries.   Basic foods such as cereals were less affected, as the value of their trade continued to increase, although slowly.   Trade in fishery products also expanded.   As a result, the experience of countries, whether developed or developing, in their agricultural exports, varied widely depending on the composition of their agricultural trade.

One of the most pernicious developments in the conduct of world trade in the past few years has been the increased incidence of protectionism.   In contrast with the 1930s when high tariffs were put in place to protect industries and employment, contemporary protectionism relies much more on a wide variety of non-tariff barriers.   Agriculture in the majority of developed countries has been highly protected for many years and the fall in international prices of agricultural commodities rendered the degree of protectionism even more pronounced.   This problem has been compounded by production surpluses partly generated by high levels of protection and disposed of on world markets with the help of contentious export subsidies.

The GATT Ministerial Session failed to produce any substantive solutions to the long-term problems of agricultural trade, which had been made worse by the recession.   However, it did set up a Committee on Trade in Agriculture within GATT to undertake a comprehensive study of measures affecting market access and supply of agricultural products.   On the other hand, the Common Fund for Commodities, the major international effort to stabilize commodity prices, did not enter into force in March 1982 as envisaged.   This deadline had to be extended as insufficient signatories had ratified the agreement.

In these troubled times, the view of the world's agricultural sector depends on the time focus.   The short-term perspective has some positive features in that world food production of the past two years has been fully up to average performance of the past decade, food stocks (particularly cereals) have increased, and lower international prices have afforded importing countries with easier access to food commodities.   Global food availability can be said to have recovered from the setbacks of 1979-80.

However, several disquieting features remain that make it uncertain how enduring and widespread the benefits of the recovery will be:

- Progress in improving dietary energy supplies has been regionally uneven, with Africa and the Least Developed Countries standing out as failing to make much progress even over the past decade or more.

- There is a trend towards greater dependency on food imports, not only in the fast-growing countries in the Near East, but also and more disturbingly in Africa, where economic growth has been erratic and uneven, and in low income countries in other regions.

- Food emergency situations still persist, particularly in Africa.  No tangible progress has been made to place emergency food aid on a reliable, adequate, multilateral basis, or to enable it to respond rapidly and effectively to emergency needs without discrimination.

- Although international prices of many agricultural commodities have declined in terms of the US dollar, demand has not responded because the dollar has strengthened against most currencies.  Many importing countries are facing severe payments problems and per caput incomes have stagnated or fallen in real terms.  It does not appear that the relatively ample global supplies of food are equitably accessible.

- The imbalance in supply and effective demand has had serious repercussions on agricultural trade and hence on those deriving their incomes from it.  Overall agricultural commodity prices have fallen to their lowest level in real terms since the early 1950s.  The effects are spread over a wide range of countries, of types of farmers and producers.  Farm incomes are depressed in many countries.

- Development assistance, hit by budgetary cutbacks in some major donor countries, has failed to maintain the momentum achieved up to the late 1970s.  Until 1981, multilateral aid proved fairly resilient and flows to Africa, particularly, were maintained. But this was before the reductions in donor contributions to some important multilateral agencies such as IDA and IFAD.  The situation in 1982 and 1983 appears less favourable.

- The farm input supply industry also has been severely depressed, particularly in developed countries.  Ex-factory prices of fertilizers have been declining during the past two years.  Yet world fertilizer consumption declined in 1981/82, for only the second time in 30 years.  Production also declined and there are now fears that insufficient production capacity will be in place to prevent sharp rises in prices should demand recover by the mid 1980s.

- Though carry-over stocks of agricultural commodities are relatively ample, particularly for some cereals, they are highly unevenly distributed, being concentrated in North America. As a consequence of the concentration of these stocks and low prices, strong incentives to reduce the acreages of cereals and cotton have been introduced in the United States. It is anticipated that these will cause sharp cutbacks in 1983 United States' production and, in turn, supplies in world markets. If and when these policies are changed, the extent to which world cereal production and stocks would once again expand is one of the major uncertainties facing food deficit countries.

Turning briefly to the two sectors associated with agriculture, fisheries and forestry, neither has escaped the effects of the recession in demand. Fisheries has been less affected because trade in edible fish products was reasonably well maintained, although with some difficulties. The sector has been recently grappling with two major changes. The first, posing challenges and opportunities, is the implementation of the extension of national jurisdiction over the seas. The second is the adjustment needed to the rise in the price of fuel. For some countries, the combination of these has had serious implications for fishing fleets.

Forestry has been more seriously affected, especially in exporting countries. Plans of some developing countries to promote their forest industries suffered a setback because of the declines in international prices of some traded forest products.

The second part of this chapter is devoted to a survey of the patterns and trends in the use of agricultural resources and inputs since the beginning of the 1970s. The section draws at times on the findings of Agriculture: Toward 2000. The opportunity is taken to discuss selected policy issues raised by the changes in resource and input use, past and potential, in particular those relating to the environment.

The discussion is structured around three clusters of resources and inputs or combinations of them: the land-labour, the labour-power (animal and tractor) and the input (improved seed, fertilizer, pesticide and - not to exclude livestock - animal feed) relationships. Agricultural research is the means to develop new technologies to economize on the basic resources of land and labour and also to permit the substitution of inputs depending on their cost and availability. Although much progress has been made, there must be greater emphasis on achieving technological breakthroughs in developing country agriculture, to increase output, raise incomes but husband resources.

# CURRENT SITUATION

RECENT TRENDS IN FOOD AVAILABILITY

Dietary Energy Supplies During the Past Decade

According to FAO World Food Balance Sheets, improvement in the world nutrition situation in terms of dietary energy supplies during the 1970s has been both slow and regionally uneven (Table 1-1). However, despite this overall disappointing picture, there have been some successes. Notable among these is the recovery since 1974-76 of some 5% in per caput supplies in the developing market economies of the Far East and the steady improvement during the decade amounting to 15% in the Asian centrally planned economies (ACPE). The latter reflects progress in China mainly: dietary energy supplies in Kampuchea, another country in this group, fell by nearly 20% on a per caput basis.

TABLE 1-1. DAILY PER CAPUT CALORIE SUPPLY AS PERCENT OF REQUIREMENTS

| | 1969-71 | 1974-76 | 1978-80 | 1977 | 1978 | 1979 | 1980 |
|---|---|---|---|---|---|---|---|
| | ......................... % ......................... | | | | | | |
| Developing market economies | 95.5 | 95.5 | 99.2 | 96.3 | 99.2 | 99.8 | 98.6 |
| Africa | 93.5 | 93.1 | 93.7 | 94.3 | 13.9 | 93.3 | 94.0 |
| Far East | 92.8 | 90.8 | 95.7 | 91.1 | 96.0 | 96.9 | 94.1 |
| Latin America | 105.8 | 106.7 | 108.9 | 107.5 | 108.4 | 108.7 | 109.4 |
| Near East | 97.2 | 106.2 | 111.0 | 108.5 | 109.7 | 111.3 | 112.1 |
| Other dev'ing market economies | 100.0 | 101.5 | 105.7 | 102.8 | 105.7 | 106.3 | 105.3 |
| Asian centrally planned economies | 90.7 | 97.7 | 104.3 | 99.1 | 101.3 | 105.0 | 106.6 |
| Total developing countries | 93.9 | 96.3 | 100.9 | 97.2 | 99.9 | 101.5 | 101.2 |
| Least Developed Countries | 88.3 | 84.1 | 84.1 | 82.9 | 84.3 | 83.1 | 85.0 |
| Total developed countries | 128.4 | 130.8 | 133.1 | 131.2 | 132.2 | 133.7 | 133.4 |
| World | 104.8 | 106.5 | 109.8 | 107.0 | 109.1 | 110.4 | 110.0 |

Source: FAO, ESS.

The situation in Africa remained extremely precarious, particularly among the Least Developed Countries (LDCs), most of which are in this region. Out of 46 countries of the region for which data are available, per caput dietary energy supplies as a percentage of requirements actually fell in 18 of them between 1969-71 and 1978-80.

These developments are influenced not only by per caput domestic food production but also by net trade movements in food products. For example, the 14% improvement in per caput dietary energy supplies in the Near East was achieved not so much by a rise in per caput food production (only 5%) as by a doubling in the volume of per caput food imports. China also depended to some extent on increased food imports to raise dietary energy supplies. However, it is Africa which shows the most alarming trends. Per caput food production declined by fully 10% and an increase in the per caput volume of food imports of over 50% combined with a decline in the volume of food exports sufficed only to maintain the average and inadequate level of per caput dietary energy. The reason why the situation deteriorated by nearly 5% during the 1970s in the LDCs was because they could not afford to increase their food imports sufficiently to offset their declining food production.

## Dietary supplies since 1980

Data since 1980 on daily per caput dietary energy supplies are not yet available. Calculations based on estimates of per caput food production and net imports have to be used, therefore, to assess the likely situation (Table 1-2).

TABLE 1-2. DAILY PER CAPUT ENERGY SUPPLY, FOOD PRODUCTION AND FOOD IMPORTS AND EXPORTS, DEVELOPING COUNTRIES, 1980-81

| | 1980 daily per caput energy supply as % of requirement | Change in per caput | | Volume of food | |
| | | Food production | | imports | exports |
| | | 1980 to 1981 | 1981 to 1982 | 1980 to 1981 | |
| | | % | | | |
| Africa | 94.0 | -1.0 | 0.4 | 5.2 | -6.7 |
| Far East | 94.1 | 4.0 | -2.2 | -2.3 | 3.5 |
| Latin America | 109.4 | 1.7 | 0.7 | -3.3 | 13.8 |
| Near East | 112.1 | -1.7 | 0.2 | 8.5 | 21.2 |
| Asian centrally planned econ. | 106.1 | 1.7 | 2.9 | - | -13.4 |
| Total developing countries | 101.2 | 1.8 | 0.4 | 1.8 | 6.7 |

Source: FAO, ESS.

During the period 1980-82, per caput food production improved significantly in the ACPE and Latin America and more moderately in the developing market economies of the Far East. However, it declined slightly in Africa but perhaps by 1% in the Near East. In all regions, the volume of food imports did not increase as rapidly as during the 1970s and this situation seems to have continued into 1982. The slowing down in food imports was particularly marked in those regions that recorded improved domestic food production. Nevertheless some increase in dietary energy supplies can be expected in Latin America, the ACPE and the Far East in 1980-82. In the Near East, the increase in volume of imported food seems to have improved the dietary energy situation only marginally because per caput food production declined at the same time. The conclusion for Africa is still more pessimistic. Food imports did not expand at previous rates and per caput food production failed to increase in 1980-82. The average dietary situation there, at best, remained stagnant.

Food Prices

Changes in consumer food prices in absolute terms and in relation to prices of other consumer goods are an alternative, if indirect, way of assessing the accessibility of food, particularly to low-income populations who spend a large proportion of their incomes on food. A disturbing feature of the 1970s has been the acceleration in food price inflation in developing countries. In 1971 the average rate of increase in consumer prices of food in developing market economies was 4%. By 1974 it had climbed to 25% and, although the rate slowed subsequently, it had returned to high levels by 1979 (Table 1-3). Looking at this situation in another way, at the beginning of the 1970s, out of the developing countries for which data are available 94% had inflation rates below 10%. By 1981 this proportion had fallen to only one-quarter and one-third encountered rates of more than 20%.

TABLE 1-3.  CHANGES IN RATES OF INFLATION AND CONSUMER PRICES OF FOOD IN DEVELOPING[1] AND ALL DEVELOPED MARKET ECONOMY COUNTRIES, 1979-81

|  | 1979 | 1980 | 1981 |
|---|---|---|---|
| Average rate of inflation in developing market economies, % [2] | 18.9 | 26.4 | 27.9 |
| Average rate of change in consumer prices of food in developing market economies, % [2] | 21.0 | 27.8 | 29.1 |
| No. of developing countries with inflation rates | | | |
| a)  below 10% | 20 | 13 | 15 |
| b)  between 10% and 20% | 30 | 27 | 26 |
| c)  20.1% or more | 12 | 22 | 21 |
| Total | 62 | 62 | 62 |
| Average rate of inflation in developed market economies, % [2] | 10.1 | 13.4 | 10.5 |
| Average rate of change in consumer prices of food in developed market economies, % [2] | 8.9 | 10.2 | 8.6 |

1/  These are the countries consistently included in the quoted sources.

2/  Weights are proportional to GDP or GNP of the preceding year in US$.

Source:  International Labour Organization Bulletin of Labour Statistics and FAO, ESP.

Earlier expectations of a substantial decline in inflation rates in developing countries in 1981 did not materialize, despite the onset of falling prices on world markets for a wide range of commodities. There were wide differences in national rates of inflation. These may have been partly caused by more flexible exchange rates. However, the changes in consumer prices of food in a majority of developing countries appear to be more directly linked to local inflation conditions and short-term changes in domestic supply.

The highest increases in food prices among the regions were again found in Latin America, where three among the largest countries - Argentina, Brazil and Peru - showed hyperinflation rates, while nearly all other countries recorded food prices increases of over 10%. Preliminary estimates for 1982 by the UN Economic Commission for Latin America point to a further deterioration in the regional rate of inflation, which may have reached 80%.

In Africa, about one-third of the countries for which information is available showed moderate rates of below 10% in 1981, although the regional average was slightly higher than in 1980. The Far East as a whole achieved a slight reduction in overall inflation rates, although food prices in India rose by 14.5%, the largest yearly increase since 1974, and those in the Republic of Korea and Pakistan also rose significantly. Most countries in the Near East showed decelerating inflation rates, in particular Egypt and Turkey, although increases in food prices remained high in both countries.

In contrast, the weighted average rate of increase in food prices in developed market economy countries was 8.6% in 1981, the lowest since 1978. Unlike developing countries, where food prices tended to rise faster than other consumer prices during 1977-81, food prices in these countries restrained overall inflation during this period. This trend was expected to continue as a result of large supplies of a number of basic food commodities, sluggish consumer demand and a slowing down in food marketing cost inflation. The rate of inflation in OECD countries was likely to decline further to about 7.5% in 1982 and food prices to still lower rates of increase in several major industrial countries. For instance, the 1982 rise in food prices in the United States - about 3.4% - was the smallest since 1976 and compares to an increase of 4.8% in non-food items.

International food prices have continued to weaken in dollar terms - in some cases quite substantially (Fig. 1-1). However, because of the strengthening of the dollar during 1981-82, unit pieces of food imports in terms of domestic currencies will not have fallen correspondingly. Furthermore, food imports have been constrained in many instances because of foreign exchange problems. Therefore, in many importing and low income developing countries, it is unlikely that consumers will have benefited greatly despite ample supplies of most food products on world markets.

## Food Emergency Situations

In early 1983 the number of countries reported to suffer from abnormal food shortages shows a disturbing increase. According to FAO's Global Information and Early Warning System on Food and Agriculture, 30 countries reported such emergencies in January and February 1983, compared to 19 in the comparable 1982 period. While in 1981 and 1982 there was a temporary improvement, particularly in Africa, reflecting some degree of recovery from the severe shortages of 1980, the situation has worsened again largely due to drought in late 1982 and early 1983 in parts of the Sahel and southern Africa (Fig. 1-2).

A declining proportion of these situations can be attributed to what may be termed man-made disasters, although many of the chronic food supply difficulties have been created by the disturbances arising from past wars or civil strife.

## Conclusion

The overall conclusion from this analysis is that, despite some successes, the improvement in food availability in developing countries during the 1970s has been insufficient and not uniform. Improvements that have occurred in many instances have been accompanied by a greater dependence on food imports with the negative implications this holds for the security of food supplies and their equitable distribution among the population.

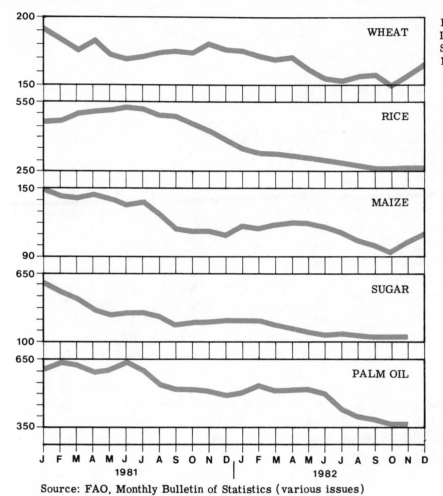

Figure 1-1
INTERNATIONAL PRICES OF
SELECTED COMMODITIES,
1981 AND 1982 BY MONTH

Source: FAO, Monthly Bulletin of Statistics (various issues)

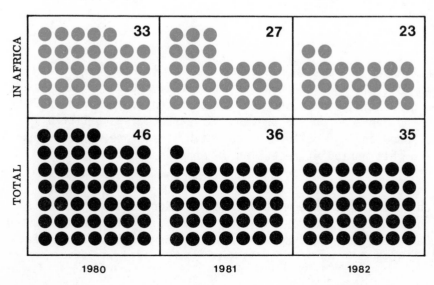

Figure 1-2
NUMBER OF COUNTRIES AFFECTED
BY ABNORMAL FOOD SHORTAGES,
1980, 1981 and 1982

Source: FAO, ESC

Despite record world production of food and declining world market prices, 1982 has not brought widespread tangible improvements from the point of view of food consumers in many developing countries.  Such a conclusion applies particularly to people with low incomes, most notably those living in Africa, although some low-income countries such as China have made significant progress.  To better understand these problems, the location of gains in food production and stocks, as well as the changing patterns of food trade and aid are examined in further detail in the following sections.

## THE IEFR

The International Emergency Food Reserve (IEFR) was established by the Seventh Special Session of the UN General Assembly in 1975 to deal with emergency food situations.  It has a minimum annual replenishment target of 500 thousand tons of cereals.  This level was exceeded in 1981 when contributions amounted to over 608 thousand tons of cereals and more than 23 thousand tons of other foods, but over half was donated specifically to refugees from Kampuchea and Afghanistan.  Contributions to the IEFR for 1982 were 454 thousand tons of cereals and 51 thousand tons of non-cereal foods.

An attempt is being made to put the resources available to the IEFR on a more reliable and predictable basis through advance pledging at a joint WFP/IEFR biennial pledging conference.  As of late March 1983, pledges amounted to 339 thousand tons of cereals and 16 thousand tons of other foods for 1983 and 177 thousand tons of cereals for 1984, quantities well below the target replenishment level.  It remains to be seen whether the next joint pledging conference will produce better results.

During 1982, FAO/WFP approved 68 emergency operations at a cost of $191.5 million compared to 54 such operations costing $178.3 million in 1981.  Nearly half (33) of these operations were to meet the needs of refugees but they accounted for 69% in terms of costs.  The balance of the assistance was to victims of natural disasters.  Twenty-eight of the total emergency operations in 1982 were in Africa.

## FOOD AND AGRICULTURAL PRODUCTION IN 1982

### Global View

World food production is estimated to have increased by 2.2% in 1982 (Table 1-4).  This was a deceleration compared to 1981, when the increase was 2.7%, but that had followed  two years of very low growth in food production.  The growth achieved in 1982 was nearly a third greater than the average for the previous 5 years but was a little lower than the 15 year average.  Food and agricultural production, therefore, by-and-large was a sustaining influence during this period of recession in other sectors.

Agricultural production, including non-food products, followed a broadly similar course although the deceleration in 1982 was more marked than that for food alone.  This was due to sharp declines in the production of some non-food commodities discussed below.  Most of these declines are probably due more to cyclical factors than to the effects of the recession.

TABLE 1-4. FAO INDEX NUMBERS OF WORLD AND REGIONAL FOOD AND
AGRICULTURAL (CROPS AND LIVESTOCK) PRODUCTION

| | 1980 | 1981 | 1982[1/] | Change 1980 to 1981 | Change 1981 to 1982 | Annual rate of change 1967 to 1982 | Annual rate of change 1978 to 1982 |
|---|---|---|---|---|---|---|---|
| | ...1969-71=100... | | | ............ % ............ | | | |
| **FOOD PRODUCTION** | | | | | | | |
| Developing market economies | 133 | 139 | 141 | 4.3 | 1.7 | 3.1 | 2.6 |
| Africa | 119 | 122 | 126 | 2.0 | 3.6 | 1.9 | 2.8 |
| Far East | 134 | 142 | 142 | 6.2 | -0.2 | 3.3 | 2.4 |
| Latin America | 138 | 144 | 149 | 4.2 | 3.2 | 3.4 | 3.0 |
| Near East | 138 | 140 | 144 | 1.1 | 3.1 | 3.1 | 2.2 |
| Asian centrally planned economies | 136 | 141 | 147 | 3.1 | 4.3 | 3.3 | 2.7 |
| Total developing countries | 134 | 139 | 143 | 3.9 | 2.5 | 3.1 | 2.6 |
| Least Developed Countries | 120 | 122 | 125 | 1.8 | 2.5 | 1.7 | 2.4 |
| Developed market economies | 121 | 125 | 126 | 3.3 | 1.4 | 1.9 | 1.7 |
| North America | 123 | 134 | 134 | 8.8 | 0.3 | 2.4 | 2.7 |
| Oceania | 123 | 132 | 120 | 7.1 | -8.9 | 2.6 | -3.6 |
| Western Europe | 123 | 121 | 125 | -1.5 | 3.8 | 1.8 | 1.9 |
| Eastern Europe and the USSR | 115 | 113 | 117 | -1.4 | 3.1 | 1.4 | -1.6 |
| Total developed countries | 119 | 121 | 123 | 1.8 | 2.0 | 1.8 | 0.6 |
| World | 125 | 129 | 131 | 2.7 | 2.2 | 2.4 | 1.5 |
| **AGRICULTURAL PRODUCTION** | | | | | | | |
| Developing market economies | 131 | 136 | 138 | 4.2 | 1.2 | 2.9 | 2.3 |
| Africa | 118 | 120 | 125 | 1.9 | 3.3 | 1.9 | 2.7 |
| Far East | 133 | 140 | 140 | 5.7 | - | 3.2 | 2.2 |
| Latin America | 135 | 142 | 144 | 5.3 | 1.2 | 3.1 | 2.6 |
| Near East | 134 | 134 | 139 | 0.5 | 3.1 | 2.8 | 1.8 |
| Asian centrally planned economies | 136 | 141 | 148 | 3.6 | 4.4 | 3.3 | 3.0 |
| Total developing countries | 133 | 138 | 141 | 4.1 | 2.2 | 3.0 | 2.5 |
| Least Developed Countries | 116 | 118 | 121 | 1.8 | 2.8 | 1.5 | 2.0 |
| Developed market economies | 120 | 124 | 125 | 3.7 | 1.0 | 1.8 | 1.6 |
| North America | 122 | 134 | 133 | 9.8 | -0.7 | 2.3 | 2.6 |
| Oceania | 116 | 123 | 114 | 6.2 | -7.1 | 2.0 | -2.6 |
| Western Europe | 123 | 121 | 125 | -1.4 | 3.8 | 1.8 | 1.9 |
| Eastern Europe and the USSR | 115 | 113 | 117 | -1.3 | 3.1 | 1.4 | -1.5 |
| Total developed countries | 118 | 120 | 122 | 2.1 | 1.7 | 1.7 | 0.6 |
| World | 124 | 128 | 130 | 3.0 | 1.9 | 2.3 | 1.5 |

1/ Preliminary.
Source: FAO, Production Yearbooks.

## Regional Patterns

For the developing countries the expansion in food production in 1982 at 2.5% was much less than that achieved in the previous year. The per caput increase was correspondingly modest at 0.4%, only half of the rate of the late 1970s (Table 1-5). Yet the Asian centrally planned economies, dominated in size by China, increased their per caput food production by nearly 3%, which was above the increase achieved in the previous year. There was some slowing down in the rate of expansion of food production in Latin America. The estimated per caput increases recorded in Africa and the Near East were only slight at 0.4% and 0.2% respectively, but at least this is better than the declines recorded in these two regions in 1981. However, neither region recovered the 1980 level of per caput food production.

The developing market economies of the Far East suffered a setback compared to 1981, particulary India. But 1981 had been generally an excellent year for food production in the region so per caput food production in 1982 was still 1% or 2% greater than in 1980.

TABLE 1-5.   FAO INDEX NUMBERS OF WORLD AND REGIONAL PER CAPUT FOOD (CROPS AND LIVESTOCK) PRODUCTION

| | | | | Change | | Annual rate of change | |
|---|---|---|---|---|---|---|---|
| | | | | 1980 to 1981 | 1980 to 1982 | 1967 to 1982 | 1978 to 1982 |
| | 1980 | 1981 | 1982[1] | | | | |
| | ...1969-71=100... | | | .............. % .......... | | | |
| Developing market economies | 104 | 106 | 105 | 1.8 | -0.7 | 0.6 | 0.2 |
| Africa | 90 | 89 | 89 | -1.0 | 0.4 | -0.9 | -0.2 |
| Far East | 107 | 111 | 109 | 4.0 | -2.2 | 1.0 | 0.2 |
| Latin America | 108 | 110 | 111 | 1.7 | 0.7 | 0.9 | 0.6 |
| Near East | 104 | 103 | 103 | -1.7 | 0.2 | 0.3 | -0.6 |
| Asian centrally planned economies | 115 | 117 | 120 | 1.7 | 2.9 | 1.5 | 1.3 |
| Total developing countries | 108 | 110 | 110 | 1.8 | 0.4 | 0.9 | 0.5 |
| Least Developed Countries | 93 | 92 | 91 | -1.0 | -0.3 | -0.9 | -0.4 |
| Total developed countries | 109 | 110 | 112 | 1.0 | 1.2 | 0.9 | -0.2 |
| World | 104 | 105 | 106 | 1.0 | 0.5 | 0.5 | -0.2 |

[1] Preliminary.

Source:  FAO, Production Yearbooks.

The fragile situation in Africa requires closer examination. Although, as stated above, food production in Africa may have recovered some of the loss incurred in 1981, this improvement was not uniform throughout the region. Indeed, of the 42 countries in Africa for which data are available, per caput food production declined in 23 of them. The sub-region worst affected was southern Africa, particularly Zimbabwe, Swaziland, Botswana and Zambia. Some countries in east-central areas, such as Burundi and Rwanda, were also affected, albeit less drastically.

For most countries of the Sahel also, 1982 was not a good year for food production. Conversely, other West African countries recorded increases. Nigeria, which has about a quarter of of the population of Sub-Saharan Africa, achieved an increase in per caput food production of nearly 2%. This accounts for a significant part of the modest gain achieved in the Africa region in 1982.

Food production growth in 1982 also varied among the developed countries. The overall increase of the previous year, which had been substantial, was not continued. Food production did not expand in North America largely because of problems of over supply carried over from the previous year. In Oceania it suffered severely from drought. On the other hand, production recovered in Western Europe, as well as in Eastern Europe and the USSR. This was the first increase in two years for the latter region.

Production of non-food commodities was most adversely affected in Latin America of the developing country regions and North America of the developed. This was due mainly to declines in production of coffee and cotton in these two regions respectively.

Major Commodities[1]

Behind these growth rates in aggregate food production lies a diverse commodity-by-commodity picture. The latest information is that in developing countries output of cereals, at 688 million tons (including rice in its milled form), increased slightly in 1982. A small increase in wheat was more or less offset by an overall decline in production of coarse grains. Rice production was unchanged. Production of pulses, rootcrops (which had declined in 1981) and edible oil crops expanded moderately, by 3 to 5%, but sugar production increased by nearly 16%. In some cases this increased output has met with weak demand on domestic and export markets and led to an accumulation of stocks and declining prices. Production of livestock products also increased in 1982 but at rather lower rates than in recent years.

Although data on catches of food fish in 1982 are not yet available, in 1981 the food fish catch of 53.5 million tons, out of a total fish catch of nearly 75 million tons, had increased by between 5-6%. Most of this increase had been in developing countries, particularly in Latin America and Asia.

In developed countries, cereal production continued to expand in 1982, although at a rate lower than in 1981. It reached 865 million tons and so exceeded the previous record quantity achieved in 1978. Output of other major food crops also expanded in most cases: root crops by 2%, pulses by over 8% and oil crops by nearly 11%. Sugar was the exception as its output declined a little. Of the livestock food products, meat output declined slightly but milk output increased.

Turning to the main non-food commodities, production of green coffee was significantly lower in 1982, falling by over 15% to a level slightly lower than that achieved in 1979. Coffee production in Latin America, the largest producing region, declined by 25% and was also somewhat reduced in Africa. Production of cotton was reduced by 2-3%, a sizeable

---

[1] The data are presented on a calendar year basis. For a detailed survey of the agricultural commodity production in 1982, see FAO, Commodity Review and Outlook 1982-83, Rome, 1983.

decline in North America being partially offset by increases in producing countries in other regions, except Latin America. Production of tobacco and natural rubber expanded by small amounts: about 0.5% and between 2-3% respectively.

As will be seen in the sections on fishery and forestry, these sectors were also affected by the economic recession in 1981 and 1982. While the catch of food fish had increased in 1981, the non-food component of the catch, roughly 20 million tons, remained unchanged mainly because of the reduced demand for fish meal, in turn due to weak world demand for livestock products. Not much change is expected to have taken place in 1982.

Production and trade in forest products have been hit particularly hard by the recession in the housing sector in some developed countries. Production of all forest products was reduced in 1981 except fuelwood and charcoal.

## INCIDENCE OF PESTS AND DISEASES IN 1982

Pests and diseases continue to pose serious problems for food production and preservation.

The rinderpest situation in Africa and the Near East worsened in 1982. In Africa, the disease broke out in several countries, including Tanzania, Chad and Egypt which had been free from the disease for many years. Outbreaks were also reported in Iran, Lebanon and most countries of the Arabian Peninsula.

Some infestations of Desert Locust and African Migratory Locusts were reported in parts of the Near East and Africa but control measures were taken, in some cases with the assistance of FAO's Technical Cooperation Programme (TCP) and bilateral donors, and major problems were averted. African armyworm also affected some localities in eastern Africa early in 1982 but widespread damage was not reported.

In Europe, several foot-and-mouth disease (FMD) outbreaks occurred during 1982. Those which occurred in Denmark and the German Democratic Republic caused serious economic losses especially in Denmark where international trade in meat products was disrupted. Sporadic outbreaks also occurred in the Federal Republic of Germany and in Spain.

Insect pests and diseases do not affect only food crops and livestock. For example, an extensive area of pine and spruce forests in northern Poland, covering 20% of the country's forest area, is being infested by the nun moth Lymantria monacha. Although control measures in 1981 exceeded all pest control activities in these forests over the past 35 years, mass occurrence of pest has not been controlled and the forests are further threatened by the entry of secondary pests.

### Outlook for Food Supplies in 1983

Overall the outlook appears to be reasonably favourable in the opening months of the year but some compositional, geographical and policy aspects are disquieting. As will be noted below, while world cereal stocks are adequate, they are concentrated in major exporting developed countries and are predominantly coarse grains.

The effects of Government policies (including farmer participation in the United States' acreage reduction programmes), developments in export markets and hence prices, input costs and subsidies as well as weather conditions until harvest in the main growing areas around the world, will have an important influence on the final outcome and size of world food production in 1983. For example, the objective of the Administration of the United States is to reduce the wheat and coarse grain acreages by 10% and rice by 15%, through the acreage reduction programmes introduced for 1982 and the payment-in-kind programme to apply as well in 1983. The total reduction from the 1982 level could be 12 million tons for wheat (76.5 million tons produced in 1982) and 41 million tons of coarse grains (256 million tons in 1982). The timely and adequate development of the monsoon in Asia, as usual, will be an important factor in determining global food supplies.

AGRICULTURAL TRADE

Overview of Trade in a Period of Recession

The current world recession has manifested itself in the area of trade by a slowing down or even decline in the volume and value of traded goods, and deteriorating terms of trade for a majority of developing countries. It has been accompanied by fluctuating exchange rates, increased levels of debt and debt servicing charges and increased protectionism. These factors have combined to render the economic difficulties that the poorer countries already face yet more intractable. The welfare of the large numbers of people who directly or indirectly derive their livelihood from the production of agricultural commodities for export will have deteriorated.

As a result of aggregate world demand, the volume of total merchandise trade in 1981 stagnated at the 1980 level, after having barely increased by 1.5% in the previous year. On a value basis world trade in 1981 actually declined for the first time since 1958, by about 1%. Preliminary estimates for 1982 point to a 2% decline in the volume of exports. Exports by industrial countries, which had declined by 1% in 1981 suffered a further 5% drop the following year. For the group of oil importing developing countries, preliminary estimates indicate a 5% fall in the value of exports in 1982, creating further pressure on their balance of payments. The deficit in their current account balances in 1982 is expected to reach US $99 thousand million, 15% more than in the previous year. The problems associated with indebtedness have become alsmost unmanageable, particularly in Latin American countries, and are threatening the stability of the world financial system as a whole. Debt servicing alone represents now about one-fifth of the total export receipts of non-oil exporting developing countries.

Exports of major commodity groups were adversely affected by the recession, more particularly minerals and fuels, resulting in a substantial reduction in the overall trade surplus of oil-exporting countries. Exports of manufactures rose by barely over 4% in 1981 in volume terms, the lowest year-to-year increase since 1975. As regards agricultural products, the volume of world exports were estimated to have risen by 3 to 5% in 1981. The rates of increase were lower than the average for the previous two decades but in excess of the 2% increase in the volume of agricultural production. On a value basis, however, world exports of agricultural, fishery and forestry products in 1981 were estimated at

US $299 thousand million, over 1% less than the previous year (Table 1-6). It was the first time since 1967 that the value of world agricultural trade failed to expand. The decline contrasted markedly with the average annual increase of more than 12% during 1977-81 and the 17% annual average achieved over the past decade.

TABLE 1-6.   VALUE AT CURRENT PRICES OF WORLD EXPORTS OF AGRICULTURAL (CROPS AND LIVESTOCK), FISHERY AND FOREST PRODUCTS

| | 1979 | 1980 | 1981[1/] | Change 1979 to 1980 | Change 1980 to 1981 | Annual rate of change 1977 to 1981 |
|---|---|---|---|---|---|---|
| | ... 000 million $ ... | | | ......... % ........... | | |
| AGRICULTURAL PRODUCTS | 203.8 | 232.5 | 230.8 | 14.1 | -0.7 | 11.9 |
| Developing market economies | 61.6 | 68.1 | 65.5 | 10.6 | -3.8 | 7.0 |
| Asian centrally planned economies | 3.8 | 4.0 | 3.5 | 5.3 | -12.5 | 7.7 |
| Total developing countries | 65.5 | 72.1 | 69.0 | 10.1 | -4.3 | 7.1 |
| Developed market economies | 128.8 | 150.6 | 152.2 | 16.9 | 1.1 | 15.2 |
| Eastern Europe and USSR | 9.6 | 9.9 | 9.7 | 3.1 | -2.0 | 11.0 |
| Total developed countries | 138.4 | 160.4 | 161.8 | 15.9 | 0.9 | 14.4 |
| FISHERY PRODUCTS | 14.2 | 15.0 | 15.6 | 5.6 | 4.0 | 13.4 |
| Developing market economies | 4.9 | 5.0 | 5.3 | 2.0 | 6.0 | 13.9 |
| Asian centrally planned economies | 0.8 | 0.9 | 0.9 | 12.5 | - | 19.3 |
| Total developing countries | 5.7 | 5.9 | 6.2 | 1.8 | 5.1 | 14.6 |
| Developed market economies | 8.1 | 8.8 | 9.0 | 8.6 | 2.3 | 12.8 |
| Eastern Europe and USSR | 0.4 | 0.4 | 0.4 | - | - | 9.7 |
| Total developed countries | 8.5 | 9.2 | 9.4 | 8.2 | 2.2 | 12.6 |
| FOREST PRODUCTS | 48.9 | 54.8 | 52.4 | 12.1 | -4.4 | 13.2 |
| Developing market economies | 8.0 | 8.2 | 8.1 | 2.5 | -1.2 | 17.1 |
| Asian centrally planned economies | 0.6 | 0.6 | 0.6 | - | - | 10.4 |
| Total developing countries | 8.6 | 8.8 | 8.7 | 2.3 | -1.1 | 16.6 |
| Developed market economies | 36.8 | 42.5 | 40.3 | 15.5 | -5.2 | 13.8 |
| Eastern Europe and USSR | 3.6 | 3.5 | 3.4 | -2.8 | -2.9 | 1.4 |
| Total developed countries | 40.4 | 46.0 | 43.7 | 13.9 | -5.0 | 12.6 |
| TOTAL | 267.0 | 302.3 | 298.8 | 13.2 | -1.2 | 12.2 |
| Developing market economies | 74.5 | 81.3 | 78.9 | 9.1 | -3.0 | 8.3 |
| Asian centrally planned economies | 5.2 | 5.5 | 5.0 | 5.8 | -9.1 | 9.6 |
| Total developing countries | 79.7 | 86.7 | 83.9 | 8.8 | -3.2 | 8.4 |
| Developed market economies | 173.7 | 201.8 | 201.6 | 16.2 | -0.1 | 14.8 |
| Eastern Europe and USSR | 13.6 | 13.7 | 13.4 | 0.7 | -2.2 | 3.5 |
| Total developed countries | 187.3 | 215.6 | 215.0 | 15.1 | -0.3 | 13.9 |
| | ......... % ......... | | | | | |
| Share of developing countries | 30 | 29 | 28 | | | |

1/ Preliminary.

Source:  FAO, Trade Yearbooks.

As the value of total merchandise trade in 1981 showed a year-to-year decline of 1%, the share of agriculture in total merchandise trade declined further to less than 15%. The decline in the value of agricultural exports, expressed in US dollars, resulted from a number of concurrent factors: abundant supplies of most agricultural products, which tended to lower prices; depressed aggregate demand, especially in industrialized countries, that affected non-food products; measures to protect domestic producers in the major trading countries; high interest rates, which led to lower inventories in importing countries; and the appreciation of the US dollar against most other currencies.

While the value of exports by developed countries as a whole in 1981 remained practically at the previous years' levels, developing countries' exports declined by over 3%. The share of developing countries in total world agricultural exports continued therefore to decline to 28% - as recently as 1977 their share had been 36%.

TABLE 1-7.  FAO INDEX NUMBERS OF VOLUME, VALUE AND UNIT VALUE OF WORLD EXPORTS OF CROP AND LIVESTOCK PRODUCTS BY MAJOR COMMODITY GROUPS

| | 1979 | 1980 | 1981[1]/ | Change 1979 to 1980 | Change 1980 to 1981 | Annual rate of change 1977 to 1981 |
|---|---|---|---|---|---|---|
| | ....1969-71=100 .... | | | ............% ............ | | |
| VOLUME | | | | | | |
| Crops and livestock, total | 147 | 156 | 162 | 5.7 | 3.8 | 5.4 |
| Food | 158 | 169 | 177 | 7.3 | 4.6 | 6.1 |
| Cereals | 176 | 198 | 208 | 12.4 | 5.1 | 8.4 |
| Feed | 187 | 207 | 220 | 10.7 | 6.4 | 8.7 |
| Raw materials | 108 | 109 | 108 | 1.5 | -1.6 | 0.8 |
| Beverages 2/ | 139 | 137 | 141 | -1.5 | 3.2 | 5.4 |
| VALUE | | | | | | |
| Crops and livestock, total | 386 | 447 | 443 | 15.7 | -0.8 | 11.7 |
| Food | 405 | 482 | 493 | 19.0 | 2.3 | 14.6 |
| Cereals | 407 | 537 | 581 | 31.9 | 8.3 | 19.8 |
| Feed | 479 | 550 | 615 | 14.8 | 11.8 | 13.0 |
| Raw materials | 277 | 302 | 290 | 9.1 | -3.9 | 7.3 |
| Beverages 2/ | 421 | 438 | 342 | 3.9 | -21.9 | -1.0 |
| UNIT VALUE | | | | | | |
| Crops and livestock, total | 271 | 294 | 274 | 8.6 | -6.8 | 4.8 |
| Food | 265 | 292 | 280 | 10.1 | -4.0 | 7.6 |
| Cereals | 250 | 286 | 289 | 14.2 | 1.2 | 9.6 |
| Feed | 222 | 236 | 235 | 6.3 | -0.7 | 2.4 |
| Raw materials | 260 | 278 | 267 | 6.9 | -3.8 | 5.7 |
| Beverages 2/ | 332 | 345 | 256 | 3.9 | -25.8 | -7.7 |

1/ Preliminary.  2/ Excluding cocoa, which is included under food.

Source:  FAO, Trade Yearbooks.

The main agricultural export commodities of developing countries were particularly hard hit in 1981, notably raw materials, forest products, tropical beverages and sugar. By contrast, the value of exports of food, particularly cereals, exported mainly by developed countries, rose although at lower rates than in the previous five years 2/.

World exports of agricultural products (crops and livestock only) in 1981 were estimated at about US $231 thousand million, 1% less than the previous year. This decline was largely price-based since, with the exception of agricultural raw materials, export volumes of the major groups of crop and livestock commodities continued to expand in 1981 (Table 1-7). Poor export performances were shared by all developing regions, but were particularly unfavourable for Asian centrally planned economies and Africa, where exports were about one-fifth smaller than in 1980 (Table 1-8). While agricultural exports continued to account for a large proportion of the total export earnings of developing countries - in 1981 about 38% in Africa, 22% in the Far East and 45% in Latin America - they contributed to finance a smaller share of their total imports - 13% for developing countries as a whole in 1981, two percentage points less than in 1980. There was a moderate increase, however, in the exports of developed countries.

The situation also differed markedly between developed and developing countries with regard to agricultural imports. Imports of crops and livestock by developed countries as a whole declined by about 4% in 1981, despite a substantial increase in import demand from Eastern European countries and the USSR. Developed countries' imports of food remained at about the previous years' levels with large purchases of cereals offsetting declines in other food products.

In contrast, imports by developing countries continued to expand, although at much lower rates than in previous years. Their imports of crops and livestock products in 1981 reached US $73 thousand million, about 7% more than in 1980. While the share of cereals, which account for about one-third of the value of total imports, remained fairly stable over the past ten years, sugar accounted for 9% of the total in 1981 compared to 5.5% in 1969-71. The share of meat products had risen from 2.8% to 5.2% of the total during the same period, and that of oilseeds and oils from 7.5% to 8.5%. On the other hand, the share of dairy products and fibres declined.

The combined effect of declining agricultural exports and rising imports resulted in an important shift in the trade balance of developing countries in 1981 when for the first time as a group they became net importers of crop and livestock products. Their overall trade deficit in these products was about US $4.2 thousand million compared to a surplus of similar magnitude in the preceding year. This shift worsened the pronounced deterioration in their overall surplus on merchandise trade which (excluding crops and livestock products) declined from $97.7 thousand million to $16.7 thousand million. The main cause of this deterioration was the decline in petroleum export earnings. However, an important factor in the growing imbalance of developing countries' agricultural trade has been the expanding import demand for food products by oil exporters and the newly industrializing countries. Another important single factor was the steep increase in food imports by the People's Republic of China, this country alone accounting for 11% of total agricultural imports of developing countries in 1981. But a large majority of low-income countries also faced deteriorating agricultural trade balances. While 66 developing countries out of a total of 90 showed a surplus on this trade balance in

---

2/ For details of individual commodity markets, see FAO, Commodity Review and Outlook, 1982-83, Rome, 1983.

TABLE 1-8.  VALUE AT CURRENT PRICES OF WORLD AGRICULTURAL TRADE
(CROPS AND LIVESTOCK) BY REGION

| | | | | | Change | | Annual rate | |
| | | | | | 1979 to 1980 | 1980 to 1981 | of change 1970 to 1981 | |
| | 1970-72 | 1979 | 1980 | 1981 | | | current | constant[1] |
|---|---|---|---|---|---|---|---|---|
| | ..... thousand million $ ..... | | | | ............. % ............. | | | |
| **Developing market econ.** | | | | | | | | |
| Export | 18.67 | 61.69 | 68.04 | 65.65 | 10.3 | -3.5 | 14.5 | 2.4 |
| Import | 10.37 | 46.00 | 59.55 | 64.06 | 29.5 | 7.6 | 19.8 | 8.6 |
| **Africa** | | | | | | | | |
| Export | 4.00 | 10.63 | 10.55 | 8.59 | -0.8 | -18.5 | 10.4 | -2.0 |
| Import | 1.77 | 8.09 | 10.21 | 10.94 | 26.2 | 7.1 | 20.2 | 8.6 |
| **Far East** | | | | | | | | |
| Export | 4.39 | 16.95 | 19.46 | 19.41 | 14.8 | -0.3 | 16.7 | 5.6 |
| Import | 3.79 | 13.20 | 16.01 | 17.67 | 21.2 | 10.4 | 16.1 | 5.6 |
| **Latin America** | | | | | | | | |
| Export | 8.03 | 28.79 | 32.22 | 31.64 | 11.9 | -1.8 | 15.8 | 3.1 |
| Import | 2.58 | 10.22 | 14.08 | 14.20 | 37.8 | 0.8 | 18.2 | 7.6 |
| **Near East** | | | | | | | | |
| Export | 2.10 | 4.64 | 5.12 | 5.49 | 10.4 | 7.2 | 9.9 | -0.2 |
| Import | 2.04 | 13.86 | 18.57 | 20.55 | 33.9 | 10.7 | 26.5 | 13.8 |
| **Asian centrally planned economies** | | | | | | | | |
| Export | 1.31 | 3.76 | 4.01 | 3.17 | 6.7 | -21.1 | 10.7 | 0.7 |
| Import | 1.38 | 6.85 | 8.61 | 9.00 | 25.8 | 4.5 | 19.8 | 9.0 |
| **Total developing countries** | | | | | | | | |
| Export | 19.97 | 65.45 | 72.05 | 68.82 | 10.1 | -4.5 | 14.2 | 2.3 |
| Import | 11.77 | 52.84 | 68.16 | 73.06 | 29.0 | 7.2 | 19.8 | 8.6 |
| **Developed market economies** | | | | | | | | |
| Export | 33.77 | 128.79 | 150.67 | 152.29 | 17.0 | 1.1 | 16.6 | 5.9 |
| Import | 45.04 | 147.08 | 157.73 | 147.28 | 7.2 | -6.6 | 13.8 | 2.4 |
| **Eastern Europe and USSR** | | | | | | | | |
| Export | 4.02 | 9.61 | 9.89 | 9.71 | 2.9 | -1.8 | 9.9 | 0.2 |
| Import | 6.14 | 23.91 | 28.83 | 31.68 | 20.6 | 9.9 | 17.7 | 5.5 |
| **Total developed countries** | | | | | | | | |
| Export | 37.79 | 138.40 | 160.55 | 162.00 | 16.0 | 0.9 | 16.0 | 5.4 |
| Import | 51.18 | 171.00 | 186.56 | 178.96 | 9.1 | -4.1 | 14.3 | 2.9 |
| **World** | | | | | | | | |
| Export | 57.77 | 203.85 | 232.61 | 230.82 | 14.1 | -0.8 | 15.4 | 4.2 |
| Import | 62.95 | 223.84 | 254.72 | 252.02 | 13.8 | -1.1 | 15.5 | 4.1 |
| **Share of developing countries in world agric.trade** | ............... % ............. | | | | | | | |
| Export | 35 | 32 | 31 | 30 | | | | |
| Import | 19 | 24 | 27 | 29 | | | | |

1/ Constant values obtained by deflating current values of trade with the indices
(1969-71 = 100) of export and import unit values of agricultural products.

Source:  FAO, Trade Yearbooks.

1969-71, the number had dropped to 49 countries by 1981. The problem was particularly acute in Africa as the region's imports of agricultural commodities which represented about 44% of its agricultural exports in the early 1970s, were 27% greater than exports in 1981.

Comprehensive information on world agricultural trade in 1982 is not yet available. However, preliminary estimates point to a further reduction in the value of agricultural trade resulting from lower income growth in both industrial and developing countries, widespread payment problems and increasing supplies of some important trade products continuing to exert downward pressure on export prices. Even if some forecasts point to a slight economic recovery during 1983, it is unlikely that it will give a sufficient stimulus to demand to solve the inherent problems of agricultural commodities currently in over-supply.

Available information for individual commodities tends to confirm these negative prospects. The value of world grain trade in 1982 was estimated at US $31-33 thousand million, or about 15% lower than the previous year. Sharp trade losses were also recorded for tropical beverages, cotton, rubber, forestry products and, more particularly, sugar and rice. Overall, the volume of agricultural exports in 1982 is estimated to have increased only marginally, while a decline of as much as 10% may be expected in their total value. This would be the largest year-to-year decline in the value of world agricultural trade in the past two decades.

## Terms of Trade

The main single factor behind the deteriorating agricultural export situation has been the steep decline in the prices of most agricultural products since the third quarter of 1980. The decline in food prices followed a period of strong quotations in which a major element had been the then buoyant price of sugar. Price declines for vegetable oilseeds and oils and tropical beverages represented an accentuation of the trends initiated in 1980. The steep drop in prices of agricultural raw materials since early 1981 followed a year of price stagnation. On the whole, the UN price index for food commodities by the third quarter of 1982 had declined by 15% below the average for 1981 and that of agricultural non-food products by 19%.

Among products of trade importance for developing countries, nominal prices of tropical beverages as a whole declined by 10% during the same period (coffee 7%, cocoa 25% and tea 5%); those of oilseeds, oils and fats declined by 22%; the reduction in prices of fruits, meat, hides and skins and textile fibres ranged from 7% to 13%. The most significant decline took place, however, in the case of free market sugar (60%). Cereals were also affected, the overall decline being 12%. But the price decline for rice was particularly severe being 36%.

The decline in agricultural prices, however, has to be assessed in the light of the strengthening of the effective exchange rate of the US dollar in which many commodity market prices are quoted. From the point of view of individual importing countries the actual impact will obviously depend on the movements of their national currencies against the US dollar. The US dollar effective exchange rate, as calculated by the IMF, rose by about 12% during 1982 against currencies weighted by their importance in US trade. This implies that US dollar prices of, for instance, tropical beverages which, as a whole, declined by 10%, actually increased somewhat in terms of most other currencies, this partially accounting for slack demand.

On the whole, however, there has been a clear decline in the prices of agricultural commodities in relation to other major commodities and products. There had been an increase of 1.5% in the weighted price index of manufactures and crude petroleum in 1981, while in the year ending September 1982 the export unit values of these goods had declined by only 5-6% in comparison to declines of 15-19% for agricultural commodities. By deflating agricultural prices by the weighted price index of these two groups of products, which represent the bulk of developing countries' total value of imports, it appears that the real prices of agricultural exports in 1981 declined by 3% in developed market economies and by as much as 16% in developing ones (Table 1-9).

TABLE 1-9.  NET BARTER AND INCOME TERMS OF TRADE OF AGRICULTURAL
EXPORTS FOR MANUFACTURED GOODS AND CRUDE PETROLEUM

|  | 1977 | 1978 | 1979 | 1980 | 1981 |
|---|---|---|---|---|---|
|  | .............. 1969-71 = 100 .............. | | | | |
| NET BARTER TERMS OF TRADE | | | | | |
| Developed market economies | 96 | 94 | 86 | 71 | 69 |
| Developing market economies | 127 | 108 | 99 | 80 | 67 |
| Africa | 136 | 116 | 107 | 81 | 64 |
| Far East | 101 | 91 | 86 | 70 | 61 |
| Latin America | 141 | 116 | 105 | 88 | 73 |
| Near East | 108 | 95 | 85 | 70 | 64 |
| INCOME TERMS OF TRADE | | | | | |
| Developed market economies | 143 | 155 | 152 | 138 | 137 |
| Developing market economies | 143 | 124 | 116 | 93 | 84 |
| Africa | 116 | 99 | 91 | 67 | 52 |
| Far East | 137 | 119 | 122 | 105 | 96 |
| Latin America | 168 | 143 | 132 | 107 | 99 |
| Near East | 100 | 102 | 76 | 60 | 62 |

Source:  UN Monthly Bulletin of Statistics (various issues) and FAO, ESP.

The increase in the volume of agricultural exports in 1981 - about 3% in developed countries and 7% in developing ones - was insufficient to compensate for declining prices. The purchasing power of agricultural exports (income terms of trade) against manufactured products continued to decline in both countries. While the loss was marginal in developed countries, for developing ones it was the fourth consecutive year of significant deterioration. The purchasing power of their exports fell thus to the lowest levels since the early 1970s.

All developing regions - except the Near East, which depends relatively less on agriculture for its export earnings - experienced heavy losses. The situation was particularly serious in Africa where, after having declined by 1.4% per annum during the 1970s, the purchasing power of the region's agricultural exports dropped by 22% in 1981 alone.

Expressed in current US dollars, the recent losses experienced by developing countries in the purchasing power of their agricultural exports appear even more alarming (Table 1-10). Until 1979 the balance of excess and deficits in real agricultural export earnings of developing market economies had been on the whole positive, with a peak gain of about US $22 thousand million in 1977, a year of export boom. Gains were reduced by nearly half the following year and continued to shrink in 1979. By 1980 there was a shift in the income balance, with developing market economies suffering an aggregate loss of US $1 600 million, the first since 1971. The year 1981 witnessed a further sharp deterioration. Of all developing regions Africa was, again, the worst affected as the losses in the purchasing power of its agricultural exports - US $4 000 million - represented over 60% of the developing market economies' total losses.

TABLE 1-10.   EXCESS AND DEFICITS IN REAL AGRICULTURAL (CROPS AND LIVESTOCK) EXPORT EARNINGS, 1979-81 1/

|  | 1979 | 1980 | 1981 |
|---|---|---|---|
|  | ............current million $ ........... | | |
| Developed market economies | 66 969 | 58 715 | 59 353 |
| Developing market economies | 11 121 | -1 584 | -6 572 |
| Africa | - 957 | -3 378 | -4 040 |
| Far East | 3 728 | 1 168 | - 389 |
| Latin America | 9 190 | 2 578 | - |
| Near East | -1 114 | -2 000 | -2 024 |

1/   Calculated by multiplying the current value of total agricultural exports by the index of income terms of trade in each year and deducting from the product the current value of agricultural exports. For instance, the 1979 figure for developed market economies - US $66 969 million - is obtained by multiplying the value of agricultural exports in 1979 - US $128.79 thousand million - by the index (1969-71 = 100) of income terms of trade of agricultural products against manufactures and crude petroleum in that year - 152 - and deducting from the result of this product - US $195.76 thousand million - the value of US $128.79 thousand million.

Source:   FAO, ESP estimates.

Agricultural Protectionism in Some Major Industrial Countries

This section reviews some recent developments in national policies affecting supply and trade of selected food products in the EEC, Japan and the United States 3/. Price support measures in this group of countries 4/ are considered in relation to world prices as a broad indicator of the levels of protection granted to the different products (ad valorem tariff equivalent). The divergence between domestic prices and world prices may be broadly assumed to reflect the cumulative effect of the various tariff and non-tariff barriers, production and export support and stabilization measures (Fig. 1-3).

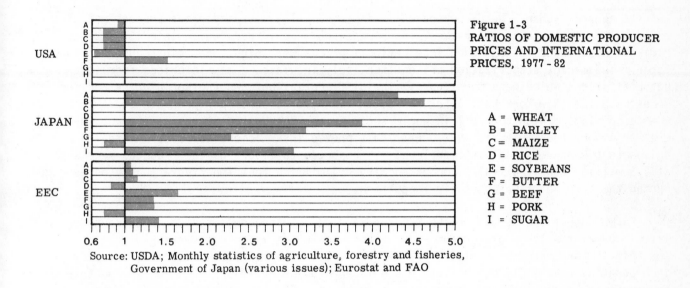

Figure 1-3
RATIOS OF DOMESTIC PRODUCER PRICES AND INTERNATIONAL PRICES, 1977 - 82

A = WHEAT
B = BARLEY
C = MAIZE
D = RICE
E = SOYBEANS
F = BUTTER
G = BEEF
H = PORK
I = SUGAR

Source: USDA; Monthly statistics of agriculture, forestry and fisheries, Government of Japan (various issues); Eurostat and FAO

There are wide differences in the prices paid to farmers in the EEC, Japan and the United States, partly reflecting the entirely different agricultural environment and cost structures in these countries 5/. Prices for cereals in the US in 1980 and 1981 were on average 50% to 75% lower than those paid in the EEC and about one-seventh of those paid in Japan. Unlike the EEC and Japan, the US farm support prices for cereals and soybeans were also well below world export prices. In addition there are fundamental differences

---

3/ For more in-depth discussions of agricultural protectionism, see the following publications. UNCTAD: Agricultural Protection and the Food Economy, Research Memo No. 46, Geneva, March 1972. FAO, Commodity Review and Outlook: 1979-80, Rome 1980, pp.109-122. Also see Valdés, Alberto and Joachim Zietz: Agricultural Protection in OECD Countries: Its Cost to Less-developed Countries, IFPRI, Research Report 21, December 1980.

4/ Price support measures are obviously not specific to these countries as many other developed and developing countries, both agricultural importers and exporters, are at least as aggressive in supporting their production.

5/ For example, the cost of mechanization per metric ton of rice in 1978 was about US $225 in Japan compared to US $22 in the US. The Japanese farmer paid US $75.63 for fertilizer for each ton of rice he produced against US $13.30 for the US farmer at comparable yield levels.

in the techniques of supporting farm incomes. In the United States direct intervention in cereal market prices is comparatively minimal and, in periods of tight supply, its producer support has been restricted to sporadic deficiency and disaster payments. Recently, however, considerable government resources have been allocated in the form of farm lending through the Commodity Credit Corporation (CCC). Farm income spending by the CCC amounted to US $15 400 million in the year ending September 1982, 69% more than in 1981 and 127% more than in 1980. Between 1981/82 and 1982/83, the levels of price support for wheat rose by 25%, for maize by 15% and for rice by 14%. While such price increases were insufficient to offset the declining trend in farm incomes as will be discussed later, they contributed to the building up of stocks of cereals and dairy products.

As regards sugar, the US Government has periodically operated price support measures through loan or purchase programmes. Such measures were introduced in late 1977, temporarily discontinued in 1980 when international prices were high, and reintroduced again later. The market stabilization price effectively insulated domestic prices from international prices which were much lower. The differential between the world price and the domestic price (New York basis) for raw sugar averaged 15 cents per pound in the third quarter of 1982. With the fall in world sugar prices the United States government increased import fees in April 1982. When this proved insufficient to raise internal prices to the market stabilization level, it resorted to import quotas. Quotas were set at 2.5 million tons, raw value, compared with 4.4 million tons imported annually on average during the five years before their imposition.

Farm support operations in the EEC are carried out through a system of guaranteed prices covering a large proportion - about three-quarters in recent years - of the Community's total agricultural production, and a system of variable import levies. By incorporating a variable charge into the delivered price of imports from third countries, the levies maintain foreign prices at or above those received by domestic producers. It has been estimated that for nine main agricultural products of the Community, the additional nominal protection from levies is 45%, over three times the average tariff rate of 14% 6/.

By January 1983, import levies for wheat represented about 55% of the support (intervention) price for bread wheat and levies for coarse grain about 55 to 60% of the intervention price. Levies for cereals, in particular wheat and barley, rose sharply in 1982 reflecting the decline in international prices. The effects of these mechanisms, insulating farmers from international competition, are reflected by the high levels of support prices granted by the Community in relation to international prices (Fig. 1-3).

High prices and relatively stable domestic demand have resulted in increasing overproduction of a number of commodities including wheat, sugar, dairy products, beef and veal. While the Community remains a net agricultural importer, it has also become the second largest agricultural exporter after the United States.

In Japan, farm support is provided through payments from tax and government bond revenues, through public corporations and through income transfers from consumers who pay prices often several times higher than world market prices. Direct and indirect agricultural subsidies during the year ending April 1981 totalled an estimated 2 455 billion yen a year (about US $11.05 billion). This figure represents over half of the total farm

---

6/ Yeats, A.J. Trade Barriers Facing Developing Countries, St. Martin's Press, New York, 1979.

income in 1980. About half of the subsidy expenditure is related to the rice programme, under which about half of the country's rice crop is purchased at supported prices and then resold to wholesalers at a loss.

However, other agricultural products, including soybeans and wheat, benefit from the government's efforts to move away from overdependence on rice. For livestock products, the profits from the sale of imported beef - for which a quota system is applied - provide subsidies and low interest loans to livestock producers. They also subsidize the storage of surplus production. A similar system is operated on the sales of imported wheat, barley and rice, the benefits of which are being used to help finance cereal subsidy programmes.

When added together the effects of the different programmes on domestic prices are considerable. Japan supports its food production at higher levels than any other major importing country, while still leaving scope for imports. However, some levelling off in support prices has recently taken place, reflecting budgetary strains, supply/demand adjustments and the decline in international prices.

## Trade Negotiations[7]

With the problems besetting world trade and particularly the apparent inability of the system of multilateral negotiations to deal with them, attention naturally was focused on the Thirty-Eighth Session of the GATT Contracting Parties held in November 1982 at ministerial level for the first time in 9 years. The concluding Declaration approved an examination of agricultural trade problems by a new GATT Committee on Trade in Agriculture. This study, designed to provide policy recommendations for the 1984 Session of the Contracting Parties, will cover all measures affecting agricultural market access and supplies. The Contracting parties also decided to carry out consultations and negotiations aimed at further liberalization of trade in tropical products including their processed and semi-processed forms and to examine factors affecting trade in forestry, fish and fisheries products.

Agreement on the Common Fund for Commodities which was reached in June 1980 and which was regarded as the cornerstone of international action to stabilize commodity prices, did not come into force on 31 March 1982 as planned because insufficient countries had ratified it. The 25 countries that had ratified extended the deadline to 30 September 1983.

## FOOD STOCKS AND WORLD FOOD SECURITY

### Food Stocks

The coincidence of relatively high levels of world production for several food commodities and rather weak effective demand has resulted in the accumulation of stocks, not only of cereals but other food commodities as well. World carry-over stocks of cereals amounted to 275 million tons by the end of the 1981/82 year, equivalent to 18% of apparent

---

[7]  For a fuller discussion of the GATT Session and the negotiations relevant to agricultural trade, see FAO, Commodity Review and Outlook, 1983/83, Rome, 1983.

consumption and an increase of about 20% over the previous year (Table 1-11). A further increase of similar magnitude is foreseen for 1982/83. For dairy products, the government-intervention agencies in the EEC and the United States held over 1.1 million tons of skim milk powder in December 1982, double the quantity of two years previously. Stocks of butter and cheese were also higher.

TABLE 1-11. WORLD STOCKS: ESTIMATED TOTAL CARRYOVERS OF CEREALS [1]

|  | Crop year ending in: | | | |
|---|---|---|---|---|
|  | 1980 | 1981 | 1982 [2] | 1983 [3] |
|  | ............... million metric tons.............. | | | |
| **BY REGION** | | | | |
| Developed countries of which: | 156.2 | 133.8 | 177.1 | 230.6 |
| USA | 78.1 | 62.2 | 104.4 | 156.7 |
| Canada | 14.3 | 12.9 | 14.9 | 18.8 |
| EEC [4] | 15.8 | 15.7 | 14.7 | 18.3 |
| USSR | 16.0 | 14.0 | 14.0 | 14.0 |
| Japan | 10.6 | 8.8 | 7.4 | 6.0 |
| Australia | 5.0 | 2.7 | 3.1 | 1.1 |
| Developing countries of which: | 99.8 | 98.5 | 97.9 | 98.1 |
| Africa | 2.9 | 3.6 | 4.7 | 4.4 |
| Far East | 82.0 | 74.7 | 74.6 | 74.9 |
| China | 53.0 | 45.5 | 43.0 | 44.0 |
| India | 10.8 | 7.1 | 7.4 | 10.2 |
| Korea, Republic of | 2.1 | 2.4 | 2.2 | 2.1 |
| Latin America | 6.4 | 11.1 | 9.2 | 9.8 |
| Argentina | 1.1 | 0.5 | 0.8 | 1.4 |
| Brazil | 1.3 | 3.8 | 2.6 | 3.5 |
| Near East | 9.4 | 10.1 | 10.3 | 9.2 |
| Turkey | 0.8 | 0.6 | 0.6 | 0.6 |
| **BY CEREAL** | | | | |
| World total cereals of which: | 256.0 | 232.4 | 275.0 | 328.7 |
| Wheat | 104.8 | 97.1 | 101.9 | 118.5 |
| Coarse grains | 109.3 | 94.1 | 131.7 | 171.4 |
| Rice (milled basis) | 42.0 | 41.1 | 41.4 | 38.9 |
|  | ...................... % ...................... | | | |
| World stocks as % of consumption | 18 | 16 | 18 | 21 |

1/ Stock data are based on an aggregate of national carryover levels at the end of national crop years and should not be construed as representing world stock levels at a fixed point of time.

2/ Estimate. 3/ Forecast. 4/ Ten member countries.

Note: Based on official and unofficial estimates. Total computed from unrounded data.

Source: FAO, ESC.

World stocks of sugar also rose by some 8 million tons in 1981/82 to 32 million tons (annual consumption is about 91 million tons), but a new record level of 37-39 million tons is expected by the end of the 1982/83 season.  An increase in the stocks of edible oils and fats is also forecast for 1983.

Although the presence of large stocks of food commodities (especially cereals) has improved world food security, this situation holds several undesirable features.

Accumulating stocks underline the current imbalance in world food supply and demand. Several developed countries are producing food in excess of domestic and export market demand.  Some of them have programmes that divert food commodities to animal feed or industrial uses.  Currently in at least one of them, the United States, programmes have been legislated that aim to reduce cereal production.  Yet in developing countries there exists a large unsatisfied demand.

Stocks, and particularly those of cereals, and dairy products are concentrated in developed countries.  For example developed countries are expected to hold 70% of world cereal stocks by the end of their 1982/83 season, an increase of 30% over 4 years.  Cereal stocks in developing countries have not increased since 1976/77.

The Seventh Session of the Committee on Food Security (CFS) in April 1982 stressed the need for a better distribution of stocks.  Stocks in many developing countries remain below target levels mainly because of lack of storage facilities and the means to purchase stocks.  Yet FAO's Food Security Assistance Scheme, aimed to improve the capacity of developing countries to maintain their food security, remains short of funds.

Coarse grains constitute over half of world cereal stocks.  On the other hand, stocks of rice and wheat by the end of 1982/83 are not forecast to be much higher than the levels of 1978/79.

Efforts to Improve World Food Security

The importance of food security as a priority objective of the world community has been reiterated at recent summit meetings such as the Western Summit in Ottawa and the North-South Summit in Cancún in 1981.  Yet there has been only limited progress these past two years in improving it.

Partly as a reflection of the lack of progress at the global level, governments of developing countries have, however, shown increasing interest in regional food security arrangements.  For example, a Regional Commission on Food Security for Asia and the Pacific was established by the FAO Council in 1982 on the recommendation of the 16th FAO Regional Conference for Asia and the Pacific.  Its purpose is to foster collective self-reliance in food supplies among member nations at regional or sub-regional levels. The first session will be held in 1983.

In Africa, countries of the Southern African Development Coordination Conference (SADCC) are in the process of carrying out feasibility studies for a number of specific projects identified for strengthening food security in the region.  An important initial component would be the establishment of an early warning system against impending food shortages.  Steps have been examined by the Comité Permanent Inter-Etats de Lutte contre la Sécheresse du Sahel (CILSS), individual governments and potential donor nations towards establishing a system of national and regional food reserves in the Sahel, and a training programme is being initiated under the Technical Cooperation Programme (TCP).

In Latin America, an Action Committee on Food Security has been set up within the framework of the Sistema Económico Latinoamericano (SELA).  It has been entrusted with the responsibility of developing the actions necessary for the establishment of a regional food security system, in line with the recommendation of a meeting of high level national experts held in Mexico in August 1981.

There has been some increase in capacities to store food grains in developing countries.  This has been assisted in part by FAO's Food Security Assistance Scheme.  However, relative to storage needs in these countries, progress has been slow.

Negotiations toward a new International Wheat Agreement reached an impasse in 1979 and are not expected to be resumed in the foreseeable future.  The Food Aid Convention (FAC), strengthened in 1980, as well as the existing Wheat Trade Convention (1971), was extended to June 1986 by the Food Aid Committee meeting in December 1982.  Yet many observers have remarked that it is disappointing that the opportunity created by abundant stocks of cereals and freedom from widespread food shortages has not been taken to build a more durable system to ensure access to essential food supplies for low-income countries.

Early consideration should be given to a possible liberalization of access to the IMF cereal import financing facility which was set up in May 1981 for an initial four-year period.  There are limitations on drawings at present because they are linked to the compensatory financing covering shortfalls in export earnings and are limited to cereal imports.  Given the current trade situation, by December 1982 10 countries had already drawn on their quota to compensate for export shortfalls and hence would be limited to only 25% of their quota to cover cereal imports.  The facility is due for a mid-term review by the IMF Executive Board in 1983.

As has been emphasized, the present world food security situation presents a mixed picture:  ample world food supplies contrasting with persistent food problems in many places amidst a discouraging economic and international cooperation climate.  The basic causes of food insecurity remain.  With this situation in mind, the Director-General of FAO has proposed a new concept of food security, new approaches towards solving world food security problems and proposals which have been supported by the FAO Council and the World Food Council.  The recommendations in his 1983 report to the Committee on World Food Security may thus lead to more concerted international efforts to establish a comprehensive and effective world food security system for the future.

## DEVELOPMENTS IN THE MEANS OF PRODUCTION

An issue of concern to agricultural policy makers particularly in developed countries, has been the price-cost squeeze in which many agricultural producers have been placed, especially in countries where agriculture is more exposed to market forces such as the United States.  In particular, the high  levels of interest rates that have prevailed in the early 1980s placed a severe burden on many farmers and led to an abnormally large number of bankruptcies.  Since mid-1982, important components of agricultural producers' costs have tended to stabilize or decline thus providing some relief to that sector. Nominal interest rates have declined although in real terms they remain at high levels (See Box).  However, at the same time, commodity prices also have been depressed although for producers in many developed countries, measures are taken to support prices well above international levels.

Fertilizer Prices, Consumption and Availability
==

Fertilizer prices have declined in the United States in line with weakening export prices (Fig. 1-4). Elsewhere they are determined more by domestic supply and demand and, if imported, by variations in exchange rates. However, except in those countries where fertilizer subsidies were removed for budgetary reasons, fertilizer prices in real terms should have eased.

The FAO Commission on Fertilizers meeting at the end of January 1983, noted with concern that current low realization prices 8/ for fertilizers could lead to inadequate investment in fertilizer production capacity and hence higher fertilizer prices in the future. In 1981/82 fertilizer production declined for the first time since the Second World War. The overall decline was 4% but it was much more in North America (16.5%). Production also declined by over 7% in Latin America. However, it expanded in Asia by over 4%.

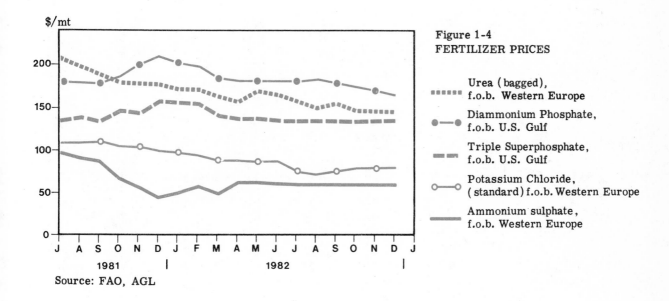

Figure 1-4
FERTILIZER PRICES

Urea (bagged),
f.o.b. Western Europe

Diammonium Phosphate,
f.o.b. U.S. Gulf

Triple Superphosphate,
f.o.b. U.S. Gulf

Potassium Chloride,
(standard) f.o.b. Western Europe

Ammonium sulphate,
f.o.b. Western Europe

Source: FAO, AGL

Fertilizer consumption also declined in 1981/82, for the second time in the last 30 years, by just over 1% (Table 1-12). Thereby production and consumption were brought more nearly into balance in 1981/82 after allowing for losses in storage and distribution and non-agricultural use. This decline in consumption was not confined to the developed market economies. Consumption also declined in Latin America and China but remained virtually unchanged in Africa. However, consumption did expand a little in the other developing regions and for all developing countries together there was almost no change. This was a disquieting reversal from the average annual increase of about 10% in the 1970s and in comparison with the required annual increase projected by AT 2000 at over 8% over the period 1980-2000.

---

8/ The price required to encourage investment in new fertilizer production capacity.

Recessionary conditions in the agricultural sector and low prices for coffee in Latin America and, in particular, high interest rates in North America clearly affected uptake. In many developing countries foreign exchange problems were curtailing the normal flow of imported fertilizers: developing market economy countries import about half their nitrogenous and phosphatic fertilizers and nearly all of their potassic fertilizers.

TABLE 1-12. FERTILIZER CONSUMPTION

| | | | | Change | | Annual rate of change | |
|---|---|---|---|---|---|---|---|
| | | | | 1979/80 to 1980/81 | 1980/81 to 1981/82 | 1977/78 to 1981/82 | 1971/72 to 1981/82 |
| | 1979/80 | 1980/81 | 1981/82 | | | | |
| | .. million metric tons .. | | | ............... % ............... | | | |
| **Total developed countries** | | | | | | | |
| Nitrogen | 34.68 | 35.73 | 35.36 | 3.0 | -1.0 | 2.9 | 4.1 |
| Phosphate | 22.94 | 22.05 | 21.69 | -3.9 | -1.6 | 0.1 | 2.0 |
| Potash | 20.36 | 20.24 | 20.10 | -0.6 | -0.7 | -0.4 | 2.6 |
| Total nutrients | 77.98 | 78.02 | 77.15 | 0.1 | -1.1 | 1.2 | 3.1 |
| **Total developing countries** | | | | | | | |
| Nitrogen | 22.57 | 24.87 | 25.08 | 10.2 | 0.8 | 8.8 | 11.7 |
| Phosphate | 8.22 | 9.40 | 9.22 | 14.4 | -1.9 | 6.5 | 9.1 |
| Potash | 3.58 | 4.03 | 3.84 | 12.6 | -4.7 | 7.6 | 10.0 |
| Total nutrients | 34.37 | 38.30 | 38.14 | 11.4 | -0.4 | 8.5 | 10.8 |
| Africa | 1.15 | 1.43 | 1.47 | 24.3 | 2.8 | 9.4 | 5.8 |
| Far East | 9.47 | 10.09 | 10.84 | 6.5 | 7.4 | 9.3 | 9.9 |
| Latin America | 6.70 | 7.52 | 6.36 | 12.2 | -15.4 | 2.7 | 8.4 |
| Near East | 3.00 | 2.95 | 3.22 | -1.7 | 9.2 | 5.7 | 9.8 |
| Asian centrally planned economies | 14.03 | 16.30 | 16.21 | 16.2 | -0.6 | 11.4 | 13.8 |
| **World** | | | | | | | |
| Nitrogen | 57.26 | 60.60 | 60.44 | 5.8 | -0.3 | 5.2 | 6.6 |
| Phosphate | 31.15 | 31.46 | 30.92 | 1.0 | -1.7 | 2.1 | 3.5 |
| Potash | 23.95 | 24.27 | 23.93 | 1.3 | -1.4 | 0.8 | 3.5 |
| Total nutrients | 112.36 | 116.33 | 115.29 | 3.5 | -0.9 | 3.4 | 5.0 |

Source: FAO, Fertilizer Yearbooks.

The FAO Commission on Fertilizers suggested that there may be possibilities for assistance by appropriate agencies such as the IMF, to be given to countries with balance of payments problems to enable them to maintain fertilizer imports.

## Agricultural Producers' Incomes and Support Measures

Agricultural producers faced unusually difficult economic conditions during the past two years. Sluggish demand confronted ample supplies of most agricultural commodities and depressed prices. While the slowing down in general inflation rates also reduced the increase in production costs, some cost elements, in particular interest rates, rose sharply (see Box). Real agricultural incomes in 1981 and 1982 tended to decline in most industrial countries although, in the EEC as a whole, a moderate recovery was recorded in 1982.

Partial data also indicate an overall unfavourable situation in farm prices and incomes in developing countries. On the positive side, lower prices for food products and agricultural raw materials have been an important element in the recent slowing down in consumer price inflation in industrial countries.

The average increase in common farm prices in European Currency Units (ECU) for the EEC was 9.5% in 1981/82, nearly double the percentage increase of the previous marketing year, and it rose further by 10.5% in 1982/83. Expressed in national currencies and taking account of all the agri-monetary adjustments adopted since the previous price decisions, the average increase in 1982/83 was 12.2%. An important factor in deciding such large price increases was the objective to compensate farmers for a sharp decline in income between 1978 and 1981. During this period agricultural producer prices had risen by 8.7% per annum, retail food prices by 10.1% and consumer prices in general by 12.2%.

The impact of the 1982/83 price decisions on consumer food prices (in national currencies) is estimated at between 4.5% and 5% for the Community as a whole, which corresponds to an increase of about 1% in the cost of living.

For the 1983/84 marketing year, the European Commission proposed an average increase of 4.4% in agricultural prices. This restrained proposal was largely based on the need to continue the fight against inflation and limit the volume of production for certain products which are currently in surplus, particularly cereals, sugar, milk and rapeseed. For these products the Commission proposed below-average price rises. While merely maintaining farm incomes at current levels, the 1983/84 farm price proposals would have only a moderate impact on food prices.

In the United States, prices paid for production inputs, interest, taxes and wage rates in 1982 are expected to rise by only 3%, after having risen by an average 11% over the past three years. The 1982 increase would be the smallest since 1968 when the index rose by 2%. However, the easing in production costs did not compensate for low farm revenues. Prices received by farmers for all farm products, which had risen by only 1.5% and 3.0% in 1980 and 1981 respectively, actually tended to decline in 1982, particularly in the second half of the year. Farmers' overall net income was estimated to have fallen to US $19 billion in 1982, from US $25 billion in the previous year.

In Canada net farm income in 1982 was also expected to decline by about 9% below the previous years' levels, reflecting a stagnation of farm cash receipts and a 3% increase in total farm operating expenses and depreciation charges. Net farm income in 1983 is likely to show a further slight decline from the 1982 level. Average farm wage rates by mid-1982 were about 7% higher than a year ealier, a substantially lower rate of increase than that of consumer prices (12.5% in 1981) and wages in other sectors. As a consequence, the gap between Canadian farm and non-farm wage rates continued to widen.

## NOMINAL AND REAL INTEREST RATES

The combined effect of monetary stringency and continued rapid inflation led to a sharp increase in interest rates, which by 1980 and 1981 had surpassed previous historical levels in several major industrial countries. An important factor behind the generalized increase in interest rates was the action of the United States Federal Reserve System to limit the growth in US money and credit. Despite parallel movements in other countries, however, interest rate differentials in favour of the US dollar tended to widen. From September 1981, a sharp decline in the US rates of interest took place, pari passu, with the easing in inflationary pressures. By January 1983 interest rates of prime lending in the United States were 11 percentage points lower than by mid-1981.

An approximate indication of the restrictiveness of interest rates or their deflationary impact may be derived from the difference between the nominal interest rate and the rate of inflation. Such comparison provides a measurement of "real" interest rates. The figure shows the evolution of the United States prime rates vis-à-vis the consumer price index in 1980-82. Real interest rates were relatively low in 1980 and, during four consecutive months, were actually negative. Since the last quarter of 1980, widely diverging trends in prime rates and consumer prices resulted in a sharp increase in real interest rates which reached peaks of 10.50% to 10.70% by mid-1981.

Real interest rates of 10% and more are without doubt a major issue in the continued recession. Although the prime rate is a basic indicator of the whole structure of commercial interest rates in the US, it applies only to first-class risk corporate borrowers, with other borrowers paying generally higher rates. Therefore interest rates paid by farmers on short-term loans were even higher than those shown.

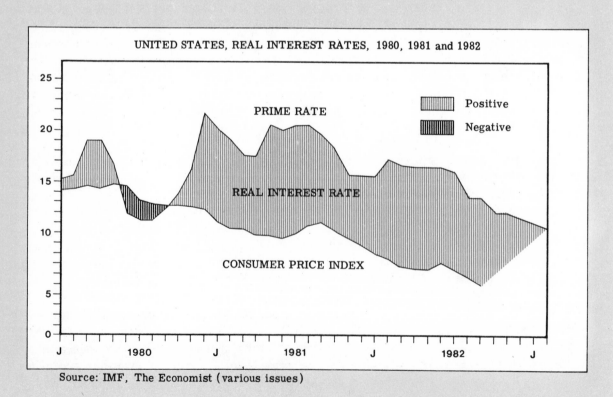

UNITED STATES, REAL INTEREST RATES, 1980, 1981 and 1982

Source: IMF, The Economist (various issues)

Recent developments in farm incomes are much less known in developing countries. The ratio of prices received by farmers to prices paid for production requisites in twelve developing countries for which information is available showed a deteriorating trend during 1978-1981 in all but two countries. Rising costs affected more severely net farm incomes in Argentina, Uruguay, Jordan, the Republic of Korea, Botswana and Mali.

In many African countries there is evidence of a persisting urban bias in agricultural and food pricing to the detriment of farm incomes. This is frequently apparent in the area of foreign trade. Overvalued exchange rates and erratic import policies for food products have contributed to reducing the incentives for domestic producers to increase food production.

Farmers in Latin America appear to have been particularly vulnerable to the slow-down in demand. Producer profits were expected to decline in 1982 as a result of low prices, high interest and inflation rates as well as higher levels of indebtedness. Some relief may be provided by the currency devaluations of several countries in the region, including Argentina, Brazil, Costa Rica, Mexico and Peru. This action should encourage exports and indirectly favour producer incomes. Producer subsidies have been important elements in the farm support policies of some major agricultural countries in the region including Brazil and Mexico. However, countries like Argentina have been forced to lower some agricultural subsidies to check the inflationary effects of the devaluation. By late 1982 also the Mexican government has drastically reduced agricultural subsidies and price controls.

Partial information for the Far East also suggests generally unfavourable farm price and cost developments requiring in many cases active support measures by government. Subsidies were granted either directly to farmers as was the case in Malaysia, or more often through the subsidized distribution of inputs. The high budgetary cost involved, however, caused some countries to reduce the scale of farm subsidization. For example, grain growers in Bangladesh suffered from a sharp reduction in input subsidies allocated in the 1982/83 budget which resulted in increases of 11% and 20% respectively in prices of fertilizers and irrigation equipment. Minimum prices for paddy and rice were increased by 9% and 11% respectively, but these were considered to be insufficient to compensate for higher production costs.


## DEVELOPMENT ASSISTANCE AND FOOD AID

Total net disbursements of Official Development Assistance (ODA) to developing countries, for all sectors including agriculture, have been increasing steadily in current terms from 1970 to 1980. For the first time, these disbursements have decreased in 1981 to $35.5 billion from $36.4 billion in 1980. This confirms the fears expressed in earlier issues of SOFA that the budgetary constraints faced by donor countries will affect negatively the flows of aid to developing countries. At the time ODA is declining, the debt of developing countries is soaring and is estimated to have reached $626 billion in 1982. Moreover, their export earnings have been dwindling as already discussed.

The situation is therefore alarming, especially if one considers the importance and role of ODA in the development efforts of low-income developing countries. The fall in ODA in 1981 was due to the decrease in OPEC bilateral aid. An increase in aid from this source in the near future is difficult to foresee since many OPEC countries are themselves facing financial difficulties as a consequence of declining oil prices. The reversal of the present trend of ODA could be achieved only if other donors and the capital surplus

OPEC countries step up substantially their aid to developing countries. This would require stronger political support of aid in the donor countries than has been shown over the past few years.

## External Assistance to Agriculture in 1981 in Comparison with Recent Years

The analysis of external assistance to agriculture is based on commitment data; statistics on disbursements are still missing and efforts are currently being made to collect them (see Box). According to preliminary data, official commitments of external assistance to agriculture "narrow definition" - that is, activities "directly" in support of the agricultural sector - decreased in 1981 by 7.5% to $7 300 million at current prices, corresponding to $4 900 million at 1975 prices (Table 1-13). The decline appears to have been particularly marked in the case of bilateral commitments, which went down for the second consecutive year, this time by 15%.

TABLE 1-13. OFFICIAL COMMITMENTS OF EXTERNAL ASSISTANCE
TO AGRICULTURE (NARROW DEFINITION)

|  | 1976 | 1977 | 1978 | 1979 | 1980 | 1981[1] |
|---|---|---|---|---|---|---|
|  | .................. million $ .................... | | | | | |
| **TOTAL COMMITMENTS** | | | | | | |
| Multilateral 2/ | 1 934 | 2 764 | 3 851 | 3 634 | 4 732 | 4 616 |
| Bilateral 3/ | 1 582 | 1 940 | 2 626 | 3 323 | 3 188 | 2 710 |
| Total at current prices | 3 516 | 4 704 | 6 477 | 6 957 | 7 920 | 7 326 |
| Total at 1975 prices 4/ | 3 516 | 4 316 | 5 182 | 4 865 | 5 013 | 4 884 |
| Total at 1980 prices 4/ | 5 555 | 6 819 | 8 188 | 7 687 | 7 920 | 7 717 |
| **CONCESSIONAL COMMITMENTS** | | | | | | |
| Multilateral | 1 132 | 1 374 | 2 040 | 2 028 | 2 638 | 2 247 |
| Bilateral | 1 449 | 1 926 | 2 590 | 3 220 | 3 159 | 2 420 |
| Total at current prices | 2 581 | 3 300 | 4 630 | 5 248 | 5 797 | 4 667 |
| Total at 1975 prices | 2 581 | 3 028 | 3 704 | 3 670 | 3 669 | 3 111 |
| **NON-CONCESSIONAL COMMITMENTS** | | | | | | |
| Multilateral | 802 | 1 390 | 1 811 | 1 606 | 2 094 | 2 369 |
| Bilateral | (133) | (14) | (36) | (103) | (29) | (290) |
| Total at current prices | 935 | 1 404 | 1 847 | 1 709 | 2 123 | 2 659 |
| Total at 1975 prices | 935 | 1 288 | 1 478 | 1 195 | 1 344 | 1 773 |

1/ Preliminary, including partial estimates.

2/ Including World Bank, IDB, AFDB/ADF, ASDB, IFAD, OFID, AFESD, ABEDA, ISDB, UNDP, FAO (TF/TCP) and commitments to CGIAR.

3/ DAC bilateral, EEC and OPEC bilateral.

4/ Deflated by the UN unit value index for the export of manufactured goods.

( ) Based on partial information.

Source: FAO and OECD.

This recent picture regarding assistance to agriculture "narrow definition" is similar to that for the "broad definition" (Table 1-14). However, there was a small increase in total Official Commitments of External Assistance to Agriculture (OCA) of less than 2% in terms of current dollars, but 7% in terms of constant dollars, gains in multilateral assistance making up for the apparent decline in bilateral assistance. As with assistance to "narrow definition", reductions have occurred particularly with concessional commitments, the decline being about 7% in 1981.

### TABLE 1-14. OFFICIAL COMMITMENTS OF EXTERNAL ASSISTANCE TO AGRICULTURE (BROAD DEFINITION)

|  | 1976 | 1977 | 1978 | 1979 | 1980 | 1981 |
|---|---|---|---|---|---|---|
|  | ................... million $ ........................ | | | | | |
| TOTAL OCA |  |  |  |  |  |  |
| Multilateral[1] | 3 016 | 4 014 | 5 238 | 5 129 | 6 689 | 7 069 |
| Bilateral | 2 237 | 3 113 | 3 837 | 4 949 | 4 598 | 4 396 |
| Total at current prices | 5 253 | 7 127 | 9 075 | 10 071 | 11 287 | 11 465 |
| Total at 1975 prices [2] | 5 253 | 6 538 | 7 260 | 7 043 | 7 144 | 7 643 |
| Total at 1980 prices [2] | 8 300 | 10 330 | 11 471 | 11 128 | 11 287 | 12 076 |
| CONCESSIONAL OCA |  |  |  |  |  |  |
| Multilateral | 1 665 | 1 704 | 2 487 | 2 730 | 3 603 | 3 432 |
| Bilateral | 1 833 | 2 933 | 3 443 | 4 578 | 4 300 | 3 926 |
| Total at current prices | 3 498 | 4 637 | 5 930 | 7 308 | 7 903 | 7 358 |
| Total at 1975 prices [2] | 3 498 | 4 254 | 4 744 | 5 111 | 5 002 | 4 905 |
| NON-CONCESSIONAL OCA |  |  |  |  |  |  |
| Multilateral | 1 351 | 2 310 | 2 751 | 2 399 | 3 086 | 3 637 |
| Bilateral | 404 | 180 | 394 | 364 | 298 | 470 |
| Total at current prices | 1 755 | 2 490 | 3 145 | 2 763 | 3 384 | 4 107 |
| Total at 1975 prices [2] | 1 755 | 2 284 | 2 516 | 1 932 | 2 142 | 2 738 |

1/ Including World Bank (IBRD/IDA), IFAD, IDB, ASDB, AFDB/ADF, OFID, AFESD, ABEDA, ISDB, UNDP, FAO (TCP/Trust Funds) and commitments to CGIAR.

2/ Deflated by the UN unit value index of the export of manufactured goods.

Source: FAO and OECD.

The recent record of external assistance to agriculture raises some important issues:

- In real terms, commitments to agriculture "narrow definition" in 1981 were barely at the same level as in 1979, while they increased by 48% during the preceding three years (1976-1978).

- The volume of assistance to agriculture "narrow definition" is still 40% short of
the internationally agreed estimate of annual requirements of $8 300 million at
1975 prices for the period 1975-1980 ($13 100 million at 1980 prices). It is also
far below the estimated requirements of $12 500 million (at 1975 prices) for 1990,
projected in the FAO study "Agriculture: Towards 2000" and mentioned in the UN
General Assembly Resolution 36/185.

- External assistance to agriculture from bilateral sources is provided mostly on
concessional terms. Not only has the amount of total bilateral assistance to
agriculure declined but its concessional component has also tended to decrease.
This indicates a hardening in the terms of external flows to developing countries'
agricultural sectors. Coinciding with the stagnation in the volume of assistance,
this hardening puts further strains on their balance of payments.

- In times of even modest cutbacks in aid overall there may be serious interruptions
of aid flows at the level of individual countries. In addition, delays in project
mobilization and other problems may create large differences between aid commitments and actual disbursements.

## The regional picture

The regional impact of the changing flows of development assistance since 1976 have
been of some consequence (Fig.1-5). In terms of real capital commitments per head of the
agricultural labour force, aid to African agriculture(broadly defined) fell back from 1977
to 1979 but subsequently recovered quite strongly even in 1981. By that year each member
of the agricultural labour force was receiving 55% more capital commitments in real terms

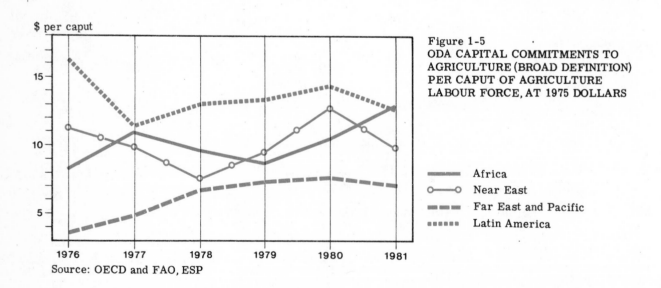

$ per caput

Figure 1-5
ODA CAPITAL COMMITMENTS TO
AGRICULTURE (BROAD DEFINITION)
PER CAPUT OF AGRICULTURE
LABOUR FORCE, AT 1975 DOLLARS

Africa
Near East
Far East and Pacific
Latin America

1976    1977    1978    1979    1980    1981
Source: OECD and FAO, ESP

than 6 years previously. Africa received greater bilateral assistance in particular.
There has been no clear trend in the Near East although the overall level of commitments
is relatively high. Aid to the region's agricultural sector suffered a sharp setback in
1981. The Far East and Pacific region has shown the most consistent increase with capital
commitments per head of the agricultural labour force being more than 100% greater in
1980 than in 1976 but still well below the other developing regions. The greater part of

## DISBURSEMENTS OF EXTERNAL ASSISTANCE TO AGRICULTURE

As part of its efforts to improve the reporting on official external assistance to agriculture, FAO has developed a data bank on loans and grants provided by bilateral and multilateral donors to developing countries for the development of their agricultural sectors.

The data stored are the amount, terms and purpose of all loans and grants committed from 1974 onwards. Technical assistance grants are the exception because data on individual transactions are not available.

The FAO data bank is up-dated annually. Moreover, an attempt has been made, in cooperation with OECD and multilateral agencies concerned, to collect data on annual disbursements of the loans and grants committed to agriculture since 1974. Some preliminary figures on disbursements made by multilateral lending agencies in the years 1979 to 1981 on loans committed from 1974 onwards are shown below.

Although these disbursement figures may be slightly underestimated because the disbursements on loans committed before 1974 are not included, the amounts actually disbursed in a year are far below the amounts committed in the same year. The volume of disbursements in a given year of course depends on the volume of commitments made earlier and how rapidly the commitments are disbursed.

A more detailed analysis of disbursements in relation to commitments of external assistance will be presented in the next issue of SOFA. It is hoped that data on bilateral disbursements will be available for their inclusion in this analysis.

### Disbursement of total multilateral external assistance in 1979-1981 1/

|  | 1979 | 1980 | 1981 |
|---|---|---|---|
|  | ...............million $............... | | |
| Agriculture "broad" definition | 2 500 | 2 900 | 3 200 |
| (as % of commitments made in same year) | (53%) | (47%) | (50%) |
| Agriculture "narrow" definition | 1 600 | 1 900 | 2 200 |
| (as % of commitments made in same year) | (49%) | (45%) | (54%) |

1/ Excluding technical assistance grants. The figures on commitments used to compute the ratios shown in the table refer to capital commitment only. Therefore, they are lower than those reported in Tables 1-13 and 1-14.

Source: FAO estimates.

the increase in commitments to agriculture in this region was from multilateral sources, but not by a large amount. The region suffered a moderate reduction in 1981. The surprising feature of the flows of aid to Latin America - as measured in Fig. 1-5 - is their level relative to other regions: in every year but one out of the period 1976-81, they received the greatest amount. But typically these countries have relatively low percentages of their populations employed in agriculture. Nevertheless during the 1970s, for example, Brazil received significantly more aid to agriculture per head of agricultural population than India.

ODA capital commitments to the 36 least developed countries (LDCs)[9] fell by 4% in current prices in 1981 according to preliminary estimates. This was a sharp reversal from the preceding 3 years when commitments had nearly doubled.

## Assistance to Africa

Despite the overall worsening climate for development assistance, aid to agriculture "broad definition" in Africa [10] has increased apart from a setback in 1978. About one-half of these commitments has usually gone into activities directly related to crops and livestock. There has been a move away from land and water development perhaps because of the problems and rising costs of implementing irrigation schemes (Fig. 1-6). Commitments

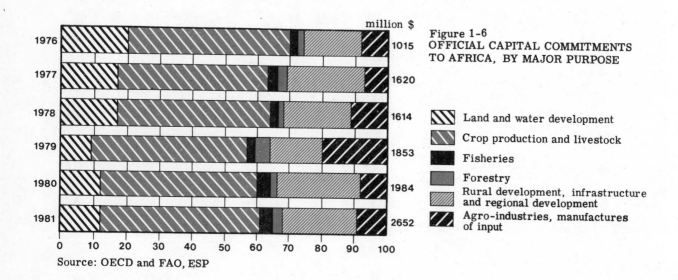

Figure 1-6
OFFICIAL CAPITAL COMMITMENTS
TO AFRICA, BY MAJOR PURPOSE

Land and water development

Crop production and livestock

Fisheries

Forestry

Rural development, infrastructure and regional development

Agro-industries, manufactures of input

Source: OECD and FAO, ESP

to agro-industries including the manufacture of fertilizers have been irregular because of the lumpy nature of capital investments. The share of concessional commitments in the total to Africa has tended to decline in line with what has happened in other regions, but the decline has been only marginal. It should be recalled that most of the Least Developed Countries are in Africa and that most of the donors agreed at the UN Conference on the LDCs held in Paris in 1981 to make special efforts to increase the flows of ODA to them [11].

---

[9] As revised by UN General Assembly, 37th Session, December 1982.

[10] Excluding Egypt, Libya and Sudan.

[11] Given the change in the list of LDCs, since the Conference, no up-dated estimates of requirements of assistance to LDCs' agriculture are available.

Assistance in 1982

Available information on official external assistance to agriculture in 1982 does not indicate a major change from the pattern for 1981. World recession and budgetary constraints which have limited the expansion in the volume of assistance in the last few years still underlie the lack of any major increase in the commitments of the major donor countries.

This situation is affecting not only bilateral but also multilateral development assistance. The World Bank's International Development Association (IDA) has had to reduce its commitments to all sectors to $2.7 billion in fiscal 1982 from $3.5 billion in the preceding year. It seems likely that IDA may also have to reduce its budgeted lending programme of $3.3 billion for fiscal year 1983, the last year of its sixth replenishment period.

The International Fund for Agricultural Development (IFAD) is also facing problems in financing its first 3 year replenishment period ending in December 1983. For this period, $630 million and $450 million had been pledged from OECD and OPEC sources respectively, but disbursements by donors have been delayed. If this situation continues, IFAD will have less than $250 million of uncommitted resources by the end of 1983, enough for only the first part of 1984, the beginning of its second replenishment period.

External Assistance for Agricultural Inputs

The provision of fertilizers and other inputs accounted for US $502 million of ODA commitments in 1981 (Table 1-15). This amounted to 4.4% of total OCA (broad definition) and showed a decline of over 11% compared to 1980 12/. The Far East region is the main recipient of fertilizer aid. It has received between 70%-90% of this aid but Africa increased its share in 1981.

Fertilizers are the major inputs provided under external assistance to agriculture, the largest share being provided by bilateral sources.

The operation of FAO's International Fertilizer Supply Scheme (IFS) has seriously diminished since it was established in 1975 in response to the then prevailing crisis in fertilizer supplies. The quantity handled by the IFS in 1981/82 was only 15 000 tons. The Commission on Fertilizers called on donors to replenish its resources so that it may continue to assist low-income countries expand their fertilizer use even in times of financial constraints.

The Far East region receives substantial assistance also for the development of its capacity to manufacture fertilizers. Total official commitments for assistance in the manufacture of inputs amounted to $806 million in 1981, a sharp increase over the previous year. However, commitments for this purpose as investments in fertilizer manufacture are very lumpy and large loans to a few projects can inflate the yearly figure.

---

12/ Alternative estimates quoted at the Fertilizer Commission put the volume of fertilizer aid at 2.0 million tons in 1981, virtually all from bilateral sources, equivalent to 5% of fertilizer consumed by developing countries in that year.

TABLE 1-15.   ODA COMMITMENTS FOR SUPPLY OF INPUTS

| | 1976 | 1977 | 1978 | 1979 | 1980 | 1981[1] |
|---|---|---|---|---|---|---|
| | ............... million $ ................ | | | | | |
| ODA COMMITMENTS FOR | | | | | | |
| Supply of fertilizers 2/ | 172 | 236 | 295 | 230 | 473 | 390 |
| Supply of other inputs 3/ | 56 | 18 | 35 | 40 | 93 | 112 |
| Total at current prices | 228 | 254 | 330 | 270 | 566 | 502 |
| Total at 1975 prices 4/ | 228 | 233 | 264 | 189 | 358 | 335 |
| Total at 1980 prices 4/ | 362 | 368 | 418 | 300 | 566 | 528 |
| ODA COMMITMENTS BY | | | | | | |
| Bilateral sources | 186 | 233 | 291 | 208 | 394 | 338 |
| Multilateral sources | 42 | 21 | 39 | 62 | 172 | 164 |
| | ................... % ................... | | | | | |
| Supply of inputs as share of total ODA commitments (broad definition) | 7 | 5 | 6 | 4 | 7 | 7 |
| Supply of inputs as share of total ODA commitments (narrow definition) | 9 | 8 | 7 | 5 | 10 | 11 |

1/   Preliminary.   2/   Excluding International Fertilizer Scheme commitments.

3/   Pesticides, agricultural equipment and machinery, seeds.

4/   Deflated by the UN unit value index for export of manufactured goods.

Source:   FAO and OECD.


Food Aid

Food aid allocations of cereals for 1982/83 stood at nearly 9.2 million tons by March 1983, a little more than was allocated at the same time in 1982 and also slightly above the quantity actually shipped in 1981/82 (Table 1-16).  The past year saw a sligtly smaller proportion of food aid being shipped to low-income food deficit countries (76% compared to 79% in 1980-81).  The proportion of cereal imports of these countries covered by food aid is at a low figure of 17%, having steadily declined in recent years.  Food aid has basically stagnated since 1976/77 while cereal imports of low-income countries have increased by over 60%.

Food aid had become slightly less concentrated in the traditional largest donors, the United States, EEC and Canada, although this trend has been recently reversed mainly because of increased contributions from the EEC.

As a means to ensure the level, predictability and continuity of emergency food aid, the Committee on Food Aid Policies and Programmes (CFA) agreed on having regular joint pledging conferences to identify resources for the World Food Programme (WFP) that comprises about 20% of all food aid, and the IEFR that the WFP administers.  The first joint pledging conference was held in March 1982 when pledges made amounted to only a little

over half of the pledging target for the WFP 1983-84 biennium of $1 200 million.  Sub-
sequently, pledges picked up and by the end of January 1983 they amounted to $993 million,
83% of the target.  Pledges for 1981-82 amounted to US $840 compared with a target of
$1 000 million.  An insufficiency of contributions in cash and in services can also be
noted for 1981-82.  They amounted to only 25% of the total compared with the target of
33%.  The Programme is thereby rendered less flexible and some development projects are
threatened if food cannot be purchased locally and its transport assured.

TABLE 1-16.  SHIPMENTS OF FOOD AID IN CEREALS, JULY/JUNE

|  | 1977/78 | 1978/79 | 1979/80 | 1980/81[1] | 1981/82[1] | 1982/83[1][2] |
|---|---|---|---|---|---|---|
|  | ............. thousand tons grain equivalent ............. | | | | | |
| Total | 9 216[3] | 9 502[3] | 8 886[3] | 8 908 | 9 026 | 9 361 |
|  | ....................... % ....................... | | | | | |
| Proportions of shipments made by the 3 largest donors:  USA, Canada & EEC | 90 | 86 | 82 | 79 | 82 | 83 |
| Share of the total to low income food-deficit countries4/ | 78 | 79 | 81 | 79 | 76 | 79[5] |
| Proportion of cereal imports of low income food deficit countries represented by food aid | 25 | 23 | 21 | 19 | 18 | 17 |

1/  Partly estimated.  2/  Allocations.

3/  In addition, according to unofficial reports, the USSR provided emergency aid to
    several countries in Asia amounting to 200 thousand tons each in 1977/78 and
    1979/80 and 400 thousand tons in 1978/79.

4/  Includes all food deficit countries with per caput income below the level used by
    the World Bank to determine eligibility for IDA assistance (i.e. with a per caput
    income of US $795 and below in 1981) which, in accordance with the guidelines and
    criteria agreed by the CFA, should be given priority in the allocation of food aid.

5/  Estimated.

Source:  FAO, ESC.

The value of net commitments of food aid under FAO/WFP in 1982 was estimated to be
$576 million compared to $488 million in 1981 when it had represented about 10% of concessional commitments to agriculture "narrow definition".  About 80% of these commitments
were to low-income food deficit countries and nearly the same proportion, about 77%, for
agricultural and rural development projects.

In reviewing food aid, the Thirteenth Session of the Committee on Food Aid Policies
and Programmes (CFA), held in April 1982, concluded that:

- Cereal food aid shipments in 1980/81 declined for the second year in a row, and allocations by donors again fell substantially short of the 10 million ton level agreed by the World Food conference.

- While the bulk of food aid continued to be directed to low-income food deficit countries, they have had to resort increasingly to commercial food imports.

- An encouraging development has been the relatively rapid increase in project-oriented food aid, particularly for the promotion of agricultural production and employment in rural areas. However, while cereal food aid for the establishment of national security reserves rose appreciably in 1980/81, it still represents only a fraction of identified needs.

- Multilateral food aid rose substantially in 1980 and, with larger contributions to the IEFR, the trend was likely to continue in 1981. However, contributions to WFP's regular resources are lagging behind the 1981-82 pledging target, and WFP shipments for development projects may have to be curtailed.

- Triangular transactions declined in 1981, mainly because of lower rice requirements for the emergency operation in Kampuchea. On the other hand, substantial purchases of maize were made by WFP in Zimbabwe for shipment to other African countries.


FISHERIES

The Situation in 1981

Commercial catches of fish, crustaceans and molluscs reached in 1981 the record level of 74.8 million tons, an increase of 2.5 million tons over the previous year (Table 1-17). There are some indications that rehabilitation of some stocks has contributed to the increase. This increase is the fourth consecutive and the most substantial after the fluctuations which marked world catches between 1972 when the anchoveta fishery in Peru collapsed, and 1977 when the extensions of national jurisdiction over marine resources became generalized.

With extended jurisdictions, the pattern of production has changed in the last few years. Less and less effort has been devoted to long-distance fisheries, where, according to preliminary estimates, the catch decreased by a further 4% in 1981. The shift to local fishing, both coastal and offshore, is also stimulated by increasing costs of fuel - though the increase of this moderated in 1981 - as well as by the uncertainty of the outcome of fishing agreements which must be renegotiated yearly. In many instances the return to local fishing by vessels once engaged in long-distance fishing has resulted in over-capacity and in excessive pressure on nearby fish stocks already intensively fished. At the same time, many countries are experiencing conflict among the various sub-sectors of their own fishing industries.

The largest part of the increase which took place in 1981 occurred in developing countries in South America and Asia. In Chile the 20% increase in landings was mainly for fish utilized by fish meal industries. Mexico's production was 26% higher than the previous year, following a major expansion in its catching capacity. Colombia (+43%) and Uruguay (+20%) also increased their output, the former to supply mainly its domestic market and the latter the export sector. Argentina's production has continued its downward trend in the face of marketing problems and it is back to the level of output prevailing before the extension of national jurisdiction.

TABLE 1-17.  WORLD AND REGIONAL CATCH OF FISH, CRUSTACEANS AND MOLLUSCS INCLUDING
ALL AQUATIC ORGANISMS EXCEPT WHALES AND SEA WEEDS

| | | | | Change | | Annual rate of change | |
| | 1979 | 1980 | 1981 | 1979 to 1980 | 1980 to 1981 | 1977 to 1981 | 1971 to 1980 |
|---|---|---|---|---|---|---|---|
| | .. million m.t. .. | | | .......... % .......... | | | |
| Developing market economies | 26.7 | 26.6 | 28.0 | -0.1 | 5.6 | 4.2 | 1.7 |
| Africa | 3.3 | 3.2 | 3.3 | -3.0 | 1.0 | -1.3 | -1.2 |
| Far East | 12.1 | 12.4 | 12.8 | 2.7 | 3.3 | 1.4 | 4.0 |
| Latin America | 10.0 | 9.6 | 10.5 | -4.2 | 9.0 | 10.0 | -0.2 |
| Near East | 0.9 | 1.0 | 1.0 | 11.0 | 3.8 | 12.1 | 4.1 |
| Other | 0.4 | 0.4 | 0.4 | 1.9 | 0.5 | 3.4 | 7.2 |
| Asian centrally planned economies | 7.4 | 7.6 | 8.0 | 3.5 | 4.8 | 1.0 | 2.8 |
| Total developing countries | 34.1 | 34.2 | 36.1 | 0.6 | 5.5 | 3.5 | 2.0 |
| Developed market economies | 26.9 | 27.5 | 27.8 | 1.9 | 1.5 | 0.6 | 0.9 |
| North America | 4.9 | 5.0 | 5.1 | 0.9 | 3.2 | 4.4 | 3.0 |
| Oceania | 0.2 | 0.2 | 0.2 | -4.6 | 2.6 | 2.9 | 3.4 |
| Western Europe | 11.2 | 11.2 | 11.2 | 0.2 | - | -1.7 | 0.3 |
| Other | 10.6 | 11.1 | 11.3 | 4.2 | 2.3 | 1.4 | 0.7 |
| Eastern Europe and USSR | 10.3 | 10.6 | 10.8 | 3.7 | 1.5 | 1.1 | 1.8 |
| Total developed countries | 37.2 | 38.1 | 38.7 | 2.4 | 1.5 | 0.7 | 1.2 |
| World | 71.3 | 72.3 | 74.8 | 1.6 | 3.4 | 2.0 | 1.5 |

Source:  FAO, Fisheries Department.

Increased fishery production was a feature for almost all Asian countries in 1981 with Thailand being the most noticeable exception.  Its fishing industry is suffering both because of problems of readjustment to the new ocean regime and because of excessive exploitation of many domestic stocks.  In India a 10% expansion of the freshwater fisheries was barely enough to outweigh decreased yields from marine waters along its coasts bordering the West Indian Ocean.

Readjustment is also constraining the physical expansion of fishing by many West African countries, even though abundant resources are still to be found off their shores. Some coastal countries have opted for the development of their own industrial fleets and have concentrated mainly on the production of high-value species demanded by international markets.  But they have had only limited success.

The developed countries, considered as a group, have not shown any significant change in their catches, and their fishing output in 1981 was only marginally higher than in 1980. However, production in Japan and the USSR rose. While global catches of both the EEC and Eastern European countries showed no change, catches of northern European countries as a group moderately recovered from the 1980 level which had been the lowest in the last six years. Coastal countries fishing in the North East Atlantic have shown marginally increased landings of food fish and the declines by and large were confined to the fishmeal and oil industry.

The catch of food fish of about 53.5 million tons was significantly (5%-6%) higher in 1981 than in the previous year, following a period of stagnation. There is evidence that at the world level the increase of fishery production accrued entirely to the direct food sector. A contribution to this increase came also from inland water fisheries which in 1981 yielded 500 thousand tons, a gain of 6.5%.

The declines in catches of fish for reduction to meal and oil were due, in part, to a decline in the demand for fishmeal. This was affected by the general stagnation in the protein meals market, which coincided with weakened economic conditions and had particularly unfavourable consequences in some large markets such as Eastern Europe. While the developing countries as a group utilized almost the same amount of fish as in the previous year for industrial purposes, the decline occurred in the developed nations as a whole. This, in some instances, was due to resource limitations on certain fisheries widely used for that purpose such as the capelin fishery in Iceland. The total for developing countries was unchanged. However, Chile expanded further its fish reduction industry and, to a lesser extent, Mexico also utilized part of its increased catch as raw material for fish meal.

In the absence of major developments in the exploitation of unconventional resources, it seems unlikely that the annual rates of increase in world fishery production will depart from those recently prevailing.

Estimates for 1982

The indication for the first part of 1982 is that seafood supplies have generally been adequate to meet demand. Current demand levels have been depressed by the unfavourable economic conditions prevailing in many large markets and the more competitive prices of meat products. A particular example is the tuna fishery which is currently going through dramatic changes with world-wide ramifications. A severe decline in consumer demand for canned tuna in 1981 and 1982 in the United States, one of the biggest markets, is leading to a major restructuring of its industry. This, in turn, has been affecting tuna producing industries in several developing countries.

The output of the fishmeal industry is expected to have increased moderately compared to 1981 although catches of some major species, such as Chilean and Japanese pilchard, cannot have sustained their most recent growth rates. Statistics for the first nine months of 1982 point to a further expansion of fishmeal production in Chile and Peru.

The Norwegian fishmeal industry also increased output with catches 7% higher in the first 11 months of 1982 than in the same period of 1981, mainly as a result of more abundant landings of capelin. In Iceland and South Africa, which also rank among the largest fishmeal producers, the downward trend continued through 1982. For the medium-term, although there is still a potential for the growth of protein meal consumption in many developing countries, the demand for it will be very dependent upon trends in the soybean meal market.

Trade in Fishery Products

The expansion of fishery trade forecast, following the change in the ocean fishery regime, has been hampered partly by the slowness in the restructuring of the production sector in those countries which acquired control over abundant resources. Also relatively large increases in prices, coinciding in some instances with reduced real incomes, have shifted consumers' demand toward non-fishery foods in some major importing countries.

However, in 1981 world trade in fishery products - especially exports from developing countries - has proved to be more resilient to the effects of the economic recession than most other groups of agricultural commodities. Based on evidence that is still preliminary for many developing countries, the current value of exports of fishery products in 1981 was above US $15 000 million, an increase of 3% over 1980, but below the world inflation rate (Table 1-18). Much of the increase accrued to the developing countries taken as a group for which fishery products accounts for 7% of total agricultural exports. However, recent annual increases in percentage terms are well below those in the years of the expansion in the 1960s and the first part of the 1970s. In 1981 developing countries specializing in exports of selected fishery commodities were adversely affected by the conditions prevailing in their main markets. Tuna, crustacean and cephalopod products, which account for a large share of their sectoral export trade, fetched on average lower prices than a year before.

TABLE 1-18. INDEX NUMBERS OF VALUE, VOLUME AND UNIT VALUE OF EXPORTS OF FISHERY PRODUCTS: WORLD, DEVELOPING AND DEVELOPED COUNTRIES

| | | | | Change | | Annual rate of change | |
|---|---|---|---|---|---|---|---|
| | | | | 1979 to 1980 | 1980 to 1981 | 1977 to 1981 | 1971 to 1980 |
| | 1979 | 1980 | 1981 | | | | |
| | ... 1969-71 = 100 ... | | | ........... % ........... | | | |
| VALUE | 479.6 | 513.0 | 520.1 | 7.0 | 1.4 | 13.2 | 17.9 |
| Developing countries | 597.7 | 627.3 | 643.0 | 5.0 | 2.5 | 14.5 | 21.0 |
| Developed countries | 425.2 | 460.3 | 463.5 | 8.3 | 0.7 | 12.4 | 16.2 |
| VOLUME | 169.6 | 169.9 | 173.7 | 0.2 | 2.2 | 6.1 | 5.5 |
| Developing countries | 220.2 | 209.4 | 215.1 | -0.5 | 2.7 | 5.6 | 8.2 |
| Developed countries | 148.6 | 152.4 | 156.0 | 2.6 | 2.4 | 6.1 | 4.0 |
| UNIT VALUE | 285.9 | 310.2 | 306.8 | 8.5 | -0.1 | 6.4 | 11.9 |
| Developing countries | 271.3 | 310.4 | 306.4 | 14.4 | -1.3 | 7.2 | 11.7 |
| Developed countries | 290.8 | 310.0 | 307.3 | 6.6 | -0.9 | 6.4 | 12.0 |

Source: FAO, Fisheries Department.

## COOPERATIVE MANAGEMENT OF FISHERY RESOURCES
## IN THE SOUTH PACIFIC OCEAN

With the establishment of the new regime for the oceans, a vast area of the western Pacific has now come under the jurisdiction of a relatively few countries, most of which are small developing and newly-independent island states. Abundant resources of highly-valued tuna pass through this area, fished largely by the fleets of Japan, the United States and a few other countries from outside the region. For the small island states the exclusive economic zones (EEZs) of 200-mile exclusive fishing zones provide a new and important source of wealth. In 1981 fish worth over US $400 million were taken from the zones of the member and observer states of the South Pacific Forum Fisheries Agency (FFA).

In order the realize fully the opportunities provided by this new wealth, the island states need to achieve a high degree of cooperation in the management of the stocks they share. The harmonization of their regimes is necessary for the collection of appropriate levels of fees from the distant-water fleets and for ensuring effective compliance with the arrangements worked out with foreign countries.

The countries of the region have taken major steps towards establishing effective cooperation. The South Pacific Forum Fisheries Agency, established in 1979, now includes 14 member countries (Australia, Cook Islands, Federated States of Micronesia, Fiji, Kiribati, Nauru, New Zealand, Niue, Papua New Guinea, Solomon Islands, Tonga, Tuvalu, Vanuatu and Western Samoa) and two observer countries (Marshall Islands and Palau).

These countries have recently agreed on a number of measures for harmonized control over foreign fishing fleets. They have agreed to establish a regional register of foreign fishing vessels and to grant fishing licences only to those vessels accorded "good standing" status on the register. Information on illegal activities of fishing vessels will be passed on to the FFA for recording.

The states have also agreed on certain minimum standards for foreign fishing vessels access. These include the requirement that foreign fishing vessels provide notification of their entry into or departure from any zone or port; that they regularly report their position; and that they complete standard log sheets giving their regional tuna catch and fishing effort.

Although there is still a long way to go, the achievement of these steps in the brief period since the establishment of the FFA provides a remarkable example of economic cooperation among developing island states.

However, the overall increase in the value of fishery trade in 1981 was due entirely to increased prices because its volume, in absolute terms, contracted for the second consecutive year. This was almost entirely attributable to decreased overseas sales of fishmeal since all the major food product groups, with the exception of canned seafoods, showed some increase in quantity. In 1981 both Japan and the USA, which together account for some 45% of total fishery imports, increased their receipts from abroad, while in the same year imports decreased in several large importers in the EEC. Among developing countries, which as a group are net exporters of fishery products, increased earnings accrued to traditional large exporters in Asia such as the Republic of Korea, Thailand and India and to some of the new entrants, such as the Philippines. Exports from Latin America reflected the decreased exports of fishmeal, while in Africa the expansion of Moroccan trade was offset by decreased overseas sales by Senegal.

In 1982 prices remained at high levels. However, in the last months of the year, following the condition of over-supply of certain food fishery products, some price decreases apparently took place. Some further substitution within seafood commodities also is likely to have continued. Although a moderate expansion of fishery trade is believed to have taken place in 1982, developments in the short-run depend mainly upon the evolution of the world economic situation.

## Management Issues

With many of the largest stocks of easily-accessible fishery resources reaching the level of maximum sustainable exploitation, more and more attention is being paid to management issues. Several fisheries in the most productive marine areas are already subject to quota regulations. Resource management problems are receiving more attention as it is felt that additional amounts of fish will be available through improvement in the management of the resources rather than in adding to catching capacity. A World Conference on Fisheries Management and Development sponsored by the FAO is being held in two sessions in 1983 and 1984. It will address itself to basic issues of management and development of the world fisheries, and to aspects of exploitation of the resources brought about by the changed regime of the oceans.

## FORESTRY

## Production and Trade

World production of major forest products was strongly influenced by the economic recession that developed in 1980 and 1981, when a sharp decline took place in housing construction in developed countries and consequently in the demand for some processed wood products. Production of sawnwood in North America is estimated to have dropped 11% in 1980 and a further 8% in 1981. In 1981 there was also a decline of 6% in sawnwood production in Western Europe, and one of 20% in the production of similar wood products in Japan following a 15% decline in 1980 (Table 1-19).

International trade in forest products was also adversely affected by the recession (Table 1-20). Imports of tropical timber in 1981 were down by over one-fifth in both Western Europe and Japan. Trade in tropical logs was reduced by 23% and that of tropical sawnwood by 21%. As a consequence a number of developing countries experienced sharp declines in their exports of forest products. Shipments of sawnwood declined by 31% in the Ivory Coast, by 19% in western Malaysia, and by 13% in the Philippines. On the other hand, trade in tropical plywood increased by 12% because an expansion in exports from Indonesia and other countries in Asia more than offset a further decrease in the Republic of Korea.

With the continuing depressed state in 1982 of the construction industry in North America, Japan and some European countries, there has been no appreciable recovery of the export of tropical timber. This has compounded the difficulties faced by exporting developing countries attempting to establish new industries based on this product.

TABLE 1-19.   WORLD OUTPUT OF MAIN FOREST PRODUCTS

| | 1979 | 1980 | 1981 | Change 1979 to 1980 | Change 1980 to 1981 | Annual rate of change 1971 to 1980 | Annual rate of change 1977 to 1981 |
|---|---|---|---|---|---|---|---|
| | .... million c.m. .... | | | .......... % .......... | | | |
| TOTAL ROUNDWOOD | 3 094 | 3 160 | 3 142 | 2.1 | -0.6 | 1.9 | 1.8 |
| Developed countries | 1 341 | 1 349 | 1 314 | 0.6 | -2.6 | 0.7 | 1.1 |
| Developing countries | 1 753 | 1 812 | 1 828 | 3.4 | 0.9 | 2.8 | 2.4 |
| Fuelwood and charcoal | 1 650 | 1 718 | 1 759 | 4.1 | 1.0 | 2.4 | 3.1 |
| Developed countries | 205 | 232 | 245 | 13.2 | 5.6 | 2.3 | 9.5 |
| Developing countries | 1 444 | 1 486 | 1 513 | 2.9 | 1.8 | 2.4 | 2.2 |
| Industrial roundwood | 1 445 | 1 442 | 1 384 | -0.2 | -0.4 | 1.2 | 0.3 |
| Developed countries | 1 136 | 1 116 | 1 069 | -1.8 | -4.2 | 0.4 | -0.4 |
| Developing countries | 309 | 326 | 315 | 5.5 | -3.4 | 4.7 | 3.0 |
| PROCESSED WOOD PRODUCTS | | | | | | | |
| Sawnwood and sleepers | 451 | 439 | 419 | -2.7 | -4.6 | 0.4 | -1.4 |
| Developed countries | 368 | 352 | 337 | -4.3 | -4.3 | -0.5 | -2.3 |
| Developing countries | 82 | 87 | 82 | 6.1 | -5.7 | 5.4 | 2.4 |
| Wood-based panels | 106 | 101 | 97 | -4.7 | -4.0 | 3.0 | -1.3 |
| Developed countries | 93 | 87 | 83 | -6.5 | -4.6 | 2.3 | -2.0 |
| Developing countries | 14 | 14 | 14 | - | - | 7.6 | 3.9 |
| | .... million m.t. .... | | | | | | |
| Woodpulp | 127 | 130 | 129 | 2.4 | -0.8 | 2.2 | 3.6 |
| Developed countries | 113 | 115 | 114 | 1.8 | -0.9 | 1.7 | 1.4 |
| Developing countries | 14 | 16 | 16 | 14.3 | - | 8.7 | 9.0 |
| Paper and paperboard | 173 | 175 | 175 | 1.2 | - | 3.0 | 3.4 |
| Developed countries | 153 | 153 | 153 | - | - | 2.4 | 3.0 |
| Developing countries | 21 | 22 | 22 | 4.8 | - | 8.0 | 6.8 |

Source:   FAO, Forestry Department.


However, this reduction in international trade was due not only to the economic recession in industrial countries but also to a deliberate policy adopted by a number of
exporting developing countries of expanding local processing by curtailing the direct
export of unprocessed logs.  For example, Indonesia's log exports have been reduced drastically but its share of tropical plywood production and exports has risen substantially.
This issue is discussed further below.

The recession in the developed countries affected the pulp and paper industry much less.  In most of the major producing countries production in 1981 was maintained at 1980 levels, and in Finland, New Zealand and the United States production of some grades reached record levels.  Japan experienced the sharpest reduction, pulp production going down by 9% and paper production by 6% as active measures were taken to reduce high levels of inventories.  In the latter part of 1981 and 1982 production of pulp and paper also fell sharply in North America and Europe to a level some 5% below the average for 1980.

TABLE 1-20.  VOLUME OF EXPORTS OF MAIN FOREST PRODUCTS, WORLD, DEVELOPING AND DEVELOPED COUNTRIES

| | | | | Change | | Annual rate of change | |
|---|---|---|---|---|---|---|---|
| | | | | 1979 to 1980 | 1980 to 1981 | 1971 to 1980 | 1977 to 1981 |
| | 1979 | 1980 | 1981 | 1980 | 1981 | 1980 | 1981 |
| | .... million c.m. .... | | | .............% ............ | | | |
| INDUSTRIAL ROUNDWOOD | 118.4 | 115.1 | 102.0 | -2.8 | -11.4 | 2.6 | -2.5 |
| Developed countries | 71.8 | 73.0 | 69.1 | 1.7 | -5.3 | 3.7 | 1.2 |
| Developing countries | 46.6 | 42.1 | 32.9 | -9.7 | -21.9 | 1.0 | -8.5 |
| PROCESSED WOOD PRODUCTS | | | | | | | |
| Sawnwood and sleepers | 83.3 | 79.8 | 72.8 | -4.2 | -8.8 | 3.3 | -0.2 |
| Developed countries | 71.3 | 68.7 | 63.5 | -3.6 | -7.6 | 2.9 | -0.4 |
| Developing countries | 12.1 | 11.0 | 9.2 | -9.1 | -16.4 | 6.7 | 1.0 |
| Wood-based panels | 16.3 | 15.7 | 15.9 | -3.7 | 1.3 | 3.7 | 1.3 |
| Developed countries | 11.2 | 11.0 | 10.8 | -1.8 | -1.8 | 4.8 | 2.0 |
| Developing countries | 5.1 | 4.7 | 5.1 | -7.8 | 8.5 | 3.7 | -0.2 |
| | .... million m.t. .... | | | | | | |
| Pulp | 18.7 | 19.9 | 19.0 | 6.4 | -4.5 | 3.3 | 5.4 |
| Developed countries | 17.4 | 18.3 | 17.3 | 5.2 | -5.5 | 2.7 | 4.1 |
| Developing countries | 1.3 | 1.6 | 1.7 | 23.1 | 6.2 | 14.6 | 25.2 |
| Paper and paperboard | 33.3 | 35.1 | 35.6 | 5.4 | 1.4 | 3.7 | 6.2 |
| Developed countries | 32.7 | 34.2 | 34.5 | 4.6 | 0.9 | 3.6 | 5.9 |
| Developing countries | 0.6 | 0.9 | 1.1 | 50.0 | 22.2 | 10.1 | 21.9 |

Source:  FAO, Forestry Department.

Among developing countries, Brazil suffered a decline in pulp and paper production after many years of sustained growth.  However, in 1982 Brazil's exports were up 60% on 1981 - the exception among exporters.  In Argentina a combination of industrial recession and high rates of inflation resulted in pulp and paper production falling in 1981 to a level below that of 1974, with only 65% utilization of established capacity.  The economic recession also led several countries to postpone announced plans to expand capacity.

Current dollar prices of forest products have increased dramatically in the decade to 1980 but there has been very wide variation in the magnitude of the increase between products. In real terms the prices of some products such as tropical logs and sawnwood and charcoal have increased substantially but the real prices of some others such as pulpwood and particleboard have tended to decline.

The trend in the terms of trade for major forest products of developing countries has thus been generally upward. However, in 1981 international market prices of most of these products reflected the depressed state of the market, and they declined 5%-10% in current dollar prices in early 1982.

The increase in fuelwood production occurring in the developing countries reflects the growth in population. It is, however, estimated that in 1980 more than 100 million people lived in areas where the population could not obtain sufficient fuelwood even through overcutting. In a much larger area production is resulting in overcutting of existing resources. The 1981 increase of real prices of fuelwood and charcoal is a clear warning signal of increasing scarcities in the fuelwood supply situation and further confirmation of the energy crisis occurring in the developing countries.

Up until the mid-1970s fuelwood consumption in the developed world was steadily decreasing. However, the oil shock led to a reversal of this trend and most developed countries are now reporting increases in their relatively low consumption levels. A new survey just completed in the United States indicates a sixfold increase in fuelwood production in that country since 1973 to a total of some 90 million $m^3$ in 1980.

Increasing Benefit from Forest Resources

Forests make up 4 200 million ha, or 30% of the world's land area; just over half this area is in developing countries. Some 11 million ha of forests are cleared for agriculture or destroyed or degraded by shifting cultivation, fuelwood gathering, overgrazing or burning each year.

Forest land is widely perceived as a source of agricultural land and forest products as goods freely available for collection. The pressure of population is such that in many areas the supply of forest products, particularly fuelwood, is being depleted and the land being taken for agriculture is of poor quality. The resulting destruction of the forest is harmful to soil and water conservation as well as to the future supply of forest products. International organizations have signalled the risks of forest depletion and some Governments have announced policies and regulations to control it. In some cases also local people, as in the 'Chipco' movement in India, have risen in protest against tree cutting 13/. Yet tangible action to reverse the trend to forest depletion has not emerged and the pressure from people to meet their immediate needs for food and fuel continues.

Total tree planting of 1 million ha per year in tropical countries is only one tenth the rate of forest clearing and destruction. However, the programme in 1982 is double the average programme during 1976-80. Major forestry projects are being instituted in several countries to mobilize local communities to conserve the forest and to plant trees for their own use.

---

13/ Chipco is a Hindu word meaning 'to hug' in a protective sense.

An important complement of the operational programme is forestry research. Its design to meet the needs of developing countries has been the subject of reconsideration by the international community. This review has pointed out the need to give greater emphasis to research into farming systems incorporating trees, to increasing the productivity of trees in the supply of biomass and energy, to conserving wood through greater efficiency of conversion to energy by improved stove design, and research into effective management and conservation of tropical forest.

The selection of species and provenances and the collection and distribution of seed and plant material to allow their propagation, is a fundamentally important component in increasing the production of wood and other products through tree planting. International collaboration is directed to the identification of priority species, the establishment of seed collection programmes to secure and to establish research trials and seed stands. The FAO seed programme coordinates the collection of seed for international use carried out by some 15 national institutions. As a result of this programme, international provenance trials and seedstands have been established for tropical, subtropical and Mediterranean species in a large number of developing countries. A recent initiative has been the establishment of a cooperative genetic resource programme between 8 developing countries in the arid and semi-arid zones on species for fuelwood production of the genera Acacia, Eucalyptus and Prosopis. As an illustration of the potential, earlier trials in 21 countries on provenances of the species Eucalyptus camaldulensis have demonstrated that selection of the best provenance may result in an increase of 600% in yield of fuelwood compared with the least suited provenance.

## Policy and Investment in Forest Industries

The forestry sector can make a valuable contribution through the value added in the manufacture of wood products either for domestic consumption or for export. In developing countries over the decade to 1981 expansion of the sawnwood and wood-based panels industries has been at the relatively rapid rates of 5.5% and 7.5% respectively per annum, although it has slowed somewhat with recessionary conditions in the last few years, as has been noted. The feature of the current period is the effort by a number of countries to develop processing industries so that they may replace exports of roundwood with exports of higher value manufactured wood products and to meet domestic requirements for them.

As has been mentioned earlier, Indonesia has combined a programme to restrict export of unprocessed roundwood with incentives and regulations to encourage investment in manufacturing. Roundwood exports have been brought down from a peak of 21 million $m^3$ in 1978 to about 3 million $m^3$ in 1982. By 1981 production of sawnwood had increased to 3.5 million $m^3$ with exports increasing to 1.2 million $m^3$ from a nominal level at the beginning of the decade. Output of plywood has risen from 25 000 $m^3$ in 1974 to over 1 million $m^3$ in 1981 and exports of this product have increased to more than 0.5 million $m^3$ from zero during this period. Malaysia (particualrly the State of Sabah) and Paraguay are further examples of countries which have recently built up a sawmilling industry for production for export rather than exporting roundwood. However, this policy, which aims to increase domestic value added through the unprocessed product, may have lost some momentum in view of depressed demand, falling prices and a low utilization of the processing capacity installed.

Investment in Brazil and Nigeria has been directed to increase production on the basis of indigenous raw materials in order to meet rapidly increasing domestic demand. Some investment in the Near East countries has been designed to meet domestic demand using imported raw materials. An investment programme based on the production of veneer, plywood and sawnwood has been instituted in Bhutan with the objective of rapid acquisition of industry experience for the planned utilization of rich indigenous forest resources.

# TRENDS IN RESOURCE AND INPUT USE FOR AGRICULTURAL PRODUCTION AND SOME SELECTED ISSUES

## INTRODUCTION

The main challenge facing world agriculture is to ensure a regular supply of food and agricultural output to match rising demands by the world's population, which is currently increasing at an overall rate of 1.7%.  This has to be achieved with resources that are either finite (such as land) or growing at slow rates (such as the agricultural labour force).

The following discussion focuses on the developing countries and their prime need to mobilize their resources to meet the challenge posed by rising demand for agricultural products and to raise incomes.  Such mobilization essentially can be one or a combination of the following approaches:

- land expansion or intensification including irrigation;

- intensified use of sources of animal or machine power to increase productivity of labour;

- wider use of modern inputs - seeds, fertilizers, pesticides, animal feeds.

The changing pattern of resource and input use can be viewed from many different perspectives.  Output gains may not be the only consideration.  Other issues not directly linked to growth in output and incomes may also be to the fore, such as inequities of access to farming resources, the creation of employment in rural areas and environmental protection so that the natural resource base is not destroyed or human health endangered.

The section provides an overview of the broad pattern of actual and potential resource and input use in developing countries.  Some reference to developed countries is made for comparison.  No systematic attempt is made in this brief survey to relate the use of different resources and inputs to output.  However, selected issues related to individual resources or inputs are raised, in particular the impact of their greater use on the environment.

## OVERALL PATTERNS OF RESOURCE AND INPUT USE

By 1980 the developing countries were producing over half of the world's crop output but only a quarter of its livestock output.  In so doing they used a widely differing combination of resources and inputs compared to developed countries (Fig. 1-7). They had about half of the total area of arable land and land under permanent crops but nearly three-quarters of the irrigated land.  Their agricultural labour force was over 90% of the world's total.  On the other hand they used less than a third of the total fertilizers consumed, one-sixth of the world's tractors and a quarter of the animal feeds.

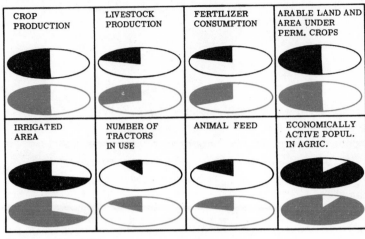

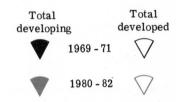

Figure 1-7
SHARES OF DEVELOPED AND
DEVELOPING COUNTRIES IN
WORLD TOTALS OF AGRICULTURAL
OUTPUT AND SELECTED INPUT USES

Source: FAO, ESS

The rates of growth of output and input use have also differed quite widely between these two groups of countries during the 1970s (Fig. 1-8). Crop production in developing

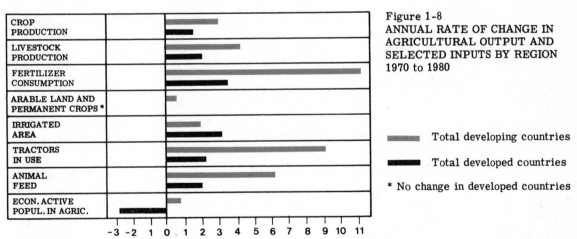

Figure 1-8
ANNUAL RATE OF CHANGE IN
AGRICULTURAL OUTPUT AND
SELECTED INPUTS BY REGION
1970 to 1980

Source: FAO, ESS

countries has increased by 2.9% per annum, double the rate of increase of developed countries. But land use increased by less than 1% per annum in the former and not at all in the latter, implying that purchased inputs have been an important element in productivity increases. Thus the developing countries' consumption of fertilizer has increased at over 11% per annum and their use of tractors as a source of power has increased at over 9% per annum. These increases in fertilizer and tractors are, however, less striking when viewed in absolute amounts. Livestock production in developing countries has increased faster than crop production, and more than twice as fast as in developed countries. But consumption of animal feed has also increased particularly rapidly in developing countries.


EMERGING PRESSURES FOR MORE AGRICULTURAL RESOURCES

The developing and developed countries differ with respect to likely future press-ures on agricultural resources. Scenario B of AT 2000 14/ projects that total demand for agricultural products of the 90 developing countries covered by the study will increase by 3.2% per annum over the period 1980-2000. This rate of increase in demand is a little higher than the past two decades (3.1%) and significantly higher than the growth achieved in agricultural production (2.8%).

In their bid to increase agricultural output more rapidly, developing countries will face issues that complicate decision making. Increasingly they will have to use modern inputs to supplement their natural resource base. Increasingly, therefore, they will face the problems of how to make these inputs available and at what cost. There will be need for emphasis on technologies and farming systems that not only are success-ful in increasing output, but also are efficient in the use of inputs. Policy decisions on whether or not to subsidize agricultural inputs will gain added importance.

As for the developed countries, Scenario B implies a slowing down in rate of growth of their agricultural output. Domestic demand in 1980-2000 is projected to increase at an annual rate of only 1.1% for the market economies and 1.5% for the centrally planned economies of the developed world. That is, rates of increase would be only one-third to one-half than those of developing countries. This compares with past rates of growth in production of 2.1% and 1.4% during the 1970s for the market and centrally planned economies respectively.


THE BASIC RESOURCES: LAND AND LABOUR


The Distribution of Land in Relation to Population

Striking differences among regions are apparent when use of arable land is ex-pressed in relation to total population or agricultural labour force (Table 1-21). For instance, the average density of agricultural labour per hectare of crop land in China and other centrally planned economies of Asia is 200 times as great as North America or Oceania.

---

14/ Agriculture: Toward 2000 (AT 2000), FAO, Rome, 1981. Two scenarios were developed: Scenario A is based on the doubling of agricultural production in the developing countries between 1980 and 2000. This would involve a growth rate of 3.7% per year. The less ambitious Scenario B is built around an 80% rise in output between 1980 and 2000, implying a 3.1% increase per year. The use of inputs and resources would have to increase more than proportionally under Scenario A, which involves more than doubling annual investments and no less than tripling current inputs alone.

TABLE 1-21.  DISTRIBUTION OF ARABLE AND PERMANENT CROP LAND IN RELATION TO TOTAL
POPULATION AND AGRICULTURAL LABOUR FORCE, 1980 1/

| | Arable and permanent crop land | Arable and Permanent crop land per person: | |
| --- | --- | --- | --- |
| | | of total population | of agricultural labour force 1/ |
| | ... million ha ... | ........... ha ............ | |
| Africa | 150.2 | 0.4 | 1.5 |
| Asia | 268.1 | 0.2 | 0.9 |
| Latin America | 162.1 | 0.4 | 4.2 |
| Near East | 87.3 | 0.4 | 2.5 |
| Other developing countries | 1.1 | 0.2 | 0.7 |
| Asian centrally planned economies | 111.7 | 0.1 | 0.4 |
| Total developing countries | 780.6 | 0.2 | 1.0 |
| North America | 235.0 | 0.9 | 87.0 |
| Western Europe | 95.1 | 0.3 | 5.7 |
| Oceania | 44.9 | 2.6 | 89.8 |
| Others | 18.9 | 0.1 | 1.9 |
| Eastern Europe and USSR | 277.8 | 0.7 | 7.2 |
| Total developed countries | 671.6 | 0.6 | 9.9 |

1/  Economically active population in agriculture.

Source:  FAO, Production Yearbook.


    There are also wide regional differences in the percentage of land in permanent
grassland but, unless livestock are raised mainly on forage feeds, the carrying capacity of this land, in terms of livestock units, does not differ so widely.  In the
Far East, where there are over 800 livestock units per $Km^2$, ruminant livestock are fed
mainly on crop residues and by-products.  In Western Europe, which also raises ruminant
livestock relatively intensively, they are fed on a variety of concentrate feeds or
forages from cropped land 15/.

    During the 1970s, the world arable land and land under permanent crops increased
by only 0.3% per annum, while crop production grew by 2.2% per annum and world population by 1.8% per annum.

---

15/  For more details and wider discussion, see Chapter 2, Table 2-9.

An analysis of data from 86 developing countries shows a strong positive association between land use in relation to the agricultural population and output and agricultural incomes.  What is the potential in this regard?

According to data assembled for AT 2000, arable land 16/ and land under permanent crops constituted by 1980 much less than half (42%) of the total of potentially cultivable land in the 90 developing countries (excluding China) analysed in the study. However, less than one-sixth of their population in 1980 lived in countries estimated as being "land abundant", with up to 40% of their potentially cultivable land being utilized.  About 50% of their total population lived in 18 countries (seven in Africa, seven in the Near East and four in the Far East) which have extremely scarce land resources and already use over 90% of their potentially cultivable land (Table 1-22).

TABLE 1-22.  ARABLE LAND IN RELATION TO POTENTIAL LAND AREA AND
POPULATION, 90 DEVELOPING COUNTRIES, 1980

| Category of country | Number of countries | Share of arable land in potential land area | Population |
|---|---|---|---|
| | | ................. % ............... | |
| Land abundant 1/ | 27 | 17 | 14 |
| Land moderately abundant 2/ | 24 | 57 | 20 |
| Land scarce 3/ | 21 | 83 | 16 |
| Extremely land scarce 4/ | 18 | 96 | 50 |
| Total | 90 | 42 | 100 |

1/ Land-abundant:  cultivating up to 40% of potential arable land.

2/ Land moderately abundant:  cultivating from 41 to 70% of potential arable land.

3/ Land-scarce:  cultivating from 71 to 90% of potential arable land.

4/ Extreme land scarcity:  cultivating over 90% of potential arable land.

Source:  FAO, AT 2000.

16/ Land under temporary crops, temporary meadows, land under market or kitchen gardens and land temporarily fallow or lying idle.  See explanatory notes to FAO Production Yearbooks.

According to these criteria the 37 countries of Africa and the 24 countries of Latin America included in AT 2000 would be regarded as land abundant. In 1980 they used respectively 32% and 27% of their potential arable land. However, they accounted for only 30% of the population. The 14 countries of the Near East covered in the study may be termed moderately land abundant using about 64% of their potential arable land but accounting for less than 9% of the population. Over 60% of the remaining population were in the 15 countries of Asia which are land scarce, cultivating on average 80% of their potential arable land. Including China, which was not covered by the AT 2000 study but which is also a land scarce country, then about 70% of the population of developing countries are living in countries that may be regarded already as land-scarce. The distribution of potential arable land is thus very uneven in relation to the distribution of population in developing countries.

Those countries which have been able to expand crop production by bringing more land into cultivation have tended not to show significant increases in average yields. For example, Brazil increased its production of paddy by nearly 175% between 1950 and 1980. The area under the crop increased by over 200% but average yields actually declined by 12%. Conversely, during the same period India increased paddy output by 132%, but the area under the crop increased by less than a third while average yields increased by over 70%.

## Increasing land productivity

As cultivable land becomes scarcer in relation to population, the pressure grows to increase its productivity. In the 1970s land productivity improved more rapidly in developing than in developed countries. In the former, cropped areas expanded only by 0.6% per annum, population by 2.2% and crop production by 2.9%. In the developed countries cropped area did not expand, population increased by less than 1% per year and crop production by only 1.5%.

Land productivity growth was highest (3.3%) in China and the other centrally planned economies of Asia, where land is scarcer in relation to population. Other countries in the Near and Far East were not far behind with an average increase in land productivity of 2.6% per annum. Latin America, which has a relatively large potential of unexploited new land, followed with 2.0%. The increase in the productivity of land was lowest (0.5% per annum) in Africa, where in general terms land is still relatively abundant.

The conventional path leading to the modernization of agriculture and increasing the productivity of land is the use of more inputs associated with improved technology, such as improved seeds, fertilizers and better water management through irrigation. Frequently, of course, the means of increasing output per unit of land go together as a package: for example, irrigation makes it feasible to use the improved technology. The response in yield to the package as a whole is greater than the sum of the responses of the inputs used individually. This has been the basis of the Green Revolution in Asia. For example, in 1975 average yields of paddy were over 150% as great in the Republic of Korea, which had an irrigation rate of 90% 17/, as in Bangladesh with an irrigation rate of 5%.

---

17/  Irrigation rate = (Harvested irrigated area/Total harvested area) x 100.

But the Republic of Korea was also using fertilizer much more intensively than Bangladesh: in 1975 their average usage of fertilizer was 202 kg and 24kg per ha respectively. Therefore irrigation can be key factor underlying improved agriculture productivity. Its use is very unevenly distributed among the regions. Africa and Latin America have the lowest shares of their cropped land irrigated - 2% and 9% respectively in 1980 - but they achieved an annual increase in irrigated area of about 3.5% in the 1970s. By contrast, countries in the Near East (22% irrigated in 1980) and the Asian centrally planned economies (44%) increased their irrigated areas by only 1.3% - 1.4% per annum during the same period. The Far East region has about 25% of its cropped land irrigated, with an annual rate of increase of over 2%.

The World Bank estimates that there are now 160 million hectares of irrigated land in the developing world, more than half of it in China and India. Twenty percent of all harvested land is irrigated and receives 60% of all fertilizer and produces 40% of all crops. As demographic pressures increase on the limited land resource, irrigation will continue to play an important role in supporting both an increase in and an improvement of reliability of crop output.

Scenario A of AT 2000 estimates that expansions in irrigated area from about 105 million ha to 148 million ha in the 90 developing countries studied could provide almost one-half of the 1980-2000 increase in crop production. The irrigated area in Africa is expected to increase most during this period, by 62%, but from a very small base. Important increases of over 40% are foreseen also for the Far East (where three quarters of the increase would be located) and Latin America. Yet the overall rate of expansion in irrigated area, at 1.7% a year, is slightly lower than the recent past. This is because the opportunities for further expansion are limited in some countries and greater emphasis has to be placed on improving and repairing existing irrigation works whose maintenance has been neglected and efficiency impaired.

It is estimated that salinity and waterlogging have damaged about half of all the world's irrigated lands. In Pakistan, out of a total of 15 million ha of irrigated land, about 11 million ha produce crops at reduced yields due to one of the above problems or a combination of both. In Syria about half of the irrigated land in the Euphrates valley is seriously affected and the proportions of affected land in Egypt and Iran are estimated to be 30% and 15% respectively.

Increasing the intensity of land use under traditional rainfed agricultural systems implies reducing the period of fallow or introducing double cropping. Without irrigation, double cropping may be difficult if not impossible unless more modern and faster methods of cultivation and quicker maturing varieties of crops are introduced.

The intensity of use of rainfed land is higher in the Far East than in the other developing regions as would be expected from its low land-person ratios. But intensifying land use by only reducing the fallow period without changing the technology used will cause yields to fall. This seems to be occurring in Africa. For example, the average yields of millet, a cereal typically grown under traditional farming systems, have declined (by 4%) during the past decade (see Box on shifting cultivation/bush fallow).


Land use and environmental issues

Bringing more land into use or intensifying its use can rapidly lead to environmental problems, as some countries have learnt to their cost.

The extent of soil degradation caused by water or wind erosion and by salinization and waterlogging arising from incorrect land practices is clearly of vital concern. The damage caused by salinization and waterlogging of irrigated land has been mentioned earlier in discussing irrigation.

As regards erosion, it is estimated that in Africa north of the Equator, for example, some 36% of the soils are affected by some degree of water erosion and 17% by wind erosion 18/. Some degree of erosion may take place without man's influence but it is often greatly accelerated when his activities cause the disappearance of protective vegetation.

Shifting cultivation is one of these possible damaging activities. Problems arise when the population exceeds the level the system can support because cropping is intensified and the fallow period shortened. The natural cycle of regeneration is broken and soil degradation sets in (see Box). The savanna soils are particularly susceptible. The extent of the area under shifting cultivation is not well established, but in Africa south of the Sahara, the minimum arable area involved is about 75 million ha, of which at least 36 million ha are harvested annually.

With mounting population pressure, shifting cultivation will have to be replaced by more permanent systems. Agrosilviculture, including the establishment of fallows of fast-growing tree species which enrich the soil, offers promise in this regard.

The pressure of population on land and the demand for forest products, particularly fuelwood, are also leading to severe deforestation and degradation of forest resources. It is estimated 19/ that closed broadleaved forests in Africa were cleared at a rate of about 1.3 million ha a year in 1976-80, or about 0.6 % annually of the area existing in 1980. The annual rates of clearance in other tropical regions of Asia and Latin America are also about 0.6%. It is more difficult to estimate the current rate of deforestation of the mixed forest and grassland tree formations (open broadleaved forests), but in Africa it appears to be about 2.6 million ha a year, equivalent to a rather lower proportion (0.5%) of the existing resources. The rates of clearance in other tropical regions tend to be higher (0.6%). This is because, especially in Asia, open forest resources represent a smaller share of the total than in Africa where large areas of these formations are not yet subject to severe population pressure.

One extreme aspect of the widespread deterioration of ecosystems under the combined pressure of adverse climate and agricultural exploitation is desertification. It is basically a problem of the misuse of land. The activities pursued in susceptible areas are inappropriate for the resources, either in nature or degree.

The United Nations Conference on Desertification held in 1977 drew attention to the hazards to which Africa's land is exposed as overexploitation continues. The area of extreme desert in Africa extends to 6.2 million ha, or 20% of the land area, but an additional 10.3 million ha, or 34% of the land area, is classified as having a very high to moderate degree of desertification hazard. Although the desertification hazard is particularly alarming in the more arid areas, it is not confined to them; the sub-humid and mountain areas also face significant hazards.

---

18/ FAO/UNEP/UNESCO. A Provisional Methodology for Soil Degradation Assessment, Rome, 1979.

19/ Tropical forest resources. FAO Forestry Paper No. 30, FAO/UNEP, Rome, 1982.

## SHIFTING CULTIVATION/BUSH FALLOW

Shifting cultivation or bush fallow farming refers to an agricultural production system in which land is cleared and cultivated for a short period alternated with a long fallow period for the restoration of fertility. The two terms have been used synonymously in many cases. However, in its original meaning, "shifting cultivation" involves movement of cultivation from one location to another, as well as relocation of the cultivator's house along with the crops. Although this practice still applies today in some countries, there is generally a development towards permanent settlement with fields being put under shorter or longer fallows. The term "bush fallow" more aptly describes the latter farming system.

One of the most important features of the bush fallow farming system is the reliance on nature, rather than on technology, to restore soil fertility. Farming in such a system, is mainly for subsistence with only small proportion of the produce available for sale. Simple farm tools are used with manual labour.

The system is an extensive form of agriculture which can be successful only if the ratio of land to population is high enough to ensure a minimum fallow period of five to ten years or even twenty years, according to climatic and soil conditions. Socio-economic changes and particularly demographic pressures cause a reduction in the availability of cultivable land. The fallow period then shortens with all other factors involved in the system remaining virtually unchanged. Yields decline as a result of inadequate recuperation of the fertility of the soil.

In Sierra Leone, for example[a/], the average fallow period steadily decreased from 10.7 years in 1972 to 9.8 years in 1974 and

8.8 in 1978. Population density increased from 35 per $km^2$ in 1970 to 38 in 1978, well above the maximum level of about 25 per $km^2$ for a bush fallow system to be sustained. The yield of upland rice in Sierra Leone fell from an average of 780 kg/ha from land fallowed for more than 10 years to an average of 540 kg/ha when the fallow lasted only 3-4 years.

Through its joint project with UNFPA, "Land Resources for Populations of the Future", FAO is attempting to determine the critical lengths of periods of cultivation and non-cultivation under different conditions of soil and climate. This may be shown by the cultivation factor R: where $R = \frac{C}{C+F} \times 100$; C = years of cultivation and F = years of fallow. Thus, three years of cultivation followed by 10 years of fallow gives an R value of $3/(3+10) \times 100 = 23$.

For example, to maintain fertility and avoid soil degradation at low level of inputs (corresponding to traditional farming methods), soil typically found in the savanna zone of Asia and Africa require only a moderate rest period: R = 35 to 40 or cultivation for two years in every 5 to 6. A compromise figure of one year cultivation in three is believed to be acceptable. Under intermediate levels of inputs use, R factors on these soils can reach 50-60, meaning cultivation somewhat more than half the time. What is clear is that - with increasing population pressures - required R factors are being exceeded, technologies are not being adopted to correct this, soils are degrading and crop yields are declining.

The improvement of the food production system in these situations of growing land and population pressures comprises, among others, the development of especially adopted soil management and input systems to ensure sustained crop yields.

---

a/ FAO/UNDP (1980). Bush fallow in Sierra Leone: An Agricultural Survey. AG: DP/SIL/73/002 Technical Report 6, Freetown.

LABOUR, ANIMAL AND TRACTOR POWER

## Agricultural Labour Force

Thus far, some land aspects of the vital land-person ratio have been briefly examined. But factors influencing the person or population side are equally important. For example, drawing on two United Nations studies on long-term population prospects, The State of Food and Agriculture 1981 drew attention to the future trends in world population growth and their implications for agriculture 20/. Rapid urbanization and accelerated migration of rural people to towns and cities, together with large increases in total population, are expected to continue in many developing countries. As shown in the following section, the agricultural labour force 21/ in these countries will not become much larger. This raises the question: will enough workers remain in agriculture to meet the expanding wants for food and other agricultural products by the people who are not on farms?

The United Nations medium-variant projections indicate that by the year 2000 just over one-half of the world's population and 44% of that of the developing countries will be living in urban areas. Not all people who remain in rural areas are dependent on agriculture. This dependence is decreasing because more and more farm households have family members who take on non-farm work full-time, part-time, or seasonally.

According to the UN projections, the agricultural labour force in the world as a whole will be growing slightly in absolute numbers, but declining as a share of the total population and labour force (Table 1-23). In the developed countries it has already been falling in absolute numbers for many years. By 2000, Africa is expected to be the only region with more than half of its total work force in agriculture.

Especially relevant to the world food situation is the question of how many people will the farmers and farm workers have to feed and supply with non-food agricultural products in the future as compared to the present. FAO calculations indicate that in both developing and developed countries the numbers of people depending on each member of the agricultural labour force for their food and other agricultural products will be increasing. Between 1980 and 2000 the ratio of total population (excluding agricultural labour force) to agricultural labour force is expected to rise from 3.8 to 5.3 in the developing market economies. The ratio in developed countries is expected to double from 25 to nearly 55. The increase in the ratio is greater in Europe than in North America, where it is already more than 80 (Table 1-24).

---

20/ FAO. The State of Food and Agriculture 1981, Rome, 1982, pp. 42-47.

21/ All economically active persons engaged principally in agriculture, fishing and hunting. The sources drawn upon are:
ILO, Labour Force, 1950-2000, Vols. I, II, III, IV, V and VI, Geneva, 1977 and FAO, Estimates and Projections of Agricultural and Non-Agricultural Population and Labour Force, 1950-2000, mimeographed, ESS/Misc/78/3, Rome, 1978.

TABLE 1-23.   AGRICULTURAL LABOUR FORCE IN DEVELOPING AND DEVELOPED
COUNTRIES, 1980 AND 2000

|  | Developing countries | Developed countries | World |
|---|---|---|---|
|  | ................. million ................. | | |
| **Agricultural labour force** | | | |
| 1980 | 759 | 68 | 827 |
| 2000 | 813 | 37 | 850 |
|  | ..................... % ................... | | |
| **Agricultural labour force as % of <u>total population</u>** | | | |
| 1980 | 23 | 6 | 19 |
| 2000 | 17 | 3 | 14 |
| **Agricultural labour force as % of <u>total labour force</u>** | | | |
| 1980 | 59 | 12 | 45 |
| 2000 | 43 | 6 | 34 |

Source:   FAO, ESS.

TABLE 1-24.   RATIO OF TOTAL POPULATION EXCLUDING AGRICULTURAL
LABOUR FORCE TO AGRICULTURAL LABOUR FORCE

|  | 1980 | 2000 | Change 1980 to 2000 |
|---|---|---|---|
|  | .................... % ..................... | | |
| Developing market economies | 3.8 | 5.3 | 40 |
| Africa | 2.7 | 4.2 | 56 |
| Latin America | 8.3 | 12.5 | 51 |
| Near East | 5.1 | 7.5 | 47 |
| Far East | 3.4 | 4.5 | 32 |
| Other developing market economies | 1.5 | 3.0 | 100 |
| Total developing countries | 3.3 | 4.9 | 49 |
| Asian centrally planned economies | 2.5 | 4.1 | 58 |
| Developed market economies | 25.2 | 54.8 | 118 |
| North America | 81.7 | 148.5 | 82 |
| Western Europe | 20.8 | 47.4 | 128 |
| Other developed market economies | 14.0 | 30.0 | 114 |
| Eastern Europe and USSR | 8.9 | 19.7 | 121 |
| Total developed countries | 16.1 | 4.9 | 117 |
| World | 4.4 | 6.2 | 41 |

Source:   FAO, ESS and ESP.

Animal and Tractor Power

One of the key questions in planning agricultural development strategies relates to the use of animal and tractor power to augment or substitute for human labour so as to raise its productivity.  There is a delicate balance between the objectives of raising output and income and that of maintaining employment opportunities.

The AT 2000 study provides an overview of the basic sources of agricultural power (Fig. 1-9) in the developing world.  Africa is the region that depends most heavily on human labour:  20 out of 37 African countries studied were estimated to rely on human labour for more than 90% of their agricultural power.

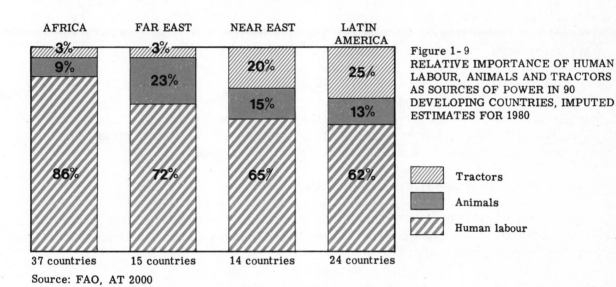

Figure 1-9
RELATIVE IMPORTANCE OF HUMAN LABOUR, ANIMALS AND TRACTORS AS SOURCES OF POWER IN 90 DEVELOPING COUNTRIES, IMPUTED ESTIMATES FOR 1980

Source: FAO, AT 2000

As regards the use of animal power, more than half of the draught animals in the 90 countries are in a single country:  India, with 84.5 million draught animals has 51% of the total.  It is followed by Bangladesh with 11.4 million (7%), Brazil 8.8 million (5%), Indonesia 6.0 million (4%) and Pakistan 5.9 million (4%).

However, numbers have to be considered in relation to the cultivable land.  The average for all 90 countries was 24 animals per 100 ha of arable land.  Mauritania heads the list with 65 per 100 ha, followed by Laos 61, Nepal 53 and then India with 50.  Countries in Africa generally have a lower intensity:  after Mauritania comes Madagascar with 38 and Ethiopia and Kenya with 37 draught animals per 100 ha.

The difficulty of introducing on a wide scale animal traction in Africa is shown by the wide disparities in its use even between adjacent countries.  Setting aside Mauritania, which has a relatively small arable land area and is a special case, Mali has 18 draught animals per 100 ha.  Yet Niger, also in the Sahel, uses only 6 per 100 ha.  A possible reason for this is that the use of ox-driven technology in the Sahel may result in increased requirements for labour in periods when its opportunity cost is relatively high

even if total labour cost per hectare of land falls 22/. Thus in Mali, on irrigated rice
farms, use of oxen enabled a large land area to be cultivated without imposing labour
constraints at other times of the season. Here animal traction has been widely adopted.
But in Upper Volta, small farmers who grow cereal crops for food find it costly to maintain cattle in the dry season; cattle have been entrusted to Fulani transhumant herdsmen.
Attempts to introduce animal traction have met with little success under these conditions.

The Sahelian experience thus shows that the constraint to adoption of animal traction
may not be farmers' attitudes as much as the difficulties created by shifting of seasonal
labour peaks within the farming system which render animal traction uneconomic.

A failure to adopt animal power may also be due to poor technology. For example,
ox-cultivation can lead to greater labour requirements; because the wider spacing of the
crop rows required, it creates greater demands for weeding later in the season. Yet it
has been noted that, even if ox-drawn weeders are part of the equipment packages, farmers
will rarely allow their crops to be weeded by animal power once the crops are above knee
height. Again, in East Africa, the most widely used ox-drawn tool is a mouldboard plough
originally developed for use in more friable temperate soils. It is difficult to use in
typical tropical soils and this single factor, together with the absence of a workable
replacement, may account for the slow spread of ox-cultivation in this sub-region even
though other factors would appear to support its wider use. Thus draught animal power
technology requires improvements and adaptation for it to succeed.

Tractor usage is more evenly dispersed, with 5 among the 90 developing countries
having 61% of the total in 1980. Brazil led, with 495 000 tractors (19% of the total),
followed by India with 326 000 (13%), Turkey 266 000 (10%), Mexico 254 000 (10%) and
Argentina 236 000 (9%). The average size and hence the working capacity of the tractors
used may differ widely among countries.

Again the distribution of tractors in relation to arable land was different. The
average for all 90 countries was 0.4 tractors per 100 ha of arable land. Suriname was
the most intensive user with 3.8 tractors per 100 ha, India was next with 1.9, followed
by Cyprus (1.8), Republic of Korea (1.7) and Uruguay (1.6).

In the 1970s, the number of tractors used in world agriculture increased by 3% per
annum. The increase was much faster in the developing countries (over 9% per annum) than
in the developed (2%). The former were, of course, starting from a much smaller base.
In the developing countries, there were particularly high rates of growth in the Asian
centrally planned economies and in the Near and Far East. But in Africa and Latin America
the rate of tractorization barely exceeded the rather low rate prevailing in western
Europe. In North America, the number of tractors has declined because of the trend towards
using larger tractors with a greater capacity.

The conflict aroused by the need to ease the drudgery of farm work and increase labour
productivity on the one hand, and the perceived need to create employment opportunities in
rural areas on the other, has been strongly felt in the broad area of mechanization and
especially tractorization 23/. The rise in the costs of energy during the 1970s appeared

---

22/ Delgado, Christopher L. and John McIntire, Oxen Cultivation in the Sahel, American
Journal of Agricultural Economics, Vol. 64, No. 2, May 1982, pp. 188-196.

23/ See, for example, SOFA 1973, Chapter 3. Agricultural Employment in Developing Countries.

to have tilted the balance away from proposing mechanization as a general prescription. Yet as evidence accumulates on the seasonal and, indeed, chronic labour shortage in many farming situations in Africa, the case for selective and appropriate mechanization to reduce labour bottlenecks and farm drudgery may need re-examination. Rural electrification could bring benefits worth exploiting.

Experience with mechanization in many developing countries has shown that its adoption may be distorted by policies that perhaps unintentionally promote its use such as over-valued exchange rates, low rates of interest and easy access to credit.

## MODERN INPUT USE

Modernization of agriculture normally involves the wider use of an array of inputs - such as improved seeds, fertilizers and pesticides - usually in the form of a package. Within technical limits the inputs may be substituted for each other depending on their relative cost and availability. Often they are associated with increased irrigation, discussed earlier.

### Improved Plant and Animal Genetic Material

The quality of improved seed cultivars can be regarded as the core element of most crop improvement programmes. Yet a recent study 24/ indicates that, while most European and North American countries had functioning seed industries for basic food, industrial, vegetable and pasture crops, the situation is much less favourable in developing countries. Agricultural research institutions were in operation in most of them, but only a few had sufficient installations for the production, quality control and distribution of improved seeds, despite recent efforts to implement seed improvement programmes.

Nevertheless some progress can be seen since the mid-1970s in the three broad areas of seed improvement: cultivar improvement, seed quality control, and seed production and distribution. By 1979/80 few developing countries reported no activities in these three areas with respect to basic food crops. But half or more of them had no programme in industrial or vegetable seeds, and there were very few programmes in pasture seed development. Overall seed improvement programmes were widely developed in South America. Programmes in Asia were oriented more towards basic food crops and vegetables and those in Africa towards industrial crops.

AT 2000 estimates that by 1980 some 27% of the developing countries' annual seed consumption was for improved varieties. Regional usage was: Latin America 44%, Near East 32%, Far East 23% and Africa only 9% 25/.

---

24/ FAO Seed Review 1979/80. AGP: SIDP 81/7.

25/ FAO (1981) op. cit. p. 168.

Constraints in the seed sector of developing countries are the lack of proper institutions including, in some cases, no statutory framework for the testing and controlled release of planting materials;  a lack of funds for facilities and equipment;  and a lack of trained manpower particularly at lower and intermediate levels.

In response to requests from member nations, FAO implemented its Seed Improvement and Development Programme (SIDP) in 1973.  By 1982, 130 countries were cooperating with the Programme.  In the early years of the programme the strategy adopted was to assess the effectiveness of seed production activities in participating countries, develop technical guidelines, introduce suitable crop varieties and formulate and implement seed projects.  Emphasis was placed on the production of quality seed of food crops but not to the exclusion of other crops of economic importance.

Since 1982, there has been a focusing of the Programme's activities towards seed utilization campaigns and the establishment of seed security reserve stocks.  Increased emphasis has been placed on technical support to strengthen national seed services.

Much concern has been voiced about the need to encourage collection, conservation, maintenance and international exchange of plant genetic materials of agricultural interest. This is not easily accomplished, for it raises questions as to the appropriate roles of various national and international entities;  the finance of such endeavours;  adequate protections against spread of plant diseases and pests;  and the proprietary rights of individual plant breeders, research centers and commercial operations.  FAO has been strongly involved in technical and organizational support of efforts to improve the situation, especially those related to access of developing nations to improved genetic materials.  These issues will be considered at the Conference of FAO in November 1983.

Although seed improvement programmes clearly refer to crop production, there is the equally important corollary for livestock - the preservation and improvement of animal genetic resources, along with encouragement of sound animal breeding and selection practices.  As discussed in Chapter 2, remarkable increases in livestock productivity, have been achieved in developed countries.  The techniques that produced these are potentially reproducible in developing countries too as shown by rapid improvements in the productivity in some countries' poultry industries.

Three points of concern should be highlighted:

- the need to generate breeding stock which comply well with a wide range of socio-economic objectives and not solely with a criterion of maximum output;

- the need to conserve indigenous genetic material which may have inestimable value in the future for disease resistance or other desirable traits;

- the need to ensure that animals are adapted to the environmental and management conditions in which they are required to perform.

Fertilizers

Consumption of fertilizer nutrients per hectare of arable and permanent crop land has nearly tripled in the developing countries since 1970 (Table 1-25).  The increase has been especially marked in China and the other Asian centrally planned economies, which now use fertilizers more intensively than developed countries as a whole. China also uses exceptionally large amounts of organic manure but these cannot supply sufficient quantities of the nutrients required to sustain high yields. Mineral fertilizers thus complement organic manure. Among developed countries a faster rate of increase in Eastern Europe and the USSR is particularly apparent.

TABLE 1-25.  FERTILIZER CONSUMPTION IN RELATION TO ARABLE LAND AND LAND UNDER PERMANENT CROPS AND COMPOSITION BY NUTRIENT, DEVELOPING AND DEVELOPED COUNTRIES.

|  | Total nutrients in 1980/81 | | Share in 1979/80 | | |
|  | per ha | % of 1970 | Nitrogen | Phosphate | Potash |
|---|---|---|---|---|---|
|  | kg/ha | .................... % ................. | | | |
| Developing market economies | 33 | 247 | 55 | 30 | 15 |
| Africa | 10 | 211 | 46 | 35 | 19 |
| Far East | 38 | 255 | 66 | 21 | 13 |
| Latin America | 46 | 229 | 39 | 37 | 24 |
| Near East | 34 | 260 | 61 | 37 | 2 |
| Asian centrally planned economies | 146 | 330 | 82 | 15 | 3 |
| Total developing countries | 49 | 273 | 66 | 24 | 10 |
| Developed market economies | 123 | 128 | 45 | 29 | 26 |
| North America | 99 | 140 | 49 | 24 | 27 |
| Oceania | 38 | 113 | 14 | 74 | 12 |
| Western Europe | 218 | 125 | 46 | 28 | 26 |
| Eastern Europe and USSR | 105 | 165 | 43 | 31 | 26 |
| Total developed countries | 116 | 140 | 45 | 29 | 26 |
| World | 80 | 164 | 51 | 28 | 21 |

Source:  FAO, Fertilizer Yearbooks.

The highest rates of use per hectare have been and continue to be in Western Europe. This partially explained by relatively large applications of fertilizers to grassland. On the average, developing countries are still applying nutrients at less than half the rates used by developed countries. Among developing regions Africa uses the least.

Developing countries, especially the Asian centrally planned economies, are tending to use higher percentages of nitrogen in the nutrient mix than developed countries, mainly because of differences in their crop patterns. They are the main producers of rice, which is a major user of nitrogen. Latin America has been consuming a smaller proportion of nitrogen than the other developing regions. Among the developed regions, Oceania has been using relatively high amounts of phosphate and low amounts of nitrogen, largely because of the predominance of pastures.

The regional averages shown in Table 1-25 conceal the very low rates of fertilizer use in many individual developing countries. In 1980/81 half of the 107 developing countries for which data are available were using less than 20 kg per ha, and a quarter were using less than 5 kg. In contrast, among 34 developing countries, fully half were using 165 kg or more per ha, and only one less than about 40 kg.

- 68 -

The pattern of fertilizer use also has some major implications for energy consumption by the agricultural sector. This is because nitrogenous fertilizers are estimated to require nearly 6 times as much energy to manufacture, pack, transport and apply as the least-energy-using potassic fertilizers 26/. By the late 1970s, nitrogenous fertilizers were consuming over 80% of all the energy used in the fertilizer sector. This is mainly because ammonia derived from natural gas is used as a feed stock for the most widely used nitrogenous fertilizers and accounts for about 55% of the energy used in their manufacture. The other 45% is accounted for by fuel costs. In contrast, phosphatic and potassic fertilizers use less energy in their manufacture than in their packing, transport and application.

The difference in the estimated energy used in the form of fertilizers per ha of land is striking: the Asian centrally planned economies apparently consume more than Western Europe per ha of land (Fig. 1-10). As fertilizer accounts for nearly 70% of the energy

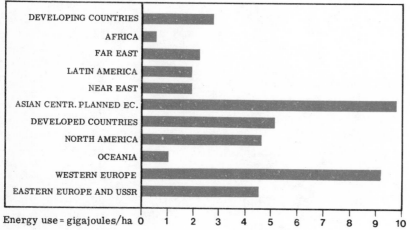

Figure 1-10
ESTIMATED RATES OF ENERGY USE PER HA. OF ARABLE LAND THROUGH FERTILIZER USE, 1978/79

Energy use = gigajoules/ha   0   1   2   3   4   5   6   7   8   9   10   (1 gigajoules = 1 thousand million joules)

Source: IFDC and FAO, ESS

used by the agricultural sector in developing countries as compared to only 40% in the developed, the relative prices charged to farmers at the farm gate could strongly influence efforts to economize on energy consumption. This issue may not appear particularly critical at this time of apparently abundant world supplies of petroleum products. Nevertheless it seems that such relative abundance stems more from the effects of the current economic recession - especially on such high energy users as steel and cement manufacturing - than on genuine energy conservation. The prices of energy, and in turn

26/ The estimates of energy use in US barrels of oil per metric ton of nutrient are: N 12.8, P 2.9, and K 2.2. See International Fertilizer Development Centre (IFDC), Energy and Fertilizer: Policy Implications and Options for Developing countries, Muscle Shoals, Alabama, 1982. See also FAO, Energy for World Agriculture, Rome, 1979, pp. 50-53.

fertilizers, could rapidly increase when economic activity picks up 27/.

For example, in India fertilizer use had spread to about 85% of the irrigated land by 1979/80. So there is much less scope to promote fertilizer use through its wider adoption on land already irrigated. The achievement of growth targets for irrigated land as set down in India's Sixth Plan, nevertheless, would go some way to promote fertilizer use in parallel. However, there is considerable economic potential to fertilizer use under rainfed conditions in India providing that the distribution network expands in these areas. Supply side considerations are also important because limiting supplies reduces the motivation of the fertilizer industry to promote sales and improve distribution. Efforts are needed to ensure adequate domestic production capacity, to utilize this capacity more fully, to manage stocks more effectively and to maintain imports as planned. It seems that many developing countries could learn from India's experience.

Clearly farmers are very conscious of relative prices of fertilizers and crops. For example in Pakistan, offtake of fertilizer which has grown 1000 fold over the past 30 years, suffered setbacks in times when the nutrient/crop price ratios deteriorated. Recent examples were in 1969-71 and 1973-75 as a result of a reduction in fertilizer subsidies 28/. Several other countries in Asia recently have had to reduce fertilizer subsidies. In Sri Lanka fertilizer prices approximately doubled between 1980/81 and 1981/82.

Despite the need and the scope for expanding fertilizer use and hence agricultural output, intensive users of fertilizers, in both developed and developing countries, may also want to examine their fertilizer policies and programmes closely in the years to come, particularly with a view of greater efficiency of use of all sources of plant nutrients within an integrated nutrient supply system. For example, in 1980/81 sixteen developing countries were consuming more than 100 kg of fertilizer nutrients per hectare of cropland and so are already moderately intensive users of fertilizers.

It is estimated that 40% to 70% of nitrogen applied is lost as far as plant nutrition goes and under wrong management some enters the ecosystem as a water pollutant. For phosphorous about 15% - 20% is utilized by the crop receiving the application. The residual phosphorous is partly available to succeeding crops and partly fixed in the soil depending on soil conditions. Losses incurred by potassic fertilizers are less.

The fertilizer manufacturers can improve the efficiency of fertilizers themselves, through the wider development of controlled-release fertilizers and materials amenable to deep placement to inhibit premature leaching, for example. However, much efficiency can be gained by improving fertilizer management. This means knowing and applying the correct dosage, having a proper balance of nutrients, and applying fertilizers at the right time and in the right place.

---

27/ Desai, Gunvant M. (1982), Sustaining Rapid Growth in India's Fertilizer Consumption: a Perspective Based on Composition of Use. IFPRI Research Report 31, Washington, August.

28/ Current Fertilizer Situation 1981-82 and Outlook 1982-83 and 1983-84. National Fertilizer Development Centre, Special Report - 10, Government of Pakistan, Islamabad, January.

Pesticides

An estimate for 1980 shows that the United States and Western Europe dominate the world market for agricultural chemicals, representing over half of the total.

Herbicides account for the largest value with about 42% of the total (Table 1-26). The same source also estimates that over half of current pesticide use is accounted for by only five crops: maize, rice cotton, soybeans and wheat.

TABLE 1-26.  ESTIMATED USE OF PESTICIDES, 1980

|  | World | United States |
|---|---|---|
|  | ............. million $ ............. | |
| Herbicides | 4 891 | 2 171 |
| Insecticides | 3 916 | 903 |
| Fungicides | 2 199 | 226 |
| Others | 559 | 199 |
| Total | 11 565 | 3 504 |

Source:  A Look at the World Pesticide Market, Farm Chemicals, September 1981.

World trade in pesticides grew at an annual rate of nearly 20% during the 1970s. Imports by developed countries account for most of this growth, notably those of North America, which increased by 30%.  The increase in the developing market economies has been slower.

Herbicide use is concentrated very much in developed countries, as is to be expected from their relative scarcity of agricultural labour.  However, the use of such chemicals as 2, 4-D appears to be increasing in such diverse developing countries as India and Mexico.

The limited data available to FAO indicate that the consumption of the "older" chlor-hydrocarbon insecticides, such as DDT and Aldrin, appears to be declining even in some developing countries because of environmental fears.  The use of parathion and other or-ganophosphates and carbamates has increased.  Some countries engaged extensively in fruit and wine production stand out as users of fungicides.

Pesticide use is limited at present by depressed prices for some agricultural com-modities, continuing environmental fears, and restrictions imposed on trade.  Other factors are the trend towards integrated pest control, whereby crop losses are reduced without relying so much on chemicals (see Box), and the use of more complex chemicals applied at lower rates and with more efficient machinery.  On the other hand, reduced tillage practices adopted for soil protection as well as to reduce energy costs and machinery use require more chemicals to control weeds and other pests.

## INTEGRATED PEST CONTROL

As a result of the various problems a-rising from the indiscriminate use of pesticides, new approaches were needed for insect control. The integrated pest control approach, advocated as early as 1954, was promoted by FAO in the early '60s. It attempts to use all the known techniques of control to maintain pest populations below the level at which they cause economic damage to crops. Under the FAO/UNEP Cooperative Global Programme for the Development and Application of Integrated Pest Control in Agriculture, a number of regional projects are now under way focusing on crops of major socio-economic importance. An example of one successfully completed project has been the control of the coconut palm Rhinoceros beetle in the South Pacific.

Information was obtained on the life-span, behaviour and ecology of this insect. Subsequently, practical and efficient integrated control techniques were developed. These were based on the prevention of the build-up of beetle populations by biocontrol agents, one of which, a virus, harmless to humans and animals, was the most important. Control measures were also directed at the elimination of potential breeding sites through environmental sanitation and re-utilization of coconut timber. Successful control programmes were carried out in the island states of the South Pacific. Later, these control techniques were also expanded to South and Southeast Asia and to the islands of the Indian Ocean.

In the past the increased use of some insecticides, such as DDT and dieldrin, gave rise to concern about their possible effects on non-target organisms. For example, in tsetse control, the application of persistent formulations of DDT and dieldrin from the ground to 10% or so of the total target area, as still used in some countries, can have a serious impact on terrestrial and acquatic fauna if care is not taken to place the insecticide in resting sites of the pest within the vegetation. However, usage of persistent formulations is rapidly declining in favour of serial applications of Endosulfan and, to some extent, Deltamethrin. Cloth screens and traps have also been used successfully in tsetse control. Research on improving insecticide formulations and application equipment is in progress so that lower dosages may be applied with greater selectivity.

Animal industries employ insecticides to control a variety of ectoparasites of livestock, such as biting flies, mites and ticks that transmit diseases, damage hides and skins or reduce animal productivity through the irritation they cause. Much work is being done to find ways of reducing the livestock industries' dependence on the use of acaricides.

Examples of these ways are new methods of applying insecticides, the exploitation of genetic resistance of the host to ectoparasites in control programmes to reduce the frequency of application of insecticides, improved knowledge of the ecology of ectoparasites to plan control programmes and stimulation of the host's resistance to ectoparasites by artificial immunization. These new approaches hold out the hope that ectoparasite control may be achieved in the future with appreciably less insecticide usage per animal unit. Not only will this reduce costs but it also will reduce the risks of pollution and generating resistance in the pests themselves.

### Animal Feed

The increased use of concentrate animal feeds such as cereals, oilseeds and milling by-products in livestock industries has been associated with marked increases in livestock output and productivity. The use of cereals and other concentrate animal feeds rose rapidly during the 1950s and 1960s in North America and both Western and Eastern Europe.

A rapid growth has also become evident more recently in developing countries where the increase averaged 9% a year in 1976-80. By 1981 nearly 600 million tons of cereals (excluding rice) were used for livestock feed, 250 million tons in the USA and the USSR alone. The use in developing countries was about 100 million tons, 17% of this in Brazil. This issue is discussed at greater length in Chapter 2.

There has been a shift in the kinds of livestock produced away from largely forage-consuming ruminants towards grain-consuming poultry and, in some countries, pigs. For example, the annual rate of increase of poultry production in 1976-80 was 7% in the world as a whole. During the same period, world production of beef and buffalo meat fell by 0.7% a year, and that of mutton and goat meat rose by only 1.4% a year.

These changes in the pattern of livestock production have influenced the extent to which countries and regions are using their domestic output of feed grains for animal production. A rough measure is provided by the percentage of their production of cereals, pulses and oilseeds that is fed to livestock. The developing countries use much less than the developed countries but, as their livestock systems intensify, they are using more of their production of these commodities as animal feed. The percentage rose from 8.5 to 14.1% in developing countries, and from 32.2 to 35.9% in developed countries between 1966-68 and 1978-80.

The rapid increase in the demand for livestock products poses particular problems for agricultural policy makers in developing countries. They must try to avoid having cereals bid away from low-income consumers by the demand for animal feed. Apart from the redistribution of incomes in favour of low-income consumers, this implies increasing cereal or other feed supplies through either domestic production or imports.

Food contamination is a pollution problem that is becoming more prevalent through the increased use of animal feeds. An example is the presence of toxic metabolites (mycotoxins), the production of which is favoured by high temperature and atmospheric humidity, conditions widely found in the humid tropics. Food and feed may also be contaminated by the heavy metals produced by some industries, and by pesticides.

The FAO/WHO Codex Alimentarius has been developing international food standards for many years. FAO, WHO and UNEP are also developing a Joint International Food and Animal Feed Contamination Monitoring Programme.


AGRICULTURAL RESEARCH, RESOURCE AND INPUT USE

With the current need to improve agricultural productivity - to raise output and incomes - the question of agricultural research to develop improved technologies takes on added importance. Agricultural research, therefore, can be regarded as a link between the 'basic' resources with which a country is naturally endowed (land, labour and water) and the use of inputs such as improved seeds, fertilizers and pesticides. Scarcities of any of the basic resources will generate pressures to develop technologies which economize in their use.

For example, in Japan the major force behind agricultural research was a growing land scarcity which led to the introduction of land-saving biological innovations. In the US, on the other hand, the need was for labour-saving technology as land was not scarce but labour was. This accelerated the development of mechanized agriculture.

However, in order for such need or requirement to be effectively reflected in new technologies, the priorities of the research programme will have to be appropriately designed. Several factors may, however, introduce biases in this process:

- The communication of needs may be weak or inadequate. Such situations may exist in developing countries where farmers need improved technologies but in practice cannot make their needs known to the administrators of agricultural research programmes. The latter have to assume the responsibility of deciding what directions such programmes should take and would gain from an effective process of extension-research feedback.

- Where technologies are introduced from other countries, either directly or through the training of researchers and administrators (situations commonly found in developing countries), the technologies themselves are orientated to the factor or resource price ratios pertaining in the originating - usually developed - country, and they may not be appropriate to the situation prevailing in the countries adopting them.

- There appear to be serious limitations or gaps in the range of innovation possibilities. For example, it is not easy to develop farm equipment that is simple and robust yet cheap. In contrast, the possibilities of developing, testing and introducing innovations that economize on land (increase crop yields, for example) are not so intractable 29/.

Agricultural research also has an important role in promoting and encouraging the substitution of inputs and economizing on their use. With the rising costs of such inputs as fertilizers and irrigation water, increasing emphasis has been given to developing crop varieties and agronomic practices that economize on the use of inputs. New directions in plant breeding have led to the development of varieties that are more pest-resistant, thereby reducing pesticide costs. Nitrogen-fixing legumes can be sown with other crops to reduce required applications of nitrogenous fertilizers.

Economic Returns and Levels of Expenditure

Numerous studies have been made of the rate of return on investments made in agricultural research, but more for developed than developing countries 30/. The rates are often well above the 10 to 15% usually considered as the opportunity cost of capital. Returns to research even above 50% are sometimes quoted. Such rates suggest that investment in agricultural research can be extremely worthwhile.

---

29/   See Binswanger, Hans P., Measuring the Impact of Economic Factors on the Direction of Technical Change in Arndt, Thomas M., Dana G. Dalrymple and Vernon W. Ruttan (eds.) Resource Allocation and Productivity in National and International Agricultural Research, Univ. of Minnesota Press, Minneapolis, USA, 1977.

30/   See several contributions in Arndt, Thomas M. et al. (1977) op. cit.

The importance of agricultural research received due recognition in the early 1970s with the creation of the system of International Agricultural Research Centres (IARC) of the Consultative Group on International Agricultural Research (CGIAR). This international agricultural research programme is sponsored by the World Bank, UNDP and FAO and has the support of both government and non-government donors.

## THE CONSULTATIVE GROUP ON INTERNATIONAL AGRICULTURAL RESEARCH (CGIAR)

The CGIAR, established in 1981, is an informal association of countries, international and regional organizations, and private foundations dedicated to supporting a system of agricultural research centres and programmes around the world. The purpose of the research effort is to improve the quantity and quality of food production in the developing countries. The World Bank, the Food and Agriculture Organization of the United Nations (FAO) and the United Nations Development Programme (UNDP) are co-sponsors of this effort. The World Bank provides the Chairman and Secretariat of the Consultative Group. The Group is advised by a Technical Advisory Committee (TAC) whose Secretariat is provided by FAO. The Group has 44 members, of which 34 are donors contributing about $150 million in 1982. The other 10 countries represent the five regions of the developing world.

The Group initially took on responsibility for four international research centres founded by two private foundations: the Rockefeller and Ford Foundations. Two of these centres, one concerned with rice and the other with wheat and maize, had already demonstrated that internationally managed research institutes, staffed and equipped to a high standard, could develop new, high-yielding varieties of seeds that bring about dramatic increases in food production. The formation of the Group enabled the existing institutes to expand and new institutes to be created on similar lines. Most food crops of major importance to the developing world have now become covered by internationally funded research.

Today there are 13 institutions in the system of international research supported by the Group. The full list is shown in the glossary of names at the beginning of this document. Their research and training activities encompass crops and animals which account for three-quarters of the food supply of the developing countries and for an even higher proportion of their protein intake. The institutions employ about 7,000 people, about 600 of whom are senior scientists recruited worldwide.

However, it is estimated that only about six developing countries have a well-developed agricultural research infrastructure, well organized and with generally adequate levels of staffing 31/. Another ten have research networks which may be reasonably well staffed but where research activities are poorly organized or managed. Fully 40 countries, each large enough to justify a comprehensive national agricultural research system, lack the necessary research infrastructure and manpower. Then there remain the many countries with a financial resource base which is too small to justify their own national programmes aimed at specific crops or livestock, but need adaptive research capability with close links to strong research institutions outside their boundaries.

---

31/  FAO National Agricultural Research in Developing Countries, C81/26, Rome, 1981, p. 8.

If the normative growth rates of agricultural production proposed in FAO's AT 2000 study are to be achieved, increases in agricultural input use by developing countries will have to be extremely large. For example, the projections indicate that fertilizer consumption in the 90 developing countries covered in the study would need to rise four or five-fold by the end of the century. Unless these countries possess or have access to vigorous agricultural research programmes that generate enhanced capabilities for effective use of inputs, overall production objectives will be jeopardized. This underlines the emphasis that needs to be placed at both national and international levels on research on crops, livestock and farming systems of developing countries. The World Food Conference in 1974 recommended that expenditure of the order of 0.5% of agricultural GDP was a reasonable target for support of agricultural research by developing countries. This figure is now exceeded by the majority of them. More recent thinking 32/, however, suggests that a 1% target is advisable at least for those countries that are relatively advanced in this field. (Developed countries typically spend about 1-2% of their agricultural GDP on research.)

It may be argued that more expenditure on agricultural research is not needed because farmers in developing countries could be much more fully utilizing existing knowledge. But it can also be argued that the faster the advance in basic knowledge, the greater are the returns from the research subsequently applied to that basic knowledge. It also seems that countries which do not have a capacity to do some significant agricultural research cannot expect to benefit fully from research done by others.

---

32/ FAO (1981), op. cit.

# 2. Livestock Production: a World Perspective

## INTRODUCTION

The topic of this chapter is livestock production in a world perspective but with particular emphasis on livestock development issues in developing countries. There are several reasons for such a focus.

- Public discussion often deals with livestock in an over-simplified manner, assuming that most animal production depends heavily on cereal feeds and that curtailment of animal production will automatically result in more food grain being accessible to malnourished people. Questions can in fact be raised about the extent to which livestock systems utilize grain, but some do not compete for sources of human food.

- During the past two decades, world attention has focused on the green revolution in crop production achieved in many developing countries. By contrast, livestock have received very little attention. Yet there are possibilities for "break-throughs" in animal production, particularly in the areas of animal breeding, feed utilization and disease control.

- Dynamic changes in world supply and demand patterns for meat, milk and other live-stock products are taking place. Agricultural leaders in developed as well as developing nations need to examine afresh their programmes and policies related to livestock production, pricing and trade. More than ever before, such reassessments will need to reflect understanding of events not only in the domestic live-stock sector but in other sectors and elsewhere in the world.

- Technological, economic and demographic changes are making it necessary for nations to address questions of basic production and marketing structure in their livestock sectors. With the growth of urban populations, large agribusinesses and international trade, it has become costly and politically difficult for many industrialized countries to continue the protection of small livestock producers and processors. In the developing countries, there are tendencies for commercial livestock operations to emerge that have little linkage to people and feed resources in existing agrarian structures.

- In this era of concern about energy supplies, ecological balance and environmental quality, several non-food attributes of livestock take on more importance. There is renewed interest in the role of animals as sources of draught power, fibre, and partially converted biomass for manure and fuel use.

- There is a need to review the broad objectives of livestock policies and programmes. The aims of livestock sector actions and assistance have often become obscured and fragmented amid the dynamic changes that have taken place in many countries in recent years.

This chapter does not provide hard-and-fast answers about what should be done.  Indeed, what is best for any one country will depend on its unique setting, capabilities and aims.  Instead, the intent here is to provide a point of departure for diagnosing in an orderly fashion what could be done in any one situation to help the livestock sector develop or adjust to changing circumstances.  Attention is drawn to important policy issues, programme decisions and economic relationships.  Much of the chapter is devoted to technical aspects and geographic settings of livestock production systems, for it is felt that economic policies and development programmes have to be in tune with these realities if they are to be effective.

Livestock production has a multi-purpose role in agriculture.  Particularly in developing countries, it is an integral part of farming systems and rural life styles that can utilize otherwise unproductive land areas and be a source of security without making people highly dependent on external inputs or complicated technologies.  Yet, the question remains: how to satisfy the rapidly increasing demand for livestock products arising in developing countries by exploiting the production potential of these systems?

The most striking gains in livestock productivity have been achieved where technologies have been imported from developed countries.  This has involved highly commercial and specialized approaches rather than the improvement of existing systems of production. It has also led to a greater dependence on imported capital goods, technical expertise and animal feeds.  Such approaches can be justified in only a limited number of development situations.

The main thesis of this chapter is that traditional farming systems involving livestock can be improved or adapted and new systems introduced that are more appropriate to the economic and social environment of most developing countries.  This improvement or adaptation rests on technological upgrading in three main areas:  livestock feeding, its breeding and health.  The possible ways to evolve animal feeding systems that are more compatible with other development and food needs require:

- effective use and management of pasture, range and waste lands for ruminant production;

- emphasis on forage grasses and legumes as integral components of crop production (which in the long run many enhance rather than compete with total cash crop production);

- wider use of crops that can be produced locally as substitutes for imported animal feeds;

- through physical and chemical treatment, changes in storage and processing and even genetic approaches, better digestibility and so fuller utilization of straw, bagasse, rice bran, banana stems, and other crop by-products;

- improvement of traditional scavenger-type production of poultry, pigs and other livestock commonly found on family holdings.

The strategies adopted with regard to livestock feeding will strongly influence those regarding breeding, the second main area for improvement.  There are several possibilities but the approach is to select and upgrade economically useful local stock, if need be, by drawing on breeding material and genetic advances in other countries.  Particular emphasis may be given to livestock breeds and species adapted to specific conditions and uses. Examples are the water buffalo for draught power, milk and meat in the humid tropics; camels, sheep and goats for arid environments; trypano-tolerant cattle, sheep and goats; and rabbits and other small stock with high reproductive rates for backyard production systems. The importance of identifying, protecting and utilizing native breeding stock should be stressed in order that genetic potentials for improved disease and environmental tolerance are not lost.

The third area of technological improvement lies in animal health. Disease monitoring networks, veterinary services and supplies, and quarantine mechanisms are at the heart of effective animal health programmes. Yet, in developing countries, these services are not always available or only inadequately so. In most cases, past efforts to prevent and control diseases affecting animal productivity have shown a high pay off. But given the continued constraint on the resources for veterinary services in most developing countries, decisions on what aspects of disease prevention and control should have priority ought to be based on a careful assessment of costs and benefits.

In focusing on this theme of integrated approaches to improvement of livestock systems, the chapter shows how livestock can serve as an important vehicle toward equitable rural development in both arid and humid settings in developing countries. Three illustrative programmes are examined. One has had considerable success in improving sheep production and grazing practices in Syria. It has used approaches which comply with the traditional independence of the nomadic people. It has also tailored water development, forage establishment and grazing practices to local agronomic conditions.

The second example is Operation Flood, a large dairy programme in India. It has centred around the development of cooperatives as a means of enabling small producers to sell processed milk to urban markets. Other forms of assistance to the producers such as improvement of feed supplies, veterinary and breeding services, and technical advice have been closely interwoven from the start. Channelling of profits into community improvements has also been a fact.

The third example is another smallholder dairy programme, this time in Kenya. This programme built on a land reform programme and the then newly-conferred ability of small-holder farmers to grow cash crops. Dairying integrated itself well into these labour-intensive farming systems, often on land settlement schemes. A reform in the pricing policy which purposely did away with supply quotas that discriminated against small-scale producers, an effective marketing system, as in India, built on a cooperative structure, and the provision of technical services, particularly artificial insemination, fortuitously worked together to ensure the programme's success.

These examples differ considerably in their style and emphasis. But common to all three is their view of livestock improvement as a means toward better human wellbeing. They also illustrate the usefulness of interdisciplinary programme approaches that go beyond conventional agency boundaries and that link with the cropping potentials, marketing and processing needs, agrarian and community structures, and the people of the particular setting at hand.

# THE ROLE OF LIVESTOCK IN DEVELOPMENT

Livestock are multi-purpose. They provide man not only with food but also with draught power. In some situations, they also serve as a means of capital accumulation. They supply manure that can be used for fuel and fertilizer and are a source of hides, skins, wool, hair and numerous other products. In many societies, especially pastoral ones, they have complex cultural values which may be an integral part of the life of both the family and the community.

It is only in the last century that livestock production and utilization has become very intensive in the industrialized countries. Yet livestock products have, for centuries past, provided the raw materials for such traditional rural industries as tanning and candle-making, and the thriving mediaeval wool industry. Modernization of the livestock industry really began through the impetus of the industrial revolution in Europe that gave new impulse to or expanded market-oriented urban centres which had to purchase their own food supply. Once the market incentives existed, the technology soon followed resulting in improvements in both animal production and product processing. In particular, new technology reduced transport costs and led to the opening up of new areas for meat production in North and South America and in Oceania. The availability of cheap grain from low cost production areas in North and South America also led to radical changes in the pattern of agricultural production. Grain began to be increasingly used in intensive meat, milk and egg production to satisfy the demands of growing industrial markets. Improvements in food technology made it possible to chill, freeze and can meat and to process milk. Such techniques considerably extended the shelf life of these perishable products. They expanded the market for animal products and gave the producer a great deal more flexibility in his production process.

TABLE 2-1.  GROSS VALUE OF LIVESTOCK PRODUCTION IN 1980

|  | Developed | Developing | Total |
|---|---|---|---|
|  | .......... Thousand million US$ .......... | | |
| Meat | 109 | 62 | 171 |
| Milk | 71 | 21 | 92 |
| Eggs | 16 | 9 | 25 |
| Hides/skins | 3 | 3 | 6 |
| Wool | 3 | 1 | 4 |
| Draught | 6 | 40 | 46 |
| Manure | 4 | 6 | 10 |
| Total | 212 | 142 | 354 |

Note.  Livestock products have been valued at market prices. Non-product values - draught and manure - have been estimated on the basis of the values of the mechanical power or chemical fertilizers which are replaced by livestock.

In developing countries this activity is carried out both on the rangelands and in close conjunction with the production of crops, particularly cereals. In the last two decades a massive international effort has gone into the improvement of cereal production by using new genetic-chemical technology. The small farmer who uses this technology rarely produces cereals in isolation, but usually pursues a mixed crop/livestock system of farming. The livestock are integrated into the system not only in generating income, but as a form of capital that can be readily liquidated, provide draught power and manure while consuming crop residues which otherwise would be unused.

Non-food values are frequently ignored when estimating the contribution of livestock to gross agricultural production. If the estimated values of draught power and utilized manure provided by livestock are included, the total annual value of livestock production increases only marginally in the developed countries but by almost one-half in the developing countries (Table 2-1).

LIVESTOCK AS A SOURCE OF FOOD

In 1980 world production of meat, milk and eggs for human consumption was estimated to be 140, 469 and 28 million tons respectively. Together with fish (about 50 million tons caught for food) these products provided in that year 33% of the global average daily intake of protein as well as 17% of the total intake of calories. Progress in raising the average levels of protein intake has been rather slow in developing countries and regional differences have been increasing (Table 2-2). The averages shown in the table also conceal major differences between countries within the regions as well as varying consumption levels within countries themselves. For example, at the national level, 1975/77 average annual intakes ranged: for meat from 120 kg per caput in the USA to 1.4 kg in India; for milk from over 300 kg in Finland to 0.4 kg in Indonesia; and for eggs from 21 kg in Israel to 0.1 kg in India.

TABLE 2-2.  GLOBAL PROTEIN INTAKES

|  | Protein of animal origin (including fish) | | | Protein of vege- table origin | Total protein |
|---|---|---|---|---|---|
|  | 1961/63 | 1969/71 | 1978/80 | 1978/80 | 1978/80 |
|  | ................ (Grams/caput/day) ................ | | | | |
| Developing market economies | 10 | 11 | 12 | 46 | 59 |
| Africa | 9 | 11 | 11 | 43 | 54 |
| Far East | 7 | 7 | 7 | 43 | 50 |
| Latin America | 25 | 25 | 28 | 39 | 66 |
| Near East | 13 | 13 | 16 | 58 | 74 |
| Asian centrally planned economies | 10 | 9 | 12 | 53 | 65 |
| Developed market economies | 44 | 51 | 56 | 43 | 99 |
| Eastern Europe and USSR | 37 | 44 | 51 | 50 | 100 |
| World | 21 | 22 | 24 | 46 | 69 |

Source:  FAO Production Yearbooks.

While there is some debate, many nutritionalists feel that humans will not have the needed amounts and kinds of amino acids unless their diets include protein from either animal (including fish) products or an unusually well designed combination of foods from plants. Per caput intakes of protein from animal sources differ widely from region to region in the world (Table 2-2). In places where little animal protein is consumed the nutritional situation of the lowest income groups is often precarious because they cannot afford enough or the right kinds of vegetable sources of protein to fill the gap.

This situation is related to the failure of animal production to keep pace with the annual growth in the human population of these countries, which has approached 3% over the past two decades. Demand has been depressed by rising prices associated with the shortfall in supply affecting low income consumers in particular. Yet shortfalls would have been even greater if pig and poultry meat production had not grown at high rates in some instances. However, much of the latter was based on the use of cereal-based concentrate feeds. This, in turn, raises further questions of nutrition policy and equity in countries where, while calorie deficiencies exist, cereals are used to produce meat for consumption by higher income groups.

TABLE 2-3.  FOOD PRODUCTION FROM SOME COMMON AGRICULTURAL SYSTEMS

| | Typical yields per annum of | |
| Type of production | Protein (kg/ha) | Gross energy (megajoules) |
| --- | --- | --- |
| Crop | | |
| Wheat | 225 | 41 000 |
| Potatoes | 450 | 78 000 |
| Vegetables | 500 | 25 000 |
| Non-ruminant livestock | | |
| Pigs | 66 | 9 700 |
| Eggs | 100 | 6 600 |
| Broiler | 100 | 4 800 |
| Intensive ruminant (crop + grass) | | |
| Milk [1]/ | 95 | 8 500 |
| Intensive beef | 55 | 6 400 |
| Extensive ruminant | | |
| Sheep | 27 | 3 300 |
| Beef cows | 32 | 4 000 |

1/  Milk data corrected to allow for replacements.

Source:  Modified after Holmes, W.  The Livestock of Great Britain as Food Producers, Nutrition, London, 29, (6) 331-336, 1975.

As a country develops, its use of grain for animal feed usually increases. Whereas currently over 60% of all grain consumed in developed countries is fed to animals, the proportion in developing countries is only 13%. Globally developing countries account for a minor proportion of world feed grain use: their share has risen only slowly from 15% in the early 1960s to 17% in 1980. Nevertheless, in absolute terms, this 1980 figure represents the feeding of close to 100 million tons of grain to livestock in these countries.

It is well recognized that livestock production is not an efficient way to produce protein and energy in situations where land can be used for crop production. Indeed, comparing crop to even intensive non-ruminant livestock production in developed countries, crops can produce at least 2 to 2½ times as much protein and energy as livestock per hectare of land (Table 2-3). For this reason it is sometimes argued that, if the wealthier countries were to reduce their consumption of animal products, sufficient land would be released for crop production to provide enough food energy to overcome deficits existing elsewhere in the world. Such arguments ignore the many complex economic issues involved in such a shift in resource use. Some of these will be addressed in the section on feed resources.

A better approach would be to give due attention to the potential for improving animal production through greater technical efficiency in the developing countries themselves. This potential is considerable (see box). If it were realized, it would undoubtedly do much to improve animal protein intakes as well as agricultural income levels in developing countries. In so doing, it would promote their development. How to realize this potential is the central issue of this chapter.

LIVESTOCK AS A SOURCE OF POWER

In developing countries animal draught power represents a major output from the livestock sector, although it is one that is usually underestimated or ignored. In fact, about half the energy these countries use for agriculture is contributed by livestock [1]. Animals provide 23% and 9% of the use of power for agricultural prduction in Asia and Africa respectively and, in this respect, are more important than tractors (see Fig 1-9). In Latin America and the Near East animals still provide about one-sixth of agricultural power though tractor use has increased rapidly in the past decade.

The use of draught animals is not restricted to the cultivation of crops. They are also used for transport - various estimates have suggested that 20% of the world's population is dependent upon animals for their transport needs - and as a source of power for processing crops and for irrigation.

Where farmers use livestock for traction purposes or burn manure for fuel this does not necessarily provide a direct income but it may save either purchased inputs or family labour. Where the ground is too hard for hand cultivation before the rains, or where double or triple cropping is practised, the timing of land preparation and planting may be critical. Without draught animals for cultivation the chances of a successful crop under these conditions may be low. In such circumstances, draught animals may be used for cultivation for only 30 to 50 days a year but without them the prevailing farming system could collapse. Similar peaks in power requirements may occur at harvest time; for example, when animals are widely used to gather and thresh grain.

---

[1] FAO, Report of the FAO Expert Consultation on Appropriate Use of Animal Energy in Agriculture in Africa and Asia, Rome, 1982.

The world's total draught animal population has been estimated to be of the order of 280 million head of which about 75% are large ruminants, 19% equines and 5% camelidae 2/. Clearly, the large scale replacement of these animals by tractors would be a costly process which would have important implications for foreign exchange requirements, employment and fossil fuel consumption. Nevertheless, a number of countries have encouraged tractorization, particularly the use of hand tractors, but their purchase and operational costs restrict the pace at which this can be carried out. Also many of the world's farms are too small to economically justify a tractor at all at present levels of output. However, some form of additional power input in the future will be essential because in most developing countries the present power available from all sources - but predominantly human labour - is considerably less than that required to achieve the full potential for improved crop yields.

Indonesia, Sri Lanka and the Philippines provide striking examples of the growing demand for draught animal power. For Indonesia's transmigration programme World Bank funds are being used to import several thousand Brahman cattle every year from Australia to meet the deficit of draught animals. In Sri Lanka, semi-feral buffaloes are being re-domesticated to replenish the rapidly growing shortage of draught animals. In the Philippines and in a number of other south-east Asian countries, a ban has been imposed on the slaughter of buffaloes to prevent the continuing depletion of draught animal power.

In its AT 2000 study, FAO calculated that power input to agriculture in developing countries would have to increase by 2.3% per annum to achieve an overall agricultural growth rate of 3.4% per annum until the year 2000. This would involve an overall increase of 15% in the number of draught animals but an increase of over 400% in tractor numbers. The required increase in tractor numbers may be hard to attain and, if so, draught animal numbers may well increase at a somewhat faster rate than that projected.

For many farming operations a pair of draught animals, or even a single animal, suffices. However, the power potential of working animals is seldom realized because of the bad harnesses and crude and inefficient implements with which they are used. They are also susceptible to losses through disease. Development and local manufacture of improved animal drawn equipment and improved veterinary services can promote the application of this source of power considerably as shown by the examples of Senegal and Sierra Leone. A recent report from the latter country indicated that ox ploughing and weeding using improved equipment cost considerably less than when the same tasks were done by either tractor or even manual labour 3/.


LIVESTOCK AS A SOURCE OF EMPLOYMENT

The role of the livestock sector as a source of employment is not easily determined in areas where a monetary economy does not exist, in areas of underemployment, or where women and children tend the stock. The opportunity cost of many tasks in animal husbandry can be low in such situations because the labour employed may not have alternative gainful employment. It is attractive as a labour activity on the family farm because much of the work can be performed by women or even children and the tasks are regular rather than seasonal.

---

2/ Ramaswamy, N.S., Report on Draught Animal Power as a Source of Renewable Energy, FAO, Rome, 1981. Another useful source is Goe, Michael R. and Robert E. McDowell. Animal Traction: Guidelines for Utilization, Cornell International Agriculture Mimeograph 81, 1980.

3/ Starkey, P.H., 1982 World Animal Review 42: 19-26.

As development proceeds, livestock production normally does not generate much gainful employment.  In arid areas of Australia, for example, one man may serve to look after 700 head of cattle equivalents.  However, this figure drops to 300 in the higher rainfall areas of Australia as it does in tropical and sub-tropical Latin America and it falls still further to 70-100 cattle equivalents on better pastoral areas in both continents.  In intensive specialized beef and dairy units in Brazil, the labour use is equivalent to 13 to 18 cattle units per man respectively 4/.  This was the type of labour intensity found in western Europe in the 1950s since which time, under the pressure of increasing labour costs, the number of stock handled per man on typical highly capital intensive dairy farms has risen to more than 100.

The impact of intensification of livestock production on labour use can be seen in the EEC where, although dairy cow numbers remained virtually constant between 1960 and 1980, the number of cows per herd almost doubled.  In Holland and the UK over 80% of cows are now in herds of 30 or more animals.  These changes have coincided with the fall in the proportion of the EEC workforce employed in agriculture which has declined from 16.6% in 1960 to 7.4% in 1979 5/.

In the early stages of industrializing and intensifying the livestock industry, it becomes more labour-intensive and jobs are created.  However, as development progresses, increasing wage rates and easier access to capital lead to a high degree of mechanization with a consequential lowering in labour inputs and a vast increase in output per man.  In the United States' poultry industry the labour used to produce 100 kilograms of turkey carcass fell from 63 to 2 man hours between 1914 and 1973;  and that to produce the same weight of broiler chicken fell from 17 hours in the late 1930s to 0.6 hours in the early 1970s.  Changes of this nature are likely to occur in developing countries too and have already started in some.  However, the existence there of considerable underemployment and lower wages, plus the shortage of capital to exploit new technologies, will probably mean that the pace of change will be somewhat slower than what occurred in developed countries.  It is also likely to be restricted to countries in the middle income group.

LIVESTOCK AS UTILIZERS OF MARGINAL LANDS AND CROP BY-PRODUCTS

The capital intensive type of livestock farming now seen so frequently in Europe and North America is well adapted to economies where capital is available, surplus grain exists and labour prices are high.  These conditions seldom prevail in developing countries where livestock agriculture is usually geared to a low input system which maximizes the use of land and waste materials otherwise unsuitable for use by man.  It is this ability of livestock, particularly ruminants, to utilize such materials and so to be  an integral part of the farming system, that constitutes a major, if largely hidden, asset in developing countries' agriculture.

The pattern of livestock feeding varies very much according to local conditions. Thus in much of the densely populated areas of Asia grazing is extremely limited, being restricted to the banks of canals and roads.  Fodder crops are rarely grown and the major feed is cereal straw.  Cattle and, in some countries, pigs are fed a variety of waste

---

4/   Jahnke, H.E. in World Animal Science Vol. 1.   Tribe, D.E. and E. Peel (eds.), Elsivier Publications, Amsterdam (in press).

5/   EEC Dairy Facts and Figures 1981, Milk Marketing Board, Thames Ditton, U.K.

materials such as vegetable refuse, ground and fermented rice hulls, cassava peelings, soybean and sweet potato vines and chopped banana stalks. As these materials are not suitable for human food there is little conflict between livestock and man for either land or source of food.

The humid and sub-humid tropics occupy 28% of the world's land surface and include permanent pastures and rough grazing land. These lands feed about 40% of the world's ruminant stock and provide about 15%, 11% and 12% respectively of the world's beef, sheep-meat and milk. Some of them have soil, topography and other features that could enable them to be used more extensively for crop production in the future. But to do so many of them would require large investments in development. Furthermore, many of the acid in-fertile soils of the lowland humid tropics yield poorly with present genetic-chemical technology. Therefore livestock are likely to play an important role in their utilization for some time hence.

The same is also true of the world's vast areas of arid and semi-arid rangelands where plant production is severely curtailed. The people inhabiting such areas have evolved a complex system of land use in which there is a delicate balance between the range ecosystem and livestock and, in some cases, wildlife. Stock have been bred for survival utilizing low quality forages, with variable patterns of rainfall and plant pro-duction. The plant species found on the range have evolved under a system of intermit-tent grazing by a variety of herbivores. The pastoralists in these areas of low crop potential have become heavily dependent on their livestock whose milk - and sometimes blood - may provide the most important components of their diet. For such societies human survival is closely related to the survival of their stock, as has been shown dra-matically by the drought in the Sahel in the early 1970s and in Ethiopia and Somalia. In such circumstances, the animal and its husbandry become closely interwoven with a society's culture. In this way communities can pursue a way of life that utilizes some of the harshest parts of the world's surface which would otherwise not be habitable by man.

Such arid zone pastoralists provide an extreme example of the use of livestock, speci-fically ruminants and camels, as converters of forages and browse to products consumable by man. But even in developed countries, some 75% of the feed intake of ruminants - as opposed to 97% in developing countries - is derived from fibrous forages. Much of this feed is produced on lands unsuitable for crop production or which otherwise would be fallowed; and much is also produced on land as part of a crop rotation.

About a quarter of the total energy content of supplementary feeds fed to livestock is derived from crop by-products which, by virtue of their characteristics such as texture, palatability and high fibre content, have a very limited potential for use as human food. In this sense, as will be discussed later, the disaggregation of the agricultural sector into crop and livestock sub-sectors is a highly artificial one in most situations.

## LIVESTOCK AS A MEANS OF CAPITAL ACCUMULATION

Apart from the value of their output, livestock may also represent an important capital asset in many farming systems. The overall investment in livestock in world agriculture, leaving aside the value of the land grazed by stock and the buildings and fences used to contain them, is, at a conservative estimate, of the order of US $400 thousand million.

In most developed countries the high costs of labour and the availability of capital associated with an efficient credit system have led to the establishment of large livestock enterprises with very high capital investment. A similar situation can be seen in the state-owned and collective enterprises of centrally planned economies. Yet even on small farms in developing countries livestock frequently represent between 20 and 50% of farm capital and contribute directly a similar proportion to farm income.

In pastoral societies livestock owners often attach greater importance to stock numbers than to their productive efficiency as they are their means of survival. Livestock have a multiple value and can represent variable combinations of wealth, prestige, and prequisites of adulthood, marriage or parenthood. They may be vital for subsistence as well as being convertible into cash.

The reproductive potential of livestock also means that they represent a form of investment in such situations where institutional saving is not possible. An animal which is not consumed or sold represents an addition to the farmer's wealth. To do so, however, it must survive drought and disease. Upgraded exotic stock may be more profitable as markets develop but, for the farmer whose goals are essentially those of capital formation and risk aversion, traditional breeds of stock may be preferred.

LIVESTOCK BY-PRODUCTS AND THEIR USES AS MANURE,
ENERGY OR INDUSTRIAL RAW MATERIALS

The faeces produced by livestock contribute to this crop-livestock interdependence by improving soil fertility. Dried ruminant faeces are also an important fuel in parts of Africa and Asia. For example, in India 60-80 million tons are estimated to be used in this way annually 6/. A number of countries have also used ruminant and pig faeces to produce methane as a source of energy.

Faeces from intensively fed livestock have a particularly high content of nutrients which can be utilized by recycling them as a feed supplement for ruminants, pigs, poultry and fish. In a number of countries of south-east Asia, for example, livestock excreta are used as feed and fertilizer for fishponds which are often integrated with duck production. Using this system, commercial yields of 10 tons fish/ha/year have been recorded 7/.

Faeces are not the only by-product produced by animals. Their carcasses provide a large number of products other than meat. These are often defined as inedible products but viscera are eaten to varying degrees in many countries, as are fats, and even hides and skins. Fat in the form of lard or tallow is often removed from the carcass. World production of these latter products in 1980 was 10.3 million tons with a market value in excess of US $1.4 thousand million, equivalent to about 5% of the value of exports of live animals and meat. Such fats may be used directly for human consumption or be rendered for the manufacture of margarine, cooking fat and other products. Lower quality animal fats are used in the manufacture of soap, glycerol and detergents. However, recently these latter markets have encountered very heavy competition from petrochemical derivatives.

Synthetics also compete strongly with wool and, to some extent hides and skins. Yet the use of these natural products continues to be important and represents between 5 and

_____

6/ Ramaswamy, N.S. op. cit.

7/ Edwards, P., A Review of Recycling Organic Wastes into Fish, With Emphasis on the Tropics. Aquaculture 21: 261-279, 1980.

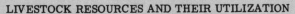

LIVESTOCK RESOURCES AND THEIR UTILIZATION

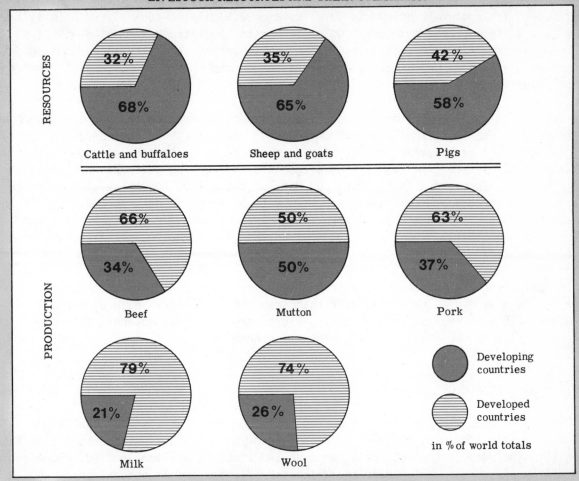

The developing countries contain 75% of the world's human population, 58% of all agricultural land, 68% of the world's cattle and buffaloes, 65% of its sheep and goats and 58% of its pigs, but produce relatively much less in terms of animal products because productivity is lower than in developed countries. This difference in productivity is well demonstrated by comparing average milk yields.

Productivity of Dairy Cattle by Region
(1969-71 to 1979-81)

| | Yield of milk per dairy cow | |
| --- | --- | --- |
| | 69-71 | 79-81 |
| | ........metric tons........ | |
| World | 1.85 | 1.92 |
| Total developed countries | 2.81 | 3.13 |
| Total developing countries | 0.61 | 0.66 |
|     Africa | 0.33 | 0.36 |
|     Far East | 0.48 | 0.51 |
|     Latin America | 0.91 | 0.95 |
|     Near East | 0.60 | 0.64 |
|     Asian Centrally Planned Economies | 0.49 | 0.67 |

Source:  FAO Production Yearbooks.

10% of the value of the animal carcass. Wool, in spite of a reduced share in a vastly expanded world fibre market, still has sales of over 2.5 million tons a year. This amount is not very different from its market volume prior to the introduction of synthetics. Hair from the camelidae and from goats is also an important commodity in certain arid or highland areas, such as Namibia, the Andean Altiplano and the Himalayas. It is used to produce a variety of garments as well as tents, blankets and handicrafts.

Fifty years ago a very wide range of products derived from animal carcass glands were used to produce pharmaceutically active compounds. However, these compounds are increasingly being either synthesized artificially or replaced by synthetic analogues. This trend is likely to accelerate under the impetus of genetic engineering which has already enabled insulin to be synthesized. In the long run many of the animal endocrine glands, which formerly produced glandular extracts, are likely to be rendered down as meat meal in the same way that bone, horn and hoof, formerly the raw materials for combs, buttons and handles, are now usually ground into bonemeal as they are rarely competitive with products made from plastics.

Indeed, among the many animal by-products formerly available for processing, it is only a few such as hides, skins and hair that seem likely to survive in widespread use in the future. This is because they possess a micro-structure that not only determines their final properties but is difficult to synthesize economically.

## LIVESTOCK AS A SOURCE OF EXPORT EARNINGS

Livestock and their products are an important component of international trade. The total annual values of meat and meat products and of milk and dairy products traded internationally, including intra-EEC trade, were US $40 thousand million in 1980, representing nearly 17.5% of current world trade in agricultural (crops and livestock) products. Most of this trade, however, takes place between developed countries, or from them to developing countries. Developing countries' exports account for less than 10% of total exports of livestock products (Table 2-4) and livestock products account for only about 6% of their exports

TABLE 2-4.  WORLD TRADE IN LIVESTOCK PRODUCTS, 1980

| | Live animals and meat | | Milk, eggs and dairy products | | Balance of trade | % of world trade | |
|---|---|---|---|---|---|---|---|
| | Exports | Imports | Exports | Imports | | Exports | Imports |
| | ................... US $ million ................... | | | | | | |
| Developing market economies | 3 269 | 5 380 | 167 | 4 713 | -6 657 | 8.6 | 24.4 |
| Africa | 554 | 695 | 3 | 1 133 | -1 271 | 1.4 | 4.4 |
| Far East | 196 | 828 | 87 | 796 | -1 341 | 0.7 | 3.9 |
| Latin America | 2 282 | 926 | 59 | 1 112 | + 303 | 5.9 | 4.9 |
| Near East | 235 | 2 754 | 18 | 1 615 | -4 116 | 0.6 | 10.6 |
| Asian centrally planned econ. | 834 | 41 | 136 | 101 | + 828 | 2.4 | 0.3 |
| Developed market economies[1/] | 19 634 | 19 954 | 12 891 | 8 516 | +4 055 | 81.6 | 68.8 |
| Eastern Europe and USSR | 2 547 | 1 988 | 427 | 647 | + 339 | 7.5 | 6.4 |
| World | 26 284 | 27 363 | 13 587 | 14 001 | -1 493 | 100.0 | 100.0 |

1/  Includes intra-EEC trade.
Source:  FAO Trade Yearbook 1980.

of agricultural products.  Yet developing countries were at the same time, responsible for 20% of the imports of meat and 34% of those for milk and milk products, and these account for about one-fifth of their agricultural imports.  Thus developed countries have benefited more from the growth in world export trade in livestock products.  Trade issues are discussed in a following section.

## LIVESTOCK:  AN INTEGRAL PART OF FARMING SYSTEMS

Apart from providing important - if variable - nutritive components of the diet, the preceding discussion shows that livestock perform a multipurpose role in agriculture.  In the context of developing countries, the main strength of livestock production as a means of promoting development lies in its integration with traditional and often small scale farming systems, both as a source of food and income and also as an input through the provision of draught power and manure.

Within both extensive pastoral systems and small scale intensive farming, livestock are of inestimable value in utilizing land resources or feed materials which otherwise cannot be used directly by man.  Labour employed in these systems often has few alternative economic pursuits.

## TRENDS IN LIVESTOCK PRODUCTION AND TRADE

In the world livestock economy, growth in demand has shifted from the developed regions over the past decades.  With population rising at an annual average rate of less than 1% and per caput demand nearing saturation point, their consumption of animal products has tended to level off and, more recently, even to decrease.  But, in the developing regions, demand has been stimulated by rising per caput incomes, rapid population growth of more than 2% per annum and high rates of urbanization, often accompanied by a rapid westernization of the diet.  Consumption has increased rapidly in the case of poultry meat and eggs.

### PRODUCTION TRENDS

Production trends have only partially followed those of demand.  In particular, in the developed market economies, agricultural policies have had difficulty in adjusting production and processing capacities to stagnating or shrinking domestic outlets.  Yet, in developing countries, domestic animal production has generally lagged behind demand.  At the beginning of the 1970s these countries were net exporters of animal products, especially meat, milk products and eggs.  In all Eastern European countries livestock production has lagged behind demand growth and the resulting deficits have been met by imports, mainly from other developed countries.

Past trends in livestock production in the developing countries have been encouraging for pig and poultry meat and eggs.  But they have been disappointing for meat and dairy products from ruminant animals where increases in production have been attained largely by increasing numbers rather than by increasing productivity (Table 2-5).

TABLE 2-5.  ANNUAL RATE OF CHANGE IN LIVESTOCK PRODUCTION, 1969/71 TO 1979/81

| | Nos. Head | Nos. Slaughtered | Carcass weight | Production |
|---|---|---|---|---|
| | ........................ | | % ........................ | |
| **Developing countries** | | | | |
| Cattle | 1.1 | 1.8 | 0.1 | 1.9 |
| Sheep and goats | 1.3 | 2.0 | ... | 2.1 |
| Pork | 4.1 | 4.1 | 0.6 | 4.8 |
| Cow milk | 2.4 | n.a. | 0.8 | 3.2 |
| Poultry | 3.6 | ... | ... | 7.5 |
| Eggs | ... | n.a. | n.a. | 5.1 |
| **Developed countries** | | | | |
| Cattle | 0.7 | 0.4 | 1.1 | 1.5 |
| Sheep and goats | -0.6 | -0.9 | - | -0.7 |
| Pork | 2.2 | 2.5 | 0.3 | 2.8 |
| Cow milk | 0.2 | n.a. | 1.1 | 1.3 |
| Poultry | 2.2 | ... | ... | 5.2 |
| Eggs | ... | n.a. | n.a. | 1.9 |

Notes.  During the 1970s the catch of fish has been increasing at an average annual rate of nearly 4.5% for developing countries but less than 1% for developed.

n.a. means "not applicable".

Source:  FAO Production Yearbooks.

Greater production in developed countries has been accompanied by more specialization and larger units. In the 1970s cattle numbers in these countries increased by less than 9% and dairy cow numbers by 4%, although production of beef and milk increased by 15% and 14% respectively. Yet the growth rate in livestock production in the developed countries has been less than that in developing ones.

Production of beef cattle and pig meat in most major producing countries has been characterized by self-perpetuating cyclical variations in both output and prices. The basic mechanism for this tendency is an inventory cycle within the breeding and fattening herds. For beef cattle the length of the cycle from peak-to-peak in production is normally 6 to 8 years if there are no external disturbances to its regular rhythm. This length of cycle appears to apply to almost three-quarters of the world's commercial beef production 8/.

Pig meat replaced bovine meat as the most important meat product in developing countries in the 1970s (Table 2-6). The share of poultry meat in their total meat output also rose

TABLE 2-6.  GROWTH RATES IN WHITE MEAT AND HEN EGG PRODUCTION IN 90 DEVELOPING COUNTRIES AND ASIAN CENTRALLY PLANNED ECONOMIES, EARLY 1960s TO LATE 1970s

| | 1961/65 | 1969/71 | 1978/80 | Per annum growth rates | | |
| | | | | 1963-70 | 1970-79 | 1980-2000 |
| | | | | Actual | | AT 2000 |
| | ....000 metric tons .... | | | ........... % ............ | | |
| **PORK** | | | | | | |
| Africa | 135 | 179 | 263 | 4.1 | 4.4 | 6.8 |
| Far East | 990 | 1 280 | 1 395 | 3.7 | 1.0 | 5.4 |
| Latin America | 1 302 | 1 655 | 2 321 | 3.5 | 3.8 | 4.4 |
| Near East | 8 | 17 | 21 | 11.4 | 2.4 | 4.2 |
| Asian centrally planned economies | ... | 10 113 | 16 079 | ... | 5.3 | ... |
| **POULTRY MEAT** | | | | | | |
| Africa | 276 | 387 | 732 | 4.9 | 7.3 | 8.1 |
| Far East | 437 | 637 | 1 045 | 5.5 | 5.7 | 8.8 |
| Latin America | 632 | 1 200 | 2 737 | 9.6 | 9.6 | 5.2 |
| Near East | 189 | 332 | 771 | 8.4 | 9.8 | 10.1 |
| Asian centrally planned economies | ... | 1 779 | 2 832 | ... | 5.3 | ... |
| **HEN EGGS** | | | | | | |
| Africa | 338 | 389 | 582 | 2.0 | 4.6 | 7.3 |
| Far East | 594 | 817 | 1 667 | 4.7 | 8.3 | 6.3 |
| Latin America | 1 102 | 1 381 | 2 341 | 3.3 | 6.0 | 4.9 |
| Near East | 271 | 328 | 702 | 2.8 | 8.8 | 8.6 |
| Asian centrally planned economies | ... | 3 451 | 4 583 | ... | 3.2 | ... |

Sources:  FAO Production Yearbooks,  AT 2000, FAO, 1981.

---

8/ FAO, Cyclical Problems in World Production and Trade in Beef and Veal:  Possibilities for Ameliorative Action.  CCP ME 75/4 Rome, 1975.

from 12% in 1970 to 17% in 1980, and since the mid 1970s their egg production has increased at a rate nearly three times that of developed countries. But the difference in the growth of milk production has been much less pronounced and is strongly influenced by structural considerations which are discussed later.

Throughout the developing regions, modern large-scale poultry and egg production and processing enterprises have now been established, mainly in the peri-urban areas, along the pattern originally evolved in North America in the late 1940s and subsequently transferred to other developed countries. To a lesser extent, similar enterprises have also been set up for the production and marketing of pig meat and, sometimes, milk.

Such large-scale operations are highly automated and capital intensive. They require a small but skilled labour force. They also require equipment and production requisites that usually have to be imported by developing countries although some of them such as Brazil, India, Korea Rep. and China are manufacturing them locally. The expansion of this activity would offer prospects for the development of local agro-industries.

The extent to which modern poultry enterprises have developed appears to be closely related to the general socio-economic development of individual countries. In the higher income and more urbanized countries of Latin America, North Africa and the Far East their share of the total national poultry production is over 80% and it has reached over 90% in some high income Near East countries. However, even in some lower income countries such as Pakistan, India, Sri Lanka, Zambia and Ghana between one-third and two-thirds of poultry production now comes from the commercial sector.

Traditional systems of poultry production are more frequently found in Africa south of the Sahara, and in a number of lower income Asian countries. Productivity is low from birds which scavenge around the homestead and are fed only on household scraps, but there is virtually no cash input involved.

With regard to milk, although the average growth rate of world production has fallen from 3% in the 1950s to less than 2% in the 1960s and the 1970s, the international dairy situation has remained one of supplies almost chronically exceeding commercial outlets in the developed countries. The surplus problem was concentrated in the United States in the first two decades after World War II and has appeared there again recenlty. But it shifted to the EEC as well in the late 1960s.

The decline in commercial demand for milk and milk products in the developed market economies partly reflects changing food consumption habits - only 17% of the milk delivered to dairies in the EEC is consumed as fresh milk - as well as structural changes in both the agricultural and the milk processing industries. The principal cause of the growing discrepancy between output and commercial outlets in these countries has been government policies in North America and some countries in Western Europe which have supported high prices for dairy farmers. These policies arising from agricultural structural problems have resulted in surpluses and the accumulation of large stocks of butter and skim milk powder. Their disposal has distorted the pattern of international trade in dairy products.

In contrast to this situation developing countries have seen their domestic supplies lagging increasingly behind demand and, as a result, they now account for the greater part of world imports of dairy products. There are many developing countries for whom dairy development is essential, not only to improve nutritional standards and reduce the foreign exchange costs of imports, but also as a means to intensify and diversify agriculture and raise small farmer incomes. However, to date, progress in dairy development, with a few outstanding exceptions, has been very slow. While there have been numerous local short-comings and failures, the over-supply situation in international markets has also been a contributory factor. It has frequently resulted in the limited funds available for agricultural development being invested in projects which offer a better return than dairy production, with a growing gap between demand and local supplies of milk products. Developing countries which, thanks to very favourable ecological conditions, would appear to be potential exporters, have little chance of realizing this potential because they would have little hope of competing with the subsidized exports of developed countries. A similar situation has also developed in meat.


## TRENDS IN CONSUMPTION AND TRADE

It has been shown that during the past two decades the growth in demand for animal products in developed countries has slowed down and on occasion consumption has even declined. In contrast, in the developing countries, where consumption levels are much lower, demand has been strong, constrained only by income levels as well as the availability of livestock products and hence their prices (Fig. 2-1). Throughout this period, the growth in consumption has exceeded that of production in developing countries, the deficit being met by imports.

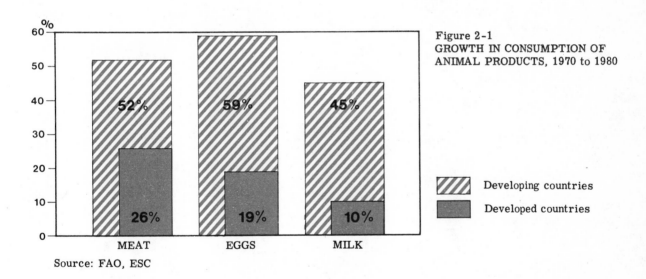

Figure 2-1
GROWTH IN CONSUMPTION OF
ANIMAL PRODUCTS, 1970 to 1980

Source: FAO, ESC

The Near East Region, reflecting petroleum export earnings and an influx of migrant labour, has experienced the most rapid rise in demand for meat and other animal products. With pig meat consumption being negligible because of religious reasons and bovine, sheep and goat meat supplies being less ample, poultry meat consumption in this region has, over the past decade, risen by more than 13% annually. Growth in poultry meat consumption has been impressive in other regions also. Pig meat and egg consumption has risen fastest in the Far East.

Growth in the consumption of animal products has been promoted by price controls and/or subsidies which have mainly benefited urban consumers. But the principal factor stimulating consumption, particularly that of poultry meat, eggs and, to a lesser extent, pig meat, has been the decrease in their prices relative to other livestock products, reflecting the technical progress in poultry and pig farming. A recent study from Brazil, Chile and Colombia

- 94 -

showed that in all three countries the prices for poultry meat and eggs fell in constant terms during the 1970s, whereas during the same period prices for beef and cow milk rose.

In those countries where foreign exchange has not been a limiting factor, imports of livestock products have grown rapidly. Developing countries now account for over 40% of world imports of dairy products. They are also net importers of eggs (Table 2-7). In meat as a whole former sizeable net export trade recently has turned into substantial net imports.

Recent FAO estimates of demand for meat and milk suggest little change in the recent pattern of demand. Growth in meat consumption will probably remain concentrated in the richer developing countries. In Eastern European countries there are likely to be some increases in retail prices that may curb demand. Japan is one of the few among the developed market economies with scope for a significant increase in meat consumption. A recovery

TABLE 2-7. DEVELOPING COUNTRIES' TRADE IN LIVESTOCK PRODUCTS

| | Shares of developing countries in the volume of world trade in livestock products | | | | Balance of trade in developing countries[1/] | | |
|---|---|---|---|---|---|---|---|
| | Imports | | Exports | | | | |
| | 1968/70 | 1978/80 | 1968/70 | 1978/80 | 1958/60 | 1968/70 | 1978/80 |
| | ....................%.................. | | | | ........'000 tons........ | | |
| Total Meat | 15 | 21 | 28 | 16 | +1 201 | +1 042 | - 394 |
| of which: | | | | | | | |
| cattle meat | 15 | 16 | 41 | 19 | + 810 | + 999 | + 440 |
| sheep/goat meat | 18 | 29 | 19 | 10 | + 59 | + 10 | - 257 |
| pigmeat | 12 | 4 | 12 | 4 | + 52 | + 6 | - 5 |
| poultry | 23 | 52 | 6 | 14 | - 10 | - 99 | - 577 |
| Eggs in shell | 20 | 31 | 15 | 12 | - 54 | - 23 | - 143 |
| Milk and milk products | 34 | 41 | 1 | 1 | -1 151 | -7 102 | -15 749 |

1/ + net export; -net import.

Source: FAO Trade Yearbooks.

of economic activity could result in some strengthening in high income countries' demand for meat but their elasticities of demand with respect to income or expenditure are now low overall 9/. Also health considerations appear to increasingly influence consumer attitudes.

Turning to possibilities to expand world meat supplies it can be argued that most of the increase is likely to come from poultry and, to a lesser extent, pig meat. It is expected that industrial systems of production such as intensive broiler production will continue to expand rapidly in developing countries and the centrally planned developed economies. But this would depend on the continued ready availability of high energy feeds.

9/ For example, in Canada in 1957 the estimated expenditure elasticity for meat was estimated to be 0.16. By 1969 this estimate was halved to 0.08.

At the same time, developing countries have unexploited feed resources that can be used by ruminant animals, as will be discussed below. Thus there is scope to expand beef production in several developing countries in Asia and Africa, primarily for domestic consumption though it would require removal of the many technical and socio-economic constraints currently hindering expansion of beef output. There is also scope to increase beef output in Eastern Europe and the USSR. On the other hand, in Western Europe, where most beef comes from the dairy herd, the continued surplus production of milk products and beef would appear to portend future reductions in cattle numbers.

Medium term prospects for the sheep sector are somewhat brighter than for bovine meat production. Nevertheless, the shift from cattle to sheep farming recently experienced in a number of countries with important pasture industries seems to be losing momentum.

For dairy products, supplies are expected to continue to exceed commercial outlets by a considerable margin for some years hence. Though the continuation of current policies to subsidize both the human consumption and feed use of some milk products in several developed countries would produce an apparent overall balance by 1985, it would conceal the wide discrepancy between output and commercial outlets. The difference would remain particularly striking in the EEC and the United States where considerable liquid and dry skim milk is used for animal feed. For example, the use of liquid and dry skim milk in animal feeds in the developed market economies in 1981 was about 1.6 million tons of skim milk powder equivalent. This was six times the volume of food aid in skim milk powder and more than twice the volume of international commercial trade in this product. Most of this usage occurred in the EEC where in addition about 30% of butter consumption is subsidized. If these dairy subsidy policies remain unchanged, the use of these products as animal feed is likely to grow considerably. This would imply that the share of the traditional low cost producing exporters in world dairy product trade would probably decline still further and there would be very little scope for export-oriented dairy development to occur in developing countries.

In contrast, in Eastern Europe and USSR milk production has actually slightly declined over the past 5 years. As a consequence imports have greatly increased. For example, net imports of dry milk products more than tripled in value between 1979 and 1981.

FAO's study AT 2000 placed considerable stress on the role of livestock development in achieving a wide range of development objectives under a high demand growth scenario. It estimated that livestock production in the 90 developing countries studied will need to grow by up to 4.5% per annum over the next 20 years. About half of the growth in demand comes from expected population growth and the remainder from increases in per caput incomes. The overall growth rate would have to be nearly double that of the last two decades. Such an increase in growth in the livestock industries of the developing countries would require major efforts and is unlikely to take place in the absence of supportive policies from the developed countries. Certainly, in the dairy sector, a continuation of the existing protectionist policies of the developed countries is unlikely to be of much help in promoting dairy development in the developing regions.

Current policies of the developed countries towards international trade in meat also restrict the prospects for developing countries for some of which this trade is becoming important (Table 2-7). For example, in 1981 about 15% of world exports of all fresh meat were from developing countries, and for fresh poultry meat the figure was 20%. Most of this was from one country, Brazil. Quantitative restrictions in the form of import embargoes, quotas, voluntary export restraint arrangements, restrictive licensing and centralized procurement have been increasingly introduced. Moreover, minimum import prices, enforced by variable levies, have been applied to an increasing extent. Barriers of a technical nature, such as animal health regulations, although recognized as necessary to prevent the introduction of diseases, also have substantial effects on international trade in livestock and animal products. At the same time, recourse has increasingly been taken to the subsidization of exports. The net effect of these various protectionist measures has been to adversely affect the export earnings of low cost producing countries, both developed and developing, and to counteract livestock development efforts.

A factor which is likely to influence the future of animal production in developing countries is the extent to which they are able to supply, either from their own production or from imports, the quantity of grain required to meet the very high growth targets suggested for their pig and poultry industries. Reference has already been made to the extent to which pig and poultry meat have substituted for ruminant meat in some countries.

Another type of substitution which has aroused considerable attention is the use of vegetable based meat or milk substitutes or extenders to replace animal based products. In general, vegetable products are cheaper than animal ones, although there are often strong consumer preferences for the latter.

The best known vegetable substitute is margarine whose early success was due to its advantages and the ease with which butter, a homogenous product without cellular structure, could be simulated. More recently, sales of margarine have been promoted on health grounds because of its high ratio of polyunsaturated to saturated fats. The substitution of milk and cheese by plant products would undoubtedly have followed that of margarine had they not been held back by legislative protection gained by the dairy farmers of the developed countries. However, more recently filled milk with butter fat being replaced by cheaper vegetable fat, has appeared on a number of markets; and extended milk, a combination of plant and animal fats and proteins, has been widely used in India. The prospects for expanding the use of these types of products should be promising in many developing countries where dairy production has limited scope but vegetable oil production could be expanded.

The use of vegetable substitutes, such as soybean protein, for meat has been constrained by technological problems and a lack of consumer acceptance. The technology has improved considerably during the past decade but is still very capital intensive and requires considerable energy inputs. Consumer acceptance problems remain ones of flavour and texture.

To date, there has been little success in introducing meat substitutes into developing countries because their price usually puts them out of reach of the income groups that require additional animal protein.


SOME KEY ISSUES ARISING FROM THE TRENDS

The issues arising from this brief survey of trends in the production, consumption and trade of livestock products are clearly demarcated between developed and developing countries. In the market economies of the first group, many issues revolve around the adjustment of production capacity to stagnating or even declining domestic markets. Such problems are particularly acute in the case of dairy products, and are closely related to questions of farm size and numbers, especially in the EEC. They have given rise to protectionist trade measures which are impinging on the interests of exporting countries which face increasingly stiff competition. In some developing countries, even their domestic livestock industries are threatened by the increasing quantities of products available on world markets at subsidized prices.

Eastern Europe and the USSR do not face such demand declines. Rather it is a question of satisfying growing demand for livestock products, which is continuing to rise at a time when foreign exchange to finance increased imports is constrained.

In the face of rapid rates of increase in demand, developing countries' production of beef and dairy products has been disappointing, but more encouraging for pig and poultry products. How best to harness their potential capacity to both satisfy increased demand while promoting rural welfare is the key issue facing livestock planners in these countries. The opportunities offered by technological advances in animal breeding, feeding and health are explored in the next section.

## THE EFFECTS OF RISING INCOMES ON THE DEMAND
## FOR LIVESTOCK PRODUCTS

When people's incomes rise above bare subsistence levels and they start to have some money to spend, the usual pattern is to use a high portion of this new income for food. Not only do they eat more but – for reasons of nutrition, taste or status – they tend also to start consuming 'preferred' food products. In many societies, livestock products such as meat and milk rank high among these preferred additions to the diet. As economists would say, livestock products tend to have a 'high income elasticity of demand'. That is, a one-percent increase in income results in more than a one-percent increase in consumption. This characteristic of the demand for animal products tends to be true for lower-and middle-income levels; people in affluent societies do reach a point when additional income results in little or no further increase in amount or quality of these commodities in their diets.

These tendencies may create basic problems for agriculture. In some situations of low income countries demand for preferred foods such as meat and dairy may rise very fast under the combined effect of rising per caput income and population.

This rise may be so rapid that domestic supplies of the products cannot keep pace. As a result, prices rise or imports have to be allowed. On the other hand, at high levels of average income, income elasticities will have significantly declined – population growth also will be less – and rates of demand growth for livestock products will be very low or even negative for some. This can create severe difficulties in adjusting supply, especially when many farmers depend on the production of these products for their livelihood.

The following table drawn from a selection of food expenditure surveys, shows the wide range of expenditure elasticities between countries with different income levels, and how these change over time. Of course, increased expenditure on a particular food item does not necessarily mean that correspondingly more of it will be consumed. The consumer may prefer to buy more expensive, better quality products. This tendency in particular applies to livestock products whose differences in quality can be wide.

Income elasticities of expenditure[a]

(i) Differences between countries

| | Per caput GNP current $ | Elasticities | |
|---|---|---|---|
| | | Meat | Fresh milk |
| Germany, F.R., 1978 | 10 300 | 0.54 | 0.61 |
| Mexico, 1977 | 1 160 | 1.02 | 1.03 |
| Tunisia, 1974/75 | 680 | 1.08 | 1.09[b] |
| Indonesia, 1978 | 340 | 2.18 | 1.93[c] |
| Sri Lanka, 1977 | 160 | 1.23 | 1.20 |
| Bangladesh, 1973/74 | 90 | 3.25 | 3.81 |

a/ A log-inverse function has been used for all examples as it is one of the best to cover a wide range of incomes and hence is valid for making international comparisons between countries.
b/ Milk and dairy products.
c/ Milk, dairy products and eggs.

Sources: FAO. Income elasticities of demand for agricultural products, forth-coming.
World Bank. World Atlas, various years.

(ii) Changes over time

| | Per caput GNP constant $ | Elasticities | |
|---|---|---|---|
| | | Beef and veal | Fresh milk |
| United Kingdom, 1960 | 5 076 | 0.25 | 0.18 |
| United Kingdom, 1973 | 6 779 | 0.10 | 0.04 |

Sources: FAO. Income elasticities of demand for agricultural products, CCP 72/W.1 Rome, 1972.
FAO. Income elasticities of demand for agricultural products, ESC/ACP/WD.76/3 Rome, 1976.

## IMPROVING THE UTILIZATION OF THE PRODUCTION RESOURCES

The productivity of domestic livestock is influenced by a variety of different environmental, social, economic and technical factors. Efforts at changing existing systems of production may involve modifying any one or all of them. In a large number of cases they have, in the past, focused upon the technical aspects of change. These tend to be easier to manipulate than environmental or socio-economic factors: the former because they are largely outside of human control except where controlled-environment housing is practical and economic; and the latter because they involve a range of political and human linkages that seldom relate to only one change agent or institution.

In contrast, changes relating to animal feeding, breeding and disease control which are likely to improve productivity can often be readily identified. Furthermore mechanisms or institutions through which they need to be implemented frequently exist. Thus efforts at livestock development over the past two decades have emphasized animal genetic improvement, feed resource utilization and disease control.

It has become recognized that research knowledge from the developed world is not necessarily suited to nor readily adopted by the farmers of the developing world. New approaches may be required if livestock productivity there is to be increased. The better utilization of the available feed resources is of paramount importance because this will influence the directions policies aimed to improve livestock genetic resources should take.


FEED RESOURCES AND THEIR UTILIZATION

Most of the available feed energy supplies come from forage feeds such as those from rangelands and pastures. In developing countries, crop residues and household wastes are important sources of feed  also (Table 2-8).

TABLE 2-8.  ESTIMATED SOURCES OF LIVESTOCK FEEDS BY TYPE OF LIVESTOCK, 1977-78

|  | Grain | Protein meal/cake | By-products | Forage & other | Total |
|---|---|---|---|---|---|
|  | ..................... % ..................... |
| Poultry | 4.5 | 1.0 | 0.8 | 0.6 | 6.9 |
| Sheep and goats | 0.3 | 0.1 | 0.4 | 11.4 | 12.2 |
| Cattle and buffalo | 5.8 | 0.5 | 2.3 | 47.1 | 55.7 |
| Pigs | 5.3 | 0.6 | 2.4 | 1.8 | 10.1 |
| Draught animals | 0.7 | 0.1 | 0.3 | 14.0 | 15.1 |
| All livestock | 16.6 | 2.3 | 6.2 | 74.9 | 100.0 |

Total estimated feed requirement was 8707.4 thousand million Mcal of energy.

Source:  Wheeler, R.O. et al.  The World Livestock Product, Feedstuff and Food Grain System, Winrock International, Morrilton, Arkansas, 1981.

The group of livestock which are basically forage eaters, including ruminants, the equidae (horses, donkeys etc.), rabbits and, to some extent, the goose, all have digestive systems that make the utilization of coarse foods possible. The ruminants are of particular interest because of their large numbers in the developing countries and their efficiency in digesting and utilizing roughages and agricultural by-products. They are also able to utilize sources of non-protein nitrogen such as urea. However, ruminants are able to do this only to a degree that meets their requirements for maintenance, late growth and moderate milk yield. For peak periods of growth and production, low energy forages are inadequate. For high productivity it is necessary, therefore, to replace poor quality roughages with high quality forage and a certain amount of grain since these contain more than twice as much energy on a dry matter basis.

There are other intrinsic limitations to the efficiency of the rumen and the ruminant. Recent research has shown that for the ruminant to function well its feed should, in addition to roughages and some easily digestible energy such as molasses, contain some high quality protein and starch which can bypass the rumen breakdown and be digested and re-absorbed in the lower parts of the intestine. Feed grains serve as a good source of appropriate bypass starch. However, in many countries feed grains for ruminants and other grass-eating stock also compete with the demand for cereals for human consumption. So throughout the world such stock are raised principally on rangelands, forages, crop residues, agro-industrial by-products and animal and food wastes.

## Permanent Pastures and Grasslands

The distribution of permanent pastures in relation to the number of ruminant livestock varies greatly between different parts of the world (Table 2-9). The number of livestock in comparison to the area of permanent pastures is very large in Asia and the Far East. Africa is the region with the largest area under pasture but with the lowest density of livestock, partially because of the presence of the tsetse fly. Latin America also has large areas under permanent grass which supports a density of livestock almost equivalent to the average for the world.

In Oceania, particularly New Zealand, very efficient milk production systems, based almost entirely on permanent pastures, have been developed. In western Europe and North America, dairy production has developed along different lines and is based on integrated crop-livestock systems in which food crops are rotated with forages and feed grains.

Obviously, grasslands differ considerably in quality and carrying capacity. The global picture given in Table 2-9 indicates only the relative importance of the permanent grasslands in different regions.

In Asia and, in particular, on the Indian subcontinent, demographic pressures and the small area of permanent pastures in relation to the livestock numbers make it necessary to rely on crop residues (mainly straw) and agro-industrial by-products as the main source of ruminant feed. In Latin America and Africa the main challenge is the utilization and improvement of available grassland.

The pressure on the rangelands can be reduced, particularly in the dry season, by providing supplementary feeding for grazing animals. This may be done through the use of fodder shrubs or trees or by giving livestock access to cultivated lands. A striking example of the success of this approach is provided by a FAO/WFP project in forest watershed grazing areas of central Turkey. The cultivation of forage legumes was introduced

TABLE 2-9.  EXTENT AND DISTRIBUTION OF PERMANENT PASTURES AND
RUMINANT LIVESTOCK, 1980

| Regions | Permanent pastures | No. of ruminant livestock units[1] | Ruminant livestock units |
|---|---|---|---|
| | million $km^2$ | millions | Nos/$km^2$ of pasture |
| Africa | 6.3 | 135 | 21 |
| Asia and Far East | 0.4 | 324 | 810 |
| Latin America | 5.4 | 229 | 42 |
| Near East | 2.8 | 69 | 25 |
| Sub-total | 14.9 | 757 | 51 |
| Asian centrally planned economies | 3.5 | 109 | 31 |
| Total developing countries | 18.4 | 866 | 47 |
| North America | 2.7 | 100 | 37 |
| Western Europe | 0.7 | 92 | 131 |
| Oceania | 4.6 | 48 | 11 |
| Others | 0.8 | 18 | 22 |
| Sub-total | 8.8 | 258 | 29 |
| Eastern Europe and USSR | 3.9 | 138 | 36 |
| Total developed countries | 12.7 | 396 | 31 |
| World | 31.1 | 1 262 | 41 |

1/  Conversion factors used:  buffalo 1.0;  cattle 0.8;  sheep and goats 0.1.

Source:  FAO Production Yearbook 1981.


on fallow land belonging to the villagers whose livestock grazed the watershed areas.  The
extra forage which then became available from the fallow land made it possible to keep the
traditional grazing areas free from livestock during the spring.  This caused a spectacular
recovery of the growth and vigour of the native range vegetation.


## Cultivated Forages

Forages from arable lands form the basis for dairy cattle and, to a lesser extent,
for other types of ruminant livestock production in Europe and North America.  The inclusion in the crop rotation of the two to three year forage crop - generally a grass legume
mixture - as a substitute for fallow became common practice among west European farmers
during the early part of the last century.  Fodder maize and other green cereals are now
finding an increasingly important role as a forage and silage crop not only in North
America but also in Europe as far north as Scandinavia.

A number of tropical forages and pasture legumes with a high potential in different ecological zones have been identified and improved through plant breeding research and development. Several tropical grasses yield as much as 50 tons of dry matter per hectare in the humid tropics when given adequate nitrogenous fertilization and appropriate management, and yields of over double this level have been recorded experimentally. Sugar-cane has also been found to have a good potential as a forage crop and offers opportunities for small farmer diversification into livestock production in some situations.

The major constraint to increased animal productivity on large parts of the grasslands in Latin America is the poor fertility of the soil. The infertile allic soils that predominate in the savannah areas cover over 300 million hectares but do not readily lend themselves to crop production. Utilization through ruminants appears to be the most promising alternative. However, more information is still required on management techniques to do this efficiently and this is an area of high priority in agricultural research programmes for the region.

Experiments in the more fertile areas of tropical Latin America have shown that productivity can be increased considerably by introducing improved techniques and methods of pasture management. A FAO/UNDP project 10/ in the Peruvian tropical lowlands (Selva) demonstrated that the traditional technique of burning the rain forests and then sowing Hyparrhenia rufa resulted in pastures with a carrying capacity below 0.5 cows per hectare. The introduction of a legume such as Stylosanthes quianensis, which is adapted to the high acidity and aluminium content of the soil,enabled both the stocking rate and the daily gain to be doubled, and gave more than a fourfold increase in total liveweight gain per hectare (over 600 kg per year).

Although the scope for increasing beef production in Latin America in this way is considerable, it will require large investments to develop the required skills and infrastructure if possibly irreversible environmental damage is to be avoided. The introduction of leguminous pastures will require the availability of phosphatic fertilizers at reasonable prices. It will also require considerable research into methods of increasing phosphorous uptake by plants as well as a better knowledge of the phosphorous requirements of different legume species.

Pastoralism is the predominant system of grassland utilization in Africa south of the Sahara. It implies communal ownership of land and water resources and private or clan ownership of livestock. In the arid and semi-arid areas, population pressure, both human and animal, has upset the balance between the regenerating capacity of the grasslands and the demands put upon them, resulting in land degradation and very low productivity per animal. Here sociological rather than technical factors impose the major constraint to the development of the rangelands.

African highland areas with their favourable climate and conditions for crop production are already very densely populated in many instances and their communal grazing areas are steadily giving way to crops. In sub-humid and humid Africa, the pasture potential is good but the development of livestock production is greatly hampered by disease, in particular trypanosomiasis (sleeping sickness in humans) and streptothricosis, a skin disease.

---

10/ Santhirasegaram, K., Recent Advances in Pasture Development in the Peruvian Tropics. 1976. World Animal Review 17: 34-39.

In the Near East and North Africa, about 23% of the land area is considered as permanent range and grassland. A further 60% can be classified as desert, although parts allow some rough grazing. The major grazing animals are sheep and goats which are managed in semi-nomadic and transhumant production systems. As in Africa south of the Sahara, overgrazing is a major problem. During the last few decades it has worsened due to the extension of cropping into areas marginal for cereal production, and because livestock numbers on the range have greatly increased.

A FAO/UNEP programme for the Ecological Management of Arid and Semi-Arid Rangelands (EMASAR) has been established to stimulate the improvement of the rangelands, particularly in this region and the Sahel, by fostering an integrated land use approach to the management of natural resources within the potentials and limitations of the various ecosystems found there.

A major policy issue concerning the cultivation of forage crops in developing countries is whether the governments of countries facing land and grain shortages should promote the use of cultivated fodders. This question has no simple answer. In mixed farming systems in the humid tropics or in irrigated areas, a well managed forage crop can compete with cereals in terms of yield of livestock feed units per year and per unit of land. But the question still remains whether human welfare would be promoted by using the land for grain production for human consumption instead.

## Feed Grains and Other Concentrates

Although pastures and fodder predominate as the most important animal feedstuffs in the world, progress in increasing output of these types of feeds has been slow. With grain output growing much faster, its use as feed has increased considerably over the past twenty years. Feed grains are by far the major form of concentrate feeds in all developed regions and in Latin America and the Near East (Table 2-10). In other developing regions grain feeding of animals is a fairly recent development and milling and by-products are still relatively more important.

The use of cereals as feed nearly doubled in developing countries between the second half of the 1960s and the same period in the 1970s. During that time the share of feed in total cereal consumption other than rice rose from 22% to 35%. Feed use of milling by-products and of oil cakes and meals increased by 44% and 81% respectively. The growth in the utilization of cereals was particularly marked in Asia, but has also been evident in Latin America and in the Near East. This results mainly from the expansion and intensification of egg, poultry meat and pig meat production, which is presently estimated to account for over two-thirds of the utilization of these concentrate feeds in developing countries. Only in Africa has the use of concentrate feed remained low, though it has also been rising.

Among the feed grains, maize is by far the most important in both the developing and the developed countries. It accounts for a little over 40% of all grain fed to livestock. In many developing countries maize is also a major grain for human consumption, in Latin America and Africa especially. In the rural areas of such countries, maize is fed to livestock only exceptionally. Barley is the second most important feed grain in both developing and developed countries. Its use is common in the Near East where surplus barley is traditionally used for fattening sheep. On a world basis, wheat ranks third in importance accounting for about 15% of all grain fed to livestock. About half of this quantity of wheat is used in the USSR.

The development of compound feed manufacture in developed countries has extended the range of products used as feedstuffs, but has tended to replace on-farm mixing rather than to create additional demand for feed. It has, however, played a role in increasing the use of grain substitutes and thereby in reducing the cereal content of rations. For example, in the Netherlands the share of cereals in compound feeds has been reduced to under 25% due to the widespread use of cereal substitutes, especially cassava.

TABLE 2-10. USE OF MAIN CONCENTRATE FEEDS 1966-70 AND 1976-80

| | Average 1966-1970 | | | | Average 1976-1980 | | | |
|---|---|---|---|---|---|---|---|---|
| | Cereals | Milling by-products | Oilcakes & meals | Total use | Cereals | Milling by-products | Oilcakes & meals | Total use |
| | ............ % ............ | | | mill. tons | ............ % ............ | | | mill. tons |
| World | 75 | 15 | 10 | 520 | 75 | 14 | 11 | 722 |
| All dev.ing countries | 46 | 42 | 11 | 97 | 55 | 34 | 11 | 174 |
| Africa | 40 | 40 | 20 | 5 | 43 | 43 | 14 | 7 |
| Latin America | 76 | 16 | 8 | 25 | 73 | 14 | 14 | 44 |
| Near East | 67 | 25 | 8 | 12 | 70 | 20 | 10 | 20 |
| Asia | 29 | 57 | 14 | 56 | 45 | 45 | 11 | 103 |

Source: FAO, ESC.

Unmixed feeds or on-farm mixing are still the main way in which concentrate diets are prepared in developing countries. However, the growth in their production of compound feeding stuffs has been rapid - over 10% per year - in the last decade, especially for poultry rations. Latin America and the Far East have been the main producing regions, although the growth rate has been fastest in the Near East.

Most feed mills in developing countries have been established in the last decade. The larger mills are often part of integrated animal production enterprises affiliated to flour milling companies. Within government programmes to increase livestock production, the compound feeding stuffs industry has received considerable incentives, such as cheap credit, tax exemptions and subsidized raw materials. Although a number of mills have computer facilities for calculating least cost formula rations, few of them- with notable exceptions in India's dairy co-operative feed plants and in Kenya, for example - make much effort to maximize the use of local by-products, particularly cereal substitutes. The growth of the compound feed industry in developing countries therefore has often been associated with rising imports of feed grains.

In quantitative terms, coarse grain imports to developing countries for use as animal feed rose from 2 million tons annually in 1966-70 to nearly 16 million tons a year in

# REDUCING MEAT CONSUMPTION TO HELP THE HUNGRY: IS IT EFFECTIVE?

In the affluent nations there are many individuals and organizations who are genuinely concerned about the wellbeing of the poor, both in their own midst and in developing countries. In their endeavours to help, sometimes these groups call for consumer boycotts against excessive consumption of meat. They hope that such reductions in meat consumption will lower the amount of grain fed to livestock and that, in turn, this will make more food grains available for malnourished people. However, the following considerations should be taken into account:

- If a noticeable lessening of demand for meat did take place, there could well be reduced demand for grain to feed livestock and downward pressures on grain prices. However, many grain producers would be likely to respond to the weakened prices by cutting back on the amount of grain they produce. One million tons less fed to livestock would not necessarily generate one million tons more for human use.

- Livestock, ruminants especially, do not live exclusively on grain. While feed grains are often used in commercial operations to fatten animals, a large proportion of the meat produced is derived from pastures, by-products and wastes. On the average livestock depend on grain to the extent of less than 20% for their feed requirements. For cattle this figure is only 10%. So the savings on grain would be less than is commonly assumed. For example, in 1978-80, on average 126 million tons of meat were produced for the use of 562 million tons of cereals (excluding rice), an average input-output ratio for the whole livestock system of 4.5 ton grain for 1 ton of meat. Assuming other things remained unchanged, a 10% reduction in meat consumption could lead to a reduction in cereal use for feed of between 55-60 million tons of cereals. But only 15% of this is wheat, or 9 million tons, equivalent to only about 2% of average wheat production in 1978-80. The remainder is coarse grains, mostly yellow maize which is not a preferred food in maize-consuming societies.

- Even if grain does become more accessible, much of it would probably be purchased for use by people and nations with relatively high incomes. Those without much money or foreign exchange would still be unable to buy the grain, even at lower prices. Hunger is often more a problem of purchasing power than of supply. There is thus a transfer problem: how to ensure that the grain saved can be consumed by those most in need?

There are, however, certain circumstances where reducing livestock production can have more direct and striking impacts on grain availability for human consumption. Examples of such situations are the centrally planned economies that use non-market mechanisms to establish food production and consumption patterns; and isolated, self-sufficient rural villages that have little or no trade interactions with the outside world.

1976-80 (Table 2-11). About 70% of these imports were made by only ten countries but many others, including some of the lowest income group, also significantly increased imports of their feed grain. A similar situation also applies to developing countries' imports of oilmeals which have risen by 20% per annum over the past decade.

TABLE 2-11.  COARSE GRAINS:  ESTIMATED UTILIZATION AND IMPORTS
AS ANIMAL FEED IN DEVELOPING COUNTRIES

|  | Utilization for feed | | Feed use as share of total utilization | | Imports for feed | | Feed imports as share of feed utilization | |
|---|---|---|---|---|---|---|---|---|
|  | 1966-70 | 1976-80 | 1966-70 | 1976-80 | 1966-70 | 1976-80 | 1966-70 | 1976-80 |
|  | million tons | | ....... % ...... | | million tons | | ....... % ...... | |
| TOTAL COARSE GRAINS | 38.8 | 84.2 | 22 | 35 | 1.9 | 15.9 | 5 | 19 |
| Africa | 1.6 | 2.9 | 5 | 8 | 0.1 | 0.7 | 5 | 26 |
| Latin America | 18.4 | 30.4 | 52 | 57 | 0.5 | 5.4 | 3 | 18 |
| Near East | 7.2 | 11.4 | 43 | 51 | 0.4 | 3.1 | 5 | 27 |
| Far East | 11.6 | 39.5 | 12 | 31 | 0.9 | 6.7 | 8 | 17 |

Source:  FAO, ESC.

The medium growth assumption (Scenario B) of FAO's study AT 2000 suggests that there will be a continuing strong rise in demand for livestock products in the developing countries over the next 20 years.  This is expected to lead to an equally strong upward growth trend of about 6% per annum in the use of feed grains.  It implies that the current feed grain use of about 100 million tons in the developing countries could triple by the end of the century.  Yet even by then this amount is likely to be less than half of the feed grain used in developed countries.  However it would mean a greater dependence on feed imports in developing countries as a group, possibly worsening their balance of payment problems that are already critical in many cases.  A basic question to be addressed, therefore, is to what extent a livestock development strategy should depend on imported feeds or whether indigenous feed resources could be exploited.  A major source of indigenous feeds are the by-products obtained from agricultural production and processing.

## Agricultural By-products

Crop agriculture produces large amounts of lignocellulosic by-products such as straws, hulls, chaffs and stalks.  The amount of straw produced annually exceeds 2 000 million tons of which slightly less than half is produced in developing countries.  Other fibrous products available in large quantities are bagasse  (112 million tons) and sugar cane tops (69 million tons) 11/.

11/  Sansoucy, R. and P. Mahadevan, Potential Lignocellulose Resources and their Utilization by Ruminants in Tropical Regions.  FAO/IAEA First Research Coordination Meeting on Isotope-aided Studies on NPN and Agro-industrial By-products Utilization by Ruminants with Particular Reference to Developing Countries.  30 November-4 December 1981.  Vienna.

### NEARLY ONE-HALF OF WORLD PRODUCTION OF WHEAT
### AND COARSE GRAINS IS FED TO LIVESTOCK

Feed grain use in developed countries rose very steeply in the 1950s and 1960s when large scale intensive systems for the production of eggs and poultry meat were introduced first in the USA and then in Europe. Similarly, intensive pig and beef production expanded and dairy cattle feed included greater proportions of concentrates. Strong demand for livestock products and the resulting use of more grain provided the main stimulus for the expansion of grain production during this period when the international demand for grain as food slackened. This use of grain as feed continued to increase up to 1973 when there was a strong rise in prices due to world shortages of grain. The primary effect of this was to reduce the quantity of grain fed to cattle, the principal consuming species.

This change reflects the high sensitivity of grain feed use to price changes, particularly for ruminants feed. In periods of high grain prices beef producers have the alternatives of resorting to pasture and by-product feeding (which, although more time consuming, are then more cost effective), or to the early slaughtering of stock. The reduction in feed grain use by ruminants was particularly marked in the large beef-lot industry in the USA where feed grain use fell by over 25% between 1973 and 1974 (see table on next page). Smaller reductions took place in some other countries, notably the USSR, but recovery was rapid and since 1975 global feed grain use expanded at an annual rate of 7%.

By 1981 nearly half (47%) of world production of wheat and coarse grain, 586 million tons, was fed to animals: 100 million tons in developing countries. A recent estimate a/ indicated that 37% of grain fed was used for cattle, 34% for pigs and 29% for poultry in 1977 (see table on following page).

_____

a/ Wheeler, R.O. et al, 1981, op.cit.

Straw constitutes the major feed for ruminants in some countries, such as Bangladesh, Pakistan and parts of India, while in many other developing countries it is a very important feed resource during certain periods of the year. But lignocellulosic by-products are characterized by low digestibility and low protein content. As their passage through the digestive tract is slow, the voluntary feed intake becomes low. In most situations straw feeding can, therefore, barely cover the maintenance requirements of ruminants. Hence, in countries where straw is the main feed resource, the basic questions are how and to what extent it might be possible to improve its feeding value or correct its deficiencies, at least partially, through appropriate supplementation.

Experience from several developing countries has shown that under village conditions, supplementation of straw rations by small amounts of minerals, urea, green fodder and oil cakes has a very positive effect on animal productivity and health and enables the utilization of lignocellulosic products to be increased 12/. Straw is usually chopped before use and a chemical treatment to improve its digestibility and feeding value has also been proposed from time to time. Recent techniques using ammonia gas, ammonium salts and urea seem to have potential particularly as they have the additional advantages of adding

_____

12/ FAO, Report of the FAO/ILCA Workshop on the Utilization of Crop Residues and Agro-Industrial By-products in Animal Feeding. Dakar, 21-25, November 1981.

Feed grain use in selected countries and US export prices for maize, 1970-81

|  | 1970 | 1971 | 1972 | 1973 | 1974 | 1975 | 1976 | 1977 | 1978 | 1979 | 1980 | 1981 |
|---|---|---|---|---|---|---|---|---|---|---|---|---|
| | ........................ $/ton ............................ |  |  |  |  |  |  |  |  |  |  |  |
| Maize price[1/], USA | 58 | 58 | 56 | 98 | 132 | 119 | 113 | 95 | 101 | 115 | 126 | 131 |
| | ..................... million tons ..................... |  |  |  |  |  |  |  |  |  |  |  |
| Feed grain use[2/] |  |  |  |  |  |  |  |  |  |  |  |  |
| WORLD | 412 | 454 | 473 | 489 | 466 | 464 | 483 | 515 | 553 | 569 | 563 | 586 |
| USA | 135 | 143 | 148 | 143 | 106 | 117 | 114 | 123 | 142 | 141 | 125 | 136 |
| USSR | 77 | 85 | 93 | 99 | 101 | 85 | 105 | 113 | 120 | 123 | 120 | 121 |
| China | 6 | 14 | 10 | 17 | 23 | 24 | 22 | 28 | 33 | 37 | 39 | 40 |
| Canada | 17 | 19 | 16 | 17 | 16 | 17 | 15 | 17 | 16 | 18 | 18 | 19 |
| France | 15 | 15 | 16 | 17 | 16 | 15 | 16 | 17 | 18 | 18 | 18 | 18 |
| Brazil | 9 | 9 | 11 | 10 | 11 | 11 | 12 | 13 | 11 | 13 | 17 | 17 |
| Japan | 9 | 10 | 10 | 12 | 13 | 12 | 13 | 15 | 16 | 17 | 17 | 17 |
| Poland | 12 | 13 | 14 | 16 | 18 | 15 | 17 | 17 | 18 | 16 | 17 | 17 |
| Germany, Fed. Rep. | 15 | 15 | 15 | 17 | 16 | 17 | 17 | 16 | 16 | 17 | 15 | 15 |
| Spain | 8 | 10 | 10 | 11 | 12 | 12 | 10 | 11 | 12 | 13 | 15 | 14 |
| TOTAL (above 10 countries) | 303 | 333 | 343 | 359 | 332 | 325 | 341 | 370 | 402 | 413 | 401 | 414 |

1/ Prices are for No. 2 US yellow maize f.o.b. gulf ports.

2/ Feed grain is defined as cereals excluding rice.

Note:   the 10 countries listed accounted for 70% or more of total feed grain use during this period.  Among developing countries, significant users of feed grain
in 1981 were (in million tons): Mexico 11.2;  Argentina 6.8;  Korea Republic
2.6;  Korea DPR 2.0;  Egypt, Iran and Venezuela 1.9;  Saudi Arabia 1.8;  Syria
1.3;  and India 1.1.  The growth rate of feed use has been rapid in some of
them, e.g. Saudi Arabia where, between 1971 and 1981, it has been more than
50% per annum.

Source:  FAO, ESS.

non-protein nitrogen to the forage.  Experiments in Bangladesh have demonstrated a practical method of using urea at the village level, though more research is required before
large scale application can be recommended 13/.

---

13/   Saadullah, M., M. Haque and F. Dolberg, Treated and Untreated Paddy Straw for
Growing Cattle.  In Proceedings of Seminar on Maximum Livestock from Minimum Land.
Bangladesh Agricultural University, Mymensingh, p. 137-155, 1981.

While lignocellulosic by-products are available on practically every farm, by-products from post harvest processing and agro-industries are much less evenly distributed. They may be available in very large quantities but in areas where there are few livestock. In developing countries large quantities of agro-industrial by-products are still being wasted and much could be used more effectively were it better processed and stored. An example is rice bran whose feed value is often reduced by poor processing, resulting in rancidity. These by-products may conveniently be divided into three groups: [14]/

a)  energy rich by-products derived from sugar cane and sugar beet, citrus fruits, bananas, coffee, pineapple etc.;

b)  protein supplements such as oilseed cakes and meals, by-products from the animal processing industry; low quality pulses not used for direct human consumption; and fishmeals, only a minor part of which are obtained from the offals and wastes of other methods of processing fish;

c)  by-products of cereal milling and milk processing which occupy an intermediate position between the first two groups in terms of nutrient content.

Several of the energy rich by-products have high feeding values and can be used as major ration components for ruminants and, sometimes, for pigs. For example waste bananas, fresh, ensiled or dried, have been shown to be an excellent feed. One ton of waste bananas balanced by a protein supplement will feed a pig to 90-100 kg, slaughter weight. Other by-products from banana plantations, such as stems, peelings and leaves, are useful as ruminant feed.

Molasses is used worldwide as an energy supplement in cattle rations. It is also used as a major basic feed for cattle in some sugar producing countries. Sugar-rich by-products lend themselves well to silage making in combination with other by-products, a number of which are used in animal rations.

A major problem with many by-products is that of utilizing them more extensively in small scale livestock production. Most of the techniques developed so far have been suitable mainly for large scale fattening schemes because the by-products are available in sufficient quantities within a limited area. Their shipment to scattered smallholders would be costly. Dehydration is widely used to facilitate the use of beet and citrus by-products in temperate countries but this technique has not yet been found economic on a commercial scale in most developing countries.

---

14/  FAO, New Feed Resources. FAO Animal Production and Health Paper No. 4, 1977.

Cassava, a traditional energy-rich food crop of the lowland humid tropics, is being used increasingly as an animal feed both in developing countries and Europe (Table 2-12). There, dried cassava chips or pellets, although not strictly by-products, have become important substitutes for grain and are being used at high levels in pig, poultry and cattle rations.

TABLE 2-12.   EEC IMPORTS OF SELECTED CEREAL SUBSTITUTES

|  | 1975 | 1976 | 1977 | 1978 | 1979 | 1980 | 1981 |
|---|---|---|---|---|---|---|---|
|  | .....................million tons......................... | | | | | | |
| Cassava and sweet potatoes | 2.3 | 3.8 | 6.0 | 5.9 | 5.4 | 4.9 | 6.2 |
| Molasses | 1.7 | 2.6 | 2.7 | 2.8 | 3.3 | 2.9 | 2.8 |
| Maize gluten | 0.9 | 1.5 | 1.5 | 2.0 | 2.3 | 2.9 | 3.0 |
| Brans | 1.2 | 2.2 | 1.9 | 2.0 | 2.0 | 1.8 | 2.0 |
| Brewery and distillery waste | 0.1 | 0.1 | 0.1 | 0.1 | 0.2 | 0.3 | 0.3 |
| Beet/citrus pulp | 0.6 | 0.8 | 1.1 | 1.3 | 1.4 | 1.6 | 1.5 |
| Total | 6.8 | 11.0 | 13.3 | 14.1 | 14.6 | 14.4 | 15.8 |

Source:   FAO, ESC.

The major suppliers to the world trade in feed cassava are Thailand and, to a lesser extent, Indonesia.  These countries have capitalized on the low import levies faced by cassava entering the EEC and have developed cassava into an important cash crop.  Thailand's total annual output of 15 million tons of fresh roots is provided mainly from producers who produce only 50-2 000 tons per annum.  Despite some drawbacks, cassava appears to be a crop with considerable potential as an animal feed in countries where it grows well but feed grains do not, and where protein supplements are also available.

Soybean is by far the most important protein supplement (Table 2-13).  The production of soybean meal has shown a steady upward trend in the last two decades.  During this time developing countries, particularly Brazil, have increased their share of both production and export.  Currently about two-thirds of world production of oilcakes and meals and three-quarters of world trade in these commodities relate  to soybean products.  Cotton-seed cake and fish meal are the next two most important livestock feeds.  Neither of them has increased in production at a rate comparable to soybean.  Fishmeal availability may well decline because those stocks of fish which normally provide the basis for fish-meal industries are either fully or over exploited.

Although the USA dominates both production and trade in oilcakes and meals, Brazil, China and India are also important.  By the early 1980s, developing countries accounted for 40% of world production and 36% of exports and 15% of imports of these products.

Meat, blood and bone meals are widely used as ration supplements in the industrialized countries.  Unfortunately, the slaughterhouse processing industries are poorly developed in most developing countries as a consequence of which these by products are often wasted.

However, animal wastes such as poultry litter and poultry manure are used increasingly as feed in both industrialized and developing countries 15/.

The third group of by-products comprises those from cereal milling and processing, including brewers' and distillers' grains, and also those from milk processing. These are almost fully utilized as feed in both developed and developing countries. The amount available varies little from year to year but increases only at a rate corresponding to the expansion of the industries concerned. Milling by-products make up a much larger part of the concentrates in developing countries where rice bran in particular is very widely used.

TABLE 2-13. OIL CAKES AND MEALS AND FISHMEAL (100% PROTEIN BASIS), PRODUCTION (1981) AND TRADE (1980)

|  | Production | Exports | Imports |
|---|---|---|---|
|  | ................'000 tons ................ | | |
| World total | 40 280 | 19 920 | 20 300 |
| Vegetable oil cakes | 37 440 | 18 570 | |
| Soybean | 25 430 | 15 590 | |
| Cottonseed | 4 090 | 360 | |
| Groundnut | 2 190 | 670 | |
| Sunflower seed | 1 860 | 640 | |
| Rapeseed | 2 070 | 480 | |
| Linseed | 460 | 330 | |
| Copra/palm kernel | 540 | 350 | |
| Fishmeal | 2 850 | 1 350 | |
| By economic region | | | |
| Developing countries | 16 200 | 7 270 | 2 710 |
| Latin America | 8 570 | 6 090 | 910 |
| Africa | 740 | 250 | 100 |
| Near East | 720 | 110 | 310 |
| Far East | 3 100 | 750 | 1 330 |
| Asian centrally planned economies | 3 040 | 40 | 590 |
| Developed countries | 24 080 | 12 640 | 17 590 |

Source: FAO Commodity Review and Outlook, 1981/82.

---

15/ For a fuller treatment of this topic see FAO 1977 (op. cit.); Muller, Z.O., Feed from Animal Wastes: State of Knowledge. FAO Animal Production and Health Paper 18: 1980, and Muller, Z.O., Feed from Animal Wastes: Feeding Manual. FAO Animal Production and Health Paper 28: 1982.

FAO estimated that 31% of the metabolizable energy of the concentrates fed in the developing countries in the period 1972/74 came from milling by-products, 57% from grain and the balance (12%) from oil cakes and meals 16/. For the developed countries the corresponding figures were 7%, 83% and 10% respectively.

## Feed Strategies for Livestock Development

Developing countries are far from being a homogenous group with regard to their projected rise in human demand for cereal products, their potential for domestic feed grain production, their alternative feed resources or their ability to import livestock products and grain. The development policy options open to them, therefore, vary considerably from country to country. However, the development of intensive large-scale poultry production seems in many countries to be considered the sole or at least the major policy option to respond to the increased demand for meat in urban areas.

Industrialized poultry production is efficient in the use of both feed and labour and is therefore commercially attractive, particularly if feed is abundantly available at low costs on the world market, the technology can be easily imported and capital is also available. However, many developing countries, which have surplus labour and crop by-products suitable for use as animal feed and yet face foreign exchange and capital constraints, cannot be advised to pursue this pattern of poultry development as the sole option. In these situations the development of small commercial units of say 100-500 layers, using commercial type feed but attempting to substitute locally produced feeds for imported grains, might be a viable proposition. Such units also offer opportunities for reducing marketing costs through cooperative efforts in egg collection, quality control and sales 17/.

An alternative strategy is that of improving traditional scavenger production. Several countries have embarked on this type of programme. For example, a large scale effort is presently under way in Pakistan to increase rural poultry production through the distribution of improved stock, backed up by vaccination services, management advice, feed distribution and the training of extension staff and farmers, including rural women who generally take care of poultry on the farm.

Milk production is another type of livestock production which has proved to be a good instrument for equitable rural development in small farmer systems. Medium to high producing dairy cows are as efficient feed converters as intensively managed poultry. In addition, dairy production is far less dependent on grain than poultry.

It has been estimated that in the late 1970s poultry used about 27% of all the feed grain consumed by livestock but produced only 9% of the human food energy provided by livestock. For pigs the corresponding relationship was 32:30 and for beef and dairy cattle

---

16/ FAO, Utilization of Grains in the Livestock Sector: Trends, Factors and Development Issues. Committee on Commodity Problems, Intergovernmental Group on Grains GR 80/5, 1979.

17/ FAO, Report of the FAO Expert Consultation on Rural Poultry and Rabbit Production, 30 November-3 December 1981, Rome, 1982.

combined 35:58 (Table 2-14). While beef cattle are poor grain converters, they can consume crops not directly utilizable by man. This attribute is often forgotten in the bid to modernize animal production by creating large scale beef cattle fattening enterprises that are based on imported feed and which have little or no impact on the development of the domestic agricultural sector.

TABLE 2-14.   USE OF FEED ENERGY AND GRAIN BY LIVESTOCK AND
THEIR OUTPUT IN TERMS OF HUMAN FOOD ENERGY

|  | Percentage of total metabolisable energy consumed by each species of livestock | Percentage of total grain used by live-stock fed to each species | Percentage of human food energy coming from individual livestock species |
|---|---|---|---|
| Beef | 32 | 17 | 18 |
| Dairy | 24 | 18 | 40 |
| Draught | 15 | 4 | - |
| Sheep and goats | 12 | 2 | 3 |
| Pigs | 10 | 32 | 30 |
| Poultry | 7 | 27 | 9 |
| Total | 100 | 100 | 100 |

Source:   Modified after Fitzhugh, H.A. et al., The Role of Ruminants in Support of Man, Winrock International, Morrilton, Ark., 1978.

Given widespread undernutrition and underemployment, plus the shortage of capital on one side, and a growing number of small farmers and landless labourers on the other, a combination of a number of systems of animal production would need to be promoted in developing regions.  Modern intensive livestock production will doubtless meet a larger share of the expanding urban demand.  However, if equity and employment creation are major concerns, more consideration needs to be devoted to the development of rural smallholder production of meat, eggs and milk.

In some developing countries it has been argued that as the feeding of small amounts of grain, minerals and oil cakes have a profound effect on the productivity and health of indigenous stock, a more equal distribution of the limited amounts of concentrate feeds would maximize their national benefits.  This could be done by making feed resources available to smallholders rather than concentrating the best feed and livestock on a limited number of intensive modern enterprises.

The advocates of this policy[18/] recommended that developing countries avoid the use of exotic dairy cattle and poultry and base their development on resources available locally, such as indigenous stock and crop residues.  Whilst this may have some attraction

18/   See, for example Jackson, M.G., F. Dolberg, C.H. Davis, M. Haque, Maximum Livestock Production from Minimum Land.  Proceedings of Seminar at Bangladesh Agricultural University, Mymensingh, 1981.

for a country whose animal feed resources are extremely limited, such as Bangladesh for example, it is not yet a developmental strategy that has been proven. All of the relatively limited number of successful livestock development programmes that have been recorded appear to have been associated with some degree of intensification and specialization.

ANIMAL GENETIC RESOURCES

The last 30 to 40 years have been a period of very intensive activity in animal breeding and selection resulting in rapid increases in animal productivity. A combination of factors is responsible, such as the introduction of national recording schemes, the unravelling of the basic concepts of quantitative genetics, the development of artificial insemination and the use of computers. Consequently, the changes that have taken place in the livestock populations of the industrialized countries over the last four decades have exceeded those occurring over hundreds of years previously. Breeds and strains which were competitive have tended to disappear rapidly.

Although these changes have been confined largely to developed countries, the techniques that produced them have also been introduced to developing countries. Large changes, therefore, are likely to occur in the composition of their livestock populations as well in the near future.

Genetic variation is the basis for future genetic change and improvement. Since it has been developed over thousands of years, care needs to be taken to ensure that potentially useful genes are not eliminated through concentration on a few outstanding breeds. It is important that breeds adapted to the often harsh environments of developing countries are not summarily discarded without evalution and replaced by non-adapted breeds which, although giving excellent production results in temperate climates, may lack the ability to withstand a harsher environment. Thus, a potential conflict exists between rapid improvement and conservation for the future. This must be recognized in applied breeding schemes.

Genetic Improvement in the Developed Countries

The effect of genetic selection, together with improvements in feeding, management and veterinary care, on animal productivity has been spectacular in the developed countries. In commercial poultry production, for instance, the amount of feed required for the production of one kg of meat has been reduced from 3 or 4 kg 30 years ago to about 1.8 kg today. The required slaughter weight of about 1.5 kg is now reached in less than 7 weeks as opposed to over 12. Parallel changes have taken place in pig production. Milk production per cow has shown marked increases. For example in Sweden the recorded output of milk per cow increased from 2 533 kg (4% fat basis) in 1900 to over 6 thousand kg in 1980. Similar improvements have occurred in the USA where in 1961/65 16.2 million cows produced 57 million tons of milk, whereas by 1980 a slightly greater quantity of milk was produced by only 10.8 million cows.

Dairy cattle breeding programmes in much of Europe and North America, are now organized by farmer cooperatives which arrange artificial insemination services, milk recording and the genetic evaluation and selection of bulls. Although an individual farmer can influence the policy and work of the cooperative, most of the important decisions relating to bull selection are made on a population basis rather than on an individual herd basis. In some countries the influence of commercial companies selling semen from their own bulls has also increased.

This process of commercialization has gone much further in poultry production where the individual producer no longer contributes to breed improvement. Breeding and selection is usually carried out by a few large international companies, several of which are subsidiaries of pharmaceutical firms which also market antibiotics, vitamins and other additives used in the poultry industry. The multiplier/hatcher buys parent stock from the breeding company for the production of commercial layer or broiler chicks. The male and female grandparents have each been produced through the crossing of at least two different lines. This guarantees a certain degree of hybrid vigour in both the parent stock and the commercial birds provided by the hatcheries. As the breeding companies retain the grandparent stock and/or the lines from which these were produced, they can ensure that their selected lines are not being directly multiplied by other producers.

## Genetic Improvement in the Developing Countries

The developing countries have two possible options for improving the genetic production potential of their livestock: (a) to build up the necessary infrastructure for selection within and between their existing livestock strains, and (b) to import breeding stock from other countries to improve their domestic populations. The two methods are not mutually exclusive. The choice of method or the optimum mix between the two approaches will depend on the species, the type of production system, climate, level of existing infrastructure and the economic situation of the country.

Dairy cattle. With some exceptions, such as the Sahiwal cattle of Pakistan and India, some Criollo strains in Central America and the Kenana and Butana cattle of the Sudan, the genetic potential for milk production from indigenous cattle in the developing countries appears to be low. As a consequence of this and of these countries' increasing demand for dairy products, cattle from the temperate regions have been imported into some of them.

The performance of these importations and of the crossbreeds derived from them has been variable because in some locations animals have their genetic potential constrained by environmental stresses and diseases of a tropical environment. But generally speaking, in both the arid and the highland areas of the tropics, if reasonable animal health and management standards are practised, it is possible to produce purebred or high-grade temperate stock through upgrading or through the development of a crossbreeding system based on animals with a high level of temperate blood. Successful examples of this type of breeding can be found in Kenya, Bolivia and the Deccan Plateau of India where artificial insemination has been found to be an excellent tool for introducing genes from temperate animals for crossbreeding and subsequent upgrading.

The real problems with temperate cattle are encountered in the humid tropics. Large-scale experiments and practical development projects in India, Thailand and elsewhere have shown that in hot, humid areas an intermediate type with 50-75% temperate blood is superior to both the European purebred whose fertility and viability is severely affected by the climate, and to the local cattle whose genetic potential for milk is insufficient. In general the first cross shows very marked hybrid vigour (see Box).

Although the use of purebred temperate dairy cattle is not therefore feasible in the humid tropics, there are at least three useful alternative approaches 19/.

---

19/ FAO, Report on Expert Consultation on Dairy Cattle Breeding in the Humid Tropics, Hissar, India, 1979.

# CROSSBRED CATTLE OUTPRODUCE PUREBREDS IN INDIA AND THAILAND

India has a long experience in cross-breeding both Indian and European-type dairy cattle. Trials have shown that milk yield rises with an increasing level of temperate breed blood and peaks at a level of 50%. After this point it declines very slowly until 75%. Beyond this point yields fall steeply. Calf mortality is at a minimum at 50-60% European blood. The superiority of the intermediate grades in terms of production per day of calving interval and per day of age at second calving was also clear. These two measures summarize the effect of three economic traits related to the efficiency of production: milk yield per lactation, age at first calving and calving interval.

Where management is optimum, the yield of the purebred may be better than that of the crossbred but the problems of poor health, low cow fertility and high calf mortality may remain. For instance, at the Thai-Danish farm in Thailand where the management, feeding and health service were excellent, the Red Danish purebred had a higher milk yield than the zebu, but its fertility and viability were low, so that overall dairy merit was higher for the crosses.

### Milk Yield per day of calving interval and per day of age at second calving in crossbreeding trials in India

| Effects | No. of observations | Milk yield kg/day of: | |
|---|---|---|---|
| | | Calving interval | Age at second calving |
| Overall mean | 781 | 5.72 | 1.61 |
| Genetic groups: | | | |
| Sahiwal | 97 | 4.52 | 1.35 |
| 25% Friesian | 121 | 5.11 | 1.39 |
| 50% Friesian | 206 | 6.40 | 1.82 |
| 62.5% Friesian | 276 | 6.58 | 1.75 |
| 75% Friesian | 81 | 5.98 | 1.76 |

Source: Dhillon, J.S. and A.K. Jain, Comparison of Sahiwal and different grades of Holstein Friesian x Sahiwal crossbreds for efficiency of milk production, Indian J. Dairy Science 30: 214-217, 1977.

### Performance of Red Danish (RD), Indian Zebu (Sahiwal and Red Sindhi) and their crossbreds in Thailand

| % genes from RD | 1st lactation yield (kg) | percent abortion | mortality | | calving interval (days) |
|---|---|---|---|---|---|
| | | | Up to 6 months | 6 months to calving | |
| 0 | 1 000 | 4.6 | 15.5 | 5.4 | 467 |
| 50 | 2 000 | 1.8 | 5.9 | 0 | 443 |
| 100 | 2 300 | 21.5 | 7.3 | 23.7 | 525 |

Source: Madsen, O. and K. Winther, Performance of purebred and crossbred dairy cattle in Thailand, Anim. Prod. 21: 209-216, 1975.

- The formation of a new breed through crossing local and temperate cattle. The few successful examples of this approach include the Jamaica Hope which is about 20% zebu (mainly Sahiwal) and 80% temperate (mainly Jersey), and the Australian Milking Zebu which is about 40% zebu and 60% Jersey. Both breeds have been quite successuful in semi-extensive production systems. A large scale crossbreeding programme is now underway in India. to develop a new dairy breed which will be about 75% temperate, based on Friesian, Jersey and Brown Swiss breeds crossed with local stock.

- Systematic crossbreeding through using semen from bulls of a temperate and a local breed alternately, in some form of continuous rotation. This system exploits hybrid vigour and, in addition, exploits the breeding progress made in the country from which the temperate breed originates. It can also be made quite flexible to allow for a higher level of temperate genes as the husbandry improves. The main problem is the scarcity of good local breeds to include in the rotation.

- Improvement of local strains. With some exceptions, listed above, indigenous cattle breeds in the developing countries have a low dairy potential. As a result, there has been a general neglect of dairy improvement programmes although, by using the best of the indigenous breeds, some improvement can be expected in the long term.

Livestock development planners will need to choose the economically most sensible alternative for a given situation from among the several technically possible. Questions concerning the need for breed importations, the role of artificial insemination and the place of embryo transfer have attracted a lot of attention.

Although there are examples of successful cattle importations, the number of unsuccessful ones with high stock mortality is embarrassingly large. For a country which has cattle available for upgraidng, it is doubtful whether large-scale importations of female stock over and above the establishment of a small nucleus herd is an appropriate dairy development strategy.

On the other hand, artificial insemination using frozen semen is an excellent method for introducing breeding material into a country. The upgrading of local cattle through the use of temperate bulls or semen produces a hardy first generation cross. Through gradual upgrading or continued crossbreeding, it is possible for the farmer to adapt his management to a more demanding and better yielding cow. In terms of rural development, this approach will be more successful than importation. A completely integrated turnkey operation with imported cows, controlled environment buildings, irrigated forage and feed production and sophisticated milk processing may still be the preferred approach for countries with sufficient financial resources.

The techniques of embryo transfer have been improved considerably during the last few years and are now used commercially. In developed countries with well-functioning artificial insemination services and progeny and performance testing programmes, the additional genetic progress to be made through the use of embryo transfer in dairy cattle appears to be small in relation to cost, and its use has, therefore, been limited so far. In developing countries, the technique would obviously permit the transfer of genetically superior material from one country to another. It also has potential for multiplying stock of specific genetic merit and could be used, for example, to transfer a large number of embryos from trypanotolerant cattle into non-tolerant ones. However, the cost would be high and it is difficult to foresee smallholder livestock owners benefiting widely from embryo transfer techniques, unless cloning of embryos becomes possible.

Beef cattle in the developing countries often have to live under harsh environmental conditions characterized by periodic droughts, shortages of feed and the occurrence of endemic diseases and parasitic problems. The hardiness of the animals is thus a production trait of major importance. Under unimproved to moderately improved conditions, well-adapted strains developed in the tropics do better than imported well-recognized breeds from the temperate zones. For instance, beef production in the tropical north of Australia is now completely dominated by zebu and zebu crosses. In Botswana, the local Tswana and Tuli cattle are superior to Afrikander cattle developed under better environmental conditions in neighbouring South Africa. The Boran cattle, which have undergone genetic improvement in Kenya, have been found to do well throughout East Africa as have Sahiwal cattle.

It is important that the productivity of these local breeds be subject to systematic evaluation. The practical recording and selection programme for beef cattle which was developed in Botswana and later introduced into Swaziland, provides a good example of what can be done 20/. Selecting for increased disease resistance also needs increased attention and more research is required along the lines of the pioneering work at the Belmont Station in Australia where a practical methodology for selection for resistance to internal and external parasites has been worked out 21/.

Sheep and goats are usually raised under the same difficult conditions as beef cattle or they occur in small scale sedentary production systems. The several strains that are found are well adapted to their local environments. The fleece from indigenous sheep breeds often has characteristics of value for traditional cottage industries. Attempts to improve local breeds through importations such as the Merino and the Corriedale, usually have been unsuccessful and, in many circumstances, improvements in feeding, management and disease control constitute the most effective way of increasing productivity.

Milk sheep and dairy goats are important in the Near East where the Awassi sheep and the Damascus goat are particularly well-known. Useful programmes have been developed for the genetic improvement of the Awassi sheep in Israel and for the Damascus goat in Syria and Cyprus.

Prolificacy varies greatly between sheep breeds. Under very harsh conditions, high prolificacy is hardly an advantage because of increased lamb mortality. However, under intensive sedentary production systems, a large lamb crop can be very desirable. There are a number of sheep breeds found in developing countries which have a very high prolificacy, such as the Barbados Blackbelly, which has an average litter of 2-2.3 lambs, the D'man sheep of Morocco (2 lambs) and the Priangan of Indonesia (1.4-2.1 lambs) 22/. These breeds warrant further development and distribution to other developing countries with similar climates and production systems.

---

20/ Trail, J.C.M. and T.W. Rennie, Botswana Performance Testing of Beef Cattle. World Animal Review 14: 37-42, 1975.

21/ Turner, H.G. and A.G. Short, Effects of Field Infestation of Gastro-intestinal Helminths and of the Cattle Tick (Boophilus microplus) on Growth of Three Breeds of Cattle. Aust. J. Agric. Res.23: 177-193, 1972.

22/ FAO, Prolific Tropical Sheep. FAO Animal Production and Health Paper 17, 1980.

Poultry production in the developing countries takes place in two parallel, often rather independent systems:  rural and industrial.  For the improved rural sector, commercial chicks are provided by hatcheries which get their parent stock from breeding units which use traditional breeding techniques, working with one "pure line" which is improved each year.  The industrialized units use breeding stock from multinational breeding companies with which they often have some kind of franchise relationship.

Many countries, particularly the oil exporting developing countries, import practically everything for their poultry industry.  The more resource-poor countries limit their imports to breeding stock and some equipment.  The poultry feed being used in these importing countries is generally of poorer quality than that in those countries where the stock are bred and selected and which, therefore, will not reach their full genetic potential.  The larger developing countries with trained manpower should consider developing their own poultry breeding programmes in order to avoid the continuous import of breeding materials and also to produce strains that would be more efficient on lower grade diets.

Underutilized Animal Genetic Resources

It has been recognized that some potentially viable animal breeds and strains in the developing countries are much underutilized 23/.  These include Boran and Sahiwal cattle, Awassi sheep, Shami goats and several prolific sheep breeds mentioned above.  In addition, the water buffalo, trypanotolerant livestock and the camelidae of the old and new world warrant more attention.

There are approximately 130 million water buffalo in the world, with the largest population in India and China.  The buffaloes of the Indo-Pakistan subcontinent and west thereof - referred to as the riverine type - are used as dairy, work and meat animals. The swamp buffalo of south-east Asia and China is the major work animal of that area but gives little milk.  In India, Pakistan and Egypt the buffalo is a dairy animal.  The buffaloes of Italy, Bulgaria and Iraq are also good milk producers and in Italy the buffalo is the foundation of a flourishing cheese-making industry.  Interest in the dairy buffalo is increasing in south-east Asia, Africa and tropical Latin America because it is assumed that it is adapted to hot, humid environments.  However, the available evidence suggests that buffaloes are heat sensitive and need constant access to water.

In spite of the importance of the buffalo, the governmental infrastructure for its improvement is weak or non-existent in most countries.  However, artificial insemination services for buffalo breeding have been developed in Egypt, India and Pakistan and in all these countries semen can now be frozen.  Services for milk recording and progeny testing of bulls, as well as for the performance testing of growth rate and draught ability need to be established or strengthened in all major buffalo countries.  In some countries, high-yielding dairy breeds or strains are known to exist such as the Murrah of India and the Nili-Ravi of Pakistan.  However, very little is known about their relative productivity and merit in comparison to breeds from other countries.

Two recent actions which should help to increase knowledge about the buffalo are the establishemnt of an International Buffalo Information Centre in Thailand sponsored by the International Development Research Centre (IDRC) and the Buffalo Research Network in Asia with the support of UNDP.

---

23/  FAO, Animal Genetic Resources Conservation and Management.  FAO Animal Production and Health Paper 24, 1981.

Trypanotolerant livestock.  A major part of the high rainfall area of Africa is infested by the tsetse fly, the vector of African trypanosomiasis, which makes livestock production difficult.  Some cattle, sheep and goat strains have, through natural selection, developed varying levels of tolerance to trypanosomiasis.  These livestock occur in varying numbers in all the west African coastal countries from Senegal to Cameroon, as well as in some of the landlocked states.  The trypanotolerant cattle are all of the taurine, straight-back type and can be divided into two groups:  the Longhorn (N'dama type) and the West African Shorthorn of which there are both full-sized and dwarf types.  Trypanotolerant sheep and goats are dwarf species which occur together throughout West Africa including the coastal zone 24/.

A FAO/ILCA/UNEP survey and further studies by ILCA show that there are approximately the following trypanotolerant numbers of livestock:  8 million cattle, 11.5 million sheep and 15 million goats.  The survey also compared the limited information on the productivity of trypanotolerant cattle with information from non-tolerant zebus kept under similar conditions, but without tsetse challenge.  For trypanotolerant cattle under light tsetse challenge, the productivity index was only 4% less than that of a wide range of indigenous zebu and Sanga cattle in non-challenge areas throughout Africa.  There was no significant difference between the two major trypanotolerant cattle groups, the N'dama and the West African Shorthorn.  The influence of the level of tsetse challenge on the productivity of the trypanotolerant livestock was marked, however.  The productivity index was 27% and 53% less for medium and high challenge respectively, compared with low challenge.  There was no evidence to suggest that the trypanotolerant breeds of sheep and goats have a lower level of productivity than other sheep and goats in Africa.

Camelidae.  The old world camels and the camelidae of the new world such as the llama and alpaca, provide important services and food for people who live under difficult environmental and economic conditions.  There are presently about 17 million camels of which less than 2 million belong to the two-humped group.  The camel is vital to the economies of countries such as Somalia (5.4 million camels) and the Sudan (2.9 million) as well as some countries of central Asia.  This is because of its high degree of adaptation to an arid environment, including its ability to live on plants inedible for other species, the widespread use of its milk and its usefulness as a pack animal and as a producer of hair and fuel.  In spite of their decreasing role in overland transportation, their number has increased by about 20% between 1950 and 1978.  The camel is likely to continue to have a role in meat and milk production on the type of rangelands which other domestic animals cannot exploit.  Very little is known about the production characteristics of different types of camels and further work in this area is needed.

The South American camelidae number about 7 million, the most important of which are the alpaca and llama.  The advantage of these two species lies in the efficient use they make of the Andean altiplano ecosystem.  Their adaptation to high altitudes make it possible for them to utilize, for food and fibre production, areas which are more than 4 000 m above sea level where crop production is impossible and cattle and sheep do not thrive.  Alpaca and llama are kept almost exclusively by resource-poor people for whom they are an important source of food and employment.  Alpaca wool fibre is of high quality and forms the basis for an important cottage industry.  Considering the unique characteristics of these two species and their importance for the livelihood of the Andean population, efforts to improve their productivity through breeding and development in general warrant greater international support.

---

24/  FAO, Trypanotolerant Livestock in West and Central Africa, vols. 1 and 2, FAO Animal Production and Health Paper 20, 1980.

Other species. Rabbit production is gaining popularity in several developing countries, particularly in backyard production systems close to the cities. Very little
has been published on the productivity and adaptability of different types of rabbits in
these conditions 25/. There are several other species which are of importance in specific
areas, such as the yak of the Himalayas and the guinea pig and capybara of Latin America.
Several wild species could become useful alternatives or complements to cattle and sheep
in rangeland areas. Interesting work is underway on the domestication of wild bovidae
and cervidae in different parts of the world, in particular the oryx and the eland.

## The Conservation of Livestock Genetic Resources

Livestock populations in developed countries have for some years been subject to
strong selection within intensified production systems, resulting in very large production
increases. Populations or breeds that did not respond well to changes in requirements
were discarded, with the result that the number of breeds has rapidly decreased. A
FAO/UNEP survey of Europe in 1975 26/ showed that 115 of the European and Mediterranean
breeds were being threatened by extinction and only 30 were holding their own. There has
been a change towards Friesian cattle in practically all of the lowland areas; and towards Simmental cattle in the moderately elevated areas of central and south-eastern
Europe. In order to save some of the rarer breeds from complete extinction, special conservation herds have been set up with public or private support in many European countries.

Crossbreeding with European-type livestock, particularly dairy cattle, and the replacement of indigenous poultry with high-yielding commercial strains are under way in many developing countries. However, it is unlikely that environmental conditions, in particular
the availability of feed and an improvement in disease prevention and control, will permit
the widespread use of either crossbred or purebred European-type livestock in the near
future. On the other hand, very little systematic work in the genetic improvement of
local livestock has yet been undertaken. The conditions for genetic resource development
are thus quite different from those in the industrialized countries where considerable
knowledge exists about the breeds currently in use. In developing countries, appropriate
systems of recording and evaluation need to be developed, taking into account not only
productivity at government stations but also at the farm level. Considerable emphasis
will have to be given to tolerance and resistance to both disease and environmental stress
to ensure that desirable genes are maintained.

## ANIMAL DISEASE CONTROL

One of the major determinants of livestock productivity and development is the health
status of the stock. Although the individual livestock owner can obviously influence this
in many ways, his control is far from absolute. In the case of diseases caused by infectious agents the health of his stock is also dependent on that of stock nearby.

---

25/   FAO,Report on the Expert Consultation on Rural Poultry and Rabbit Production
      (13 November to 3 December 1981), Rome, 1982.

26/   FAO, Pilot Study on Conservation of Animal Genetic Resources, 1975.

It is generally accepted that a state veterinary service is essential to control the spread of major diseases. The standard reached by such services varies widely from country to country. In most developed and in many developing countries national veterinary services now include both diagnostic laboratories and appropriately distributed field services with necessary supporting staff and vaccine production laboratories. The necessity for the latter depends on the diseases involved, size of the country and the availability of safe, effective vaccines from other sources. An animal quarantine service is also mandatory since the volume of trade and the speed of transportation have greatly increased in recent years and distance is no longer an important barrier to the spread of disease.

The damage that can be done when a disease enters a country that was previously free can be illustrated by the outbreaks of foot-and-mouth disease (FMD) in Denmark in 1982 which, although eliminated within a period of a few weeks, cost approximately US $20 million as compensation for slaughtered animals alone. Furthermore, restrictions imposed on agriculture and on other industries and on exports increased the cost by several million dollars a week.

The shortage of trained manpower is one of the constraints to building up a strong veterinary service in developing countries, especially in Africa. However, some countries are attempting to overcome this by innovative approaches, designed specifically for local conditions and using lower level personnel such as animal health assistants. These play an important role in the Indian Dairy Development Programme (Operation Flood) described later, as do the nomadic scouts appointed and paid for by village communities in Ethiopia, Madagascar and Niger. Although it may still be too early to evaluate the effectiveness of these 'barefoot vets', they represent a realistic approach to providing a low cost animal health service, particularly in countries which are unable to afford a field service staffed by highly trained professionals.

## The Control of Major Infectious Animal Diseases

A prime function of most state veterinary services is either to eradicate certain diseases or to reduce their incidence. These are usually diseases that:

- are of major economic importance

- have public health implications, such as rabies, brucellosis

- have recently been introduced and threaten to disrupt the industry, such as African swine fever (ASF) in Latin America

- can be effectively controlled by vaccination, such as rinderpest.

Many countries have made strenuous and continuous efforts to eradicate major diseases such as bovine brucellosis, tuberculosis, glanders, FMD, classical swine fever (CSF), sheep pox, Newcastle disease (ND), rabies, East Coast fever (ECF), babesiosis and its major vector tick Boophilus microplus. As a result, some of these diseases have been eradicated either from countries or from regions of the world. Today, the industrialized countries enjoy freedom from most of the major classic epizootic diseases. In Europe efforts are now being concentrated on the eradication of the residual foci of such diseases as ASF, CSF and ND.

Other diseases such as rinderpest and contagious bovine pleuropneumonia (CBPP), which once appeared sporadically in some European countries, have been eradicated. The incidence of FMD in Europe has been considerably reduced and several countries are now free from it.

Progress has been much slower in the developing world. Although there have been a number of successes, disease eradication has been fraught with difficulties and frustrations. Yet ASF has been successfully eradicated from Cuba, the Dominican Republic and Malta. Babesiosis has been eradicated from large areas of Argentina and Mexico. ECF has been eliminated in a number of southern African countries, although its tick vector Rhipicephalus appendiculatus persists. CBPP has been eradicated from the Central African Republic, glanders from the majority of countries in Africa and Asia and Brucella melitensis from sheep and goats in Cyprus. FMD has been eradicated from all central American countries and also from Chile, although it occurs in all other countries in Latin America and is widespread in Africa, Asia and the Near East.

A coordinated vaccination campaign against rinderpest known as Joint Project 15 (JP 15) which was carried out between 1963 and 1973, coupled with the general strengthening of veterinary services in many African countries, contributed to a recent significant decrease in the incidence of rinderpest. However, the disease was, and still is, enzootic in Sudan and in Ethiopia and probably in some other countries in Africa. Recently its resurgence has been reported from some countries in western Africa. In response, emergency action supported by FAO, OIE 27/ and the EEC was taken to organize vaccination campaigns in ten of them.

However, the majority of the cattle population in the region is still fully susceptible to rinderpest due to the absence of follow-up vaccination campaigns. Since it is very difficult to control or to monitor livestock movements across national borders in Africa, it was inevitable that unless more thorough efforts were made to eradicate rinderpest, it would spread again and threaten the region's beef and dairy industries. The recent severe and widespread resurgence of the disease has dramatically underlined this point.

## Control of Chronic Diseases

The large group of chronic diseases have effects which are more insidious and less obvious than the major infectious diseases and their importance is frequently overlooked or seriously underestimated. Although outwardly less noticeable, they frequently have an important economic impact through their effects on production or reproductive performance. Examples are enzootic pneumonias of pigs, mastitis in dairy cattle and chronic respiratory diseases of poultry. These diseases can be controlled or prevented by managerial procedures or by prophylactic animal health measures such as medication and vaccination, the application of which is facilitated when stock are raised under intensive conditions. This allows the environment to be adapted to reduce or eliminate the possibility of infection or infestation and it ensures close veterinary supervision and permits improved animal nutrition, a factor which frequently enhances disease resistance. Nevertheless, unless associated with disease preventive measures, intensification of livestock production can increase the risk of disease because of increased stocking rates and higher levels of stress.

---

27/ OIE: International Office of Epizootics.

## Trypanosomiasis

Very large areas of Africa are without cattle and other livestock because of the presence of tsetse flies and the trypanosomes they transmit. Trypanosomes are protozoa which cause wasting diseases-sleeping sickness in man and trypanosomiasis in animals. Losses arise not only from morbidity and death but also from the virtual exclusion of affected areas from agricultural livestock development.

The tsetse fly is present in 37 countries of Africa, infesting some 9 million $km^2$ or 42% of the total land area. Much of this land has an excellent potential either for pasture production or for other agricultural use and it could support an estimated additional 100 million head of livestock if it were free from this pest.

The rational utilization of the tsetse-infested areas for food production, involving the integration of livestock and crop production, is of vital importance to the future of Africa. This can be achieved if trypanosomiasis is brought under control by attacking either the causative trypanosome or the principal vector, the tsetse fly.

The mostwidely practised control method is insecticidal spraying of the 10% to 15% of the vegetation which provides the dry season resting places for the tsetse fly. An alternative approach is to work directly on the trypanosome. During the two decades, 1940-1960, a number of drugs were developed to treat trypanosomiasis. They were: (a) curative drugs effective with a single dose; and (b) prophylactic drugs affording protection for several weeks or months. The latter proved to be of particular value for livestock exposed to temporary challenge as, for example, during the passage of trade stock through tsetse fly belts.

It is possible to maintain livestock in tsetse infested areas under the protection afforded by these drugs, provided treatment of infected animals is carried out on a sustained basis at intervals commensurate with the trypanosomiasis risk. Currently at least 25 million doses of these drugs are used each year. In using either curative or prophylactic drugs, they must be administered correctly since underdosage can readily lead to resistance of the trypanosomes to further treatment.

Attempts to produce a vaccine for the immunization of domestic stock have not proved successful so far, but a major research effort is being undertaken by the International Laboratory for Research in Animal Disease (ILRAD) in Kenya.

Another important development option is the use of trypanotolerant livestock, as discussed earlier. They can live and breed in the presence of moderate trypanosomiasis challenge but if the infection to which they are exposed is severe or if the animal's vitality is weakened by stress through poor feeding, lack of water, other parasites or overwork, then they too will sicken and may die from the disease.

Thus, all of the control options suffer from some limitations. The distribution of tsetse also is not static and varies as a result of changes in the ecology due to human activities or weather conditions. Nevertheless, successful tsetse control operations have been carried out in, for example, Nigeria where, through selective spraying, it was possible to free about 205 000 $km^2$ from tsetse in the period from 1956 to 1978. Similar but smaller scale campaigns have also been carried out in a number of other African countries.

In the past,the use of land cleared of tsetse has not always been optimal. Land use planning supported by necessary legislation and the creation of appropriate infrastructures have not kept pace with the elimination of the fly.

FAO has mounted a trypanosomiasis control programme to help overcome the problem. The prime focus is on regional and/or community development using tsetse and trypanosome control methods as planned components for developing areas where the presence of trypanosomiasis effects both man and livestock.

## AFRICAN SWINE FEVER (AFS): A COSTLY VISITOR

Under 2% of the world's pigs are found in Africa. Their numbers there have increased very slowly mainly because of the existence of ASF, a virus disease for which there is no effective vaccine or treatment and which can kill up to 90% of pigs in infected herds. For example, the entire domestic pig population in Sao Tomé and Principe had to be eliminated following the sudden appearance of the disease in the country in 1979. Outbreaks of the disease in Cameroon in 1982 ruined years of effort to increase pig production there.

The disease spread from Africa to Portugal in 1957 and to Spain in 1960 and became enzootic in those countries causing substantial annual losses. In Spain the annual cost for compensation alone for the 3% of the national herd that are slaughtered for disease control exceeds US $14 million and the total direct programme costs to date approach US $200 million. Outbreaks have also occurred in France,

Italy and Malta where prompt and drastic action eliminated the disease with the exception of Sardinia (Italy) where sporadic outbreaks continue to occur. In Malta, the eradication campaign entailed slaughter of the entire pig population of 80 thousand at a total cost (including indirect costs) to the national economy estimated at US $45 million.

The disease was introduced into Cuba in 1981 and later to Brazil, Dominican Republic, Haiti and, once again, Cuba. In both Cuba and the Dominican Republic, ASF has been eliminated but in the former country eradication necessitated the slaughter of over 400 thousand pigs while in the latter death and voluntary slaughter together eliminated the entire pig population of 1.4 million. A similar operation is under way in Haiti where the entire pig population is having to be eliminated.

## The Cost of Animal Disease

According to FAO estimates, at least 5% of cattle, 10% of sheep and goats, and 15% of pigs die annually due to disease. Besides these direct losses there are production losses due to poor reproductive efficiency, retarded rates of growth and low levels of production. But because costs for labour, drugs, transport and other inputs are continually rising and veterinary services have to compete with others for limited government funds, measures to control animal diseases also compete for funds. Decisions on priorities and sizes of disease control programmes generally should be made through appropriate cost-benefit analysis. A number of such studies have indicated that well planned and organized disease control programmes can be very attractive economically. For example, a benefit/cost ratio of 4:1 has been recorded for animal morbidity measures in Mexico; 5:1 for CBPP control in Nigeria; 23:1 for fascioliasis control in Spain; and 14:1 for bovine tuberculosis eradication in Hungary 28/.

---

28/ Ellis, P.R., Bull. Off. Int. Epiz. 93: 763-767, 1981.

Prior to 1950, rinderpest killed some 2 million cattle annually in Asia, Africa and parts of Europe. The estimated cost of the JP-15 vaccination campaign against this disease was more than US $20 million but it almost eliminated the disease in most countries involved in the campaign, especially in West Africa. In Nigeria, where the disease was eradicated in 1972, the benefit/cost ratio of the campaign was nearly 2.5:1. Cattle owners responded to the ecological pressure brought about by larger herds by changing herd structures towards greater efficiency. There is clear evidence that the reduction in mortality in this situation did not lead to greater pressure on the land 29/.

However, rinderpest is almost unique among animal diseases in its epizootiological simplicity. Few other diseases are likely to be as simple to control. Polyvalent vaccines are needed for many virus diseases and frequently they confer immunity for only a limited time. Nevertheless, even with such diseases, well-planned vaccination programmes can yield a high return. For example, a control programme for FMD permitted Botswana to export beef to Europe and a vaccination programme against the disease in Kenya proved to be very effective.

---

29/ Felton, M.R., 1976, Studies on the control of Rinderpest in Nigeria, M.Sc. Thesis, University of Reading, 1976.

# SOME EXPERIENCES OF LIVESTOCK DEVELOPMENT

The central theme of this chapter is that, in attempting to meet the increased demand arising for livestock products in developing countries, careful development of their livestock sectors can satisfy other objectives as well.  The strategies adopted will depend on and profoundly influence the use of the resources available in terms of feed and genetic potential, as shown in the previous sections.

Patience and perseverance are also required where these strategies adapt and build on existing technologies and patterns of resource use if success is to be achieved.  A bringing together of various complementary activities and actions is required in the light of a comprehensive understanding of the production system involved.  Agrarian reform or the modification of access to the land resource, producer incentives, the provision of credit and processing and marketing facilities, together with the improvement of technology of animal feeding, breeding and health, are all likely components of a livestock development programme.  It is the blending of these often disparate activities, frequently administered by different institutions, and understanding the production system, that constitute the major hurdles to making these programmes a success.

The following experiences of some major livestock development programmes undertaken under widely differing conditions are, therefore, instructive.

## LIVESTOCK DEVELOPMENT ON ARID AND SEMI-ARID LANDS

More than one-third of the land surface of the globe is arid or semi-arid.  Over half of this area, or more than 2 300 million hectares, lies in developing countries.  This is an area 50% greater than all of the arable and permanent crop lands in both developed and developing countries.  It is an area of high agricultural risk where the scarcity and variability of rainfall are the dominant features.

In these arid lands the environment is normally too dry to permit the successful growth of crops.  Nomadism and transhumance constitute the way of life, involving the utilization of ephemeral pastures during the rains and withdrawing to more favoured areas in the dry season.  Camels, sheep and goats are the principal livestock in such areas.

The situation is similar in many tropical semi-arid lands which represent transitional zones comprising fragile eco-systems between a purely pastoral economy and one which introduces cropping into its agricultural systems.  Because the rainfall is unreliable, harvests are unpredictable, so that a combination of crops and livestock is adopted by some societies; transhumance is common.

Such lands can be both conserved and utilized productively as occurs, for example, in Australia and Mexico where arid lands are grazed under a ranching system.  This requires, however, that there is identifiable ownership of both stock and land by an individual or a group of individuals, so that there is an appropriate incentive for preserving the eco-system.  The land tenure changes required to bring this about in collectively owned arid rangelands are not simple to identify or to introduce, given the rapid increases in both human and livestock populations that have recently occurred.

In the arid and semi-arid zones together, the human and livestock populations rose by 75% and 79% respectively between 1949 and 1974.  These increases in both human and livestock populations in only 25 years have led to encroachments of cultivated areas onto traditional grazing lands which are now carrying more stock. They have resulted in severe overexploitation and deterioration of grazing and, not infrequently, have also led to conflicts between pastoralists and cultivators 30/.

Yet the arid and semi-arid zones have continued to hold about 12% of the large ruminant stock of tropical developing countries and to supply about 12% of the beef produced by them. However, the pace of desertification has advanced to such a degree that this level of productivity may be difficult to maintain unless the range is improved. Livestock development projects have a poor reputation in these arid and semi-arid areas. Despite the immense expenditure that has gone into arid land development schemes, little has been accomplished in improving the lot of the pastoralist, the productivity of his stock or the quality of the range which he uses.

The record of the recent past must inevitably raise questions on the soundness of intervention strategies in arid zones. Past efforts have frequently ignored the complex structure of pastoral society which is a workable adaptation to the need to manage not only livestock but also available feed and water. In such societies there is normally a logical management hierarchy of decision making responsibility, with different levels of tribal authority deciding on different issues, such as stock, labour, water and movement regimes. The tribal corporate structure is based on centuries of experience on how to survive in the face of drought, fire, disease, flood or other disaster. But recently these disasters have often been of a magnitude to raise serious questions about the efficacy of traditional approaches to the utilization of arid and semi-arid lands.

Nevertheless, attempts to develop arid lands have seldom capitalized on this experience or on the expressed needs of the pastoralist. More often they have tried to impose on him a ranching model that arbitrarily tries to control the number of stock on a given area of land. Such models are usually based on North American or Australian experience and avoid consideration of the socio-economic and cultural relationships of pastoral societies.

In arid areas there are sound ecological reasons why a unit of land management needs to be very large to allow for periodic movements of livestock. Alienating the land and allocating smaller units as private property may be not only technically questionable but also offers a tremendous risk to equity. Likewise, efforts to settle nomads, either by force or by inducement have not been very successful, although spontaneous settlement is widespread as nomads are drawn into the expanding modern economy. However, the settlement of formerly nomadic groups does not necessarily indicate a change that will lead to self-sustaining society;  rather it reflects their increasing reliance upon urban centres.

Appropriate interventions for change have to take into account the opportunities for increasing not only production but also income and equity. At the same time, they must be conscious of the need for conserving the environment. Perhaps the easiest route to change is to learn more from the pastoralist himself and not to assume that the technology already exists for improving range management, disease control and livestock marketing. For example, the assumption that pastoralists will sell livestock in response to price rises

---

30/  For an excellent discussion of grazing on arid and semi-arid lands the reader is referred to:  UNESCO - Tropical Grazing Land Ecosystems 1979. See also:  Oxby, Clare. Group Ranches:  A Study of Group Cooperative Livestock Enterprises and their Application in Tsetse and Trypanosomiasis Control Programmes with Special Reference to Cattle, FAO, Rome, 1981.

needs challenging. Pastoralists are individualists, on the fringes of the monetary economy and so their responses may not be identical with smallholders who have wider access to
purchased inputs or consumer goods. It is also necessary to re-examine whether the emphasis
given to controlling stock numbers should be determined within the context of the way in
which existing communal systems operate - see, for example, the discussion on the hema system later in this chapter. There may be much to learn from self-managing pastoral societies
which function largely outside of government. Yet such societies seldom seem to have been
examined in the formulation of arid zone development strategies. Nevertheless, the real
problem of pastoral society is the explosion in the human population which has led to a
build up in stock on communal lands well in excess of their grazing capacity.

One possible approach for alleviating pressure on nomadic areas is that of stratification, based on comparative advantages in resources, skills or location. In this way the
more arid areas may be used as specialized breeding zones, using traditional management, as
is done in Northeast Kenya. The less arid areas may be used for raising grower stock, which
may ultimately be fattened in areas of high potential or where by-product feeds are available. For such a strategy to be attractive to the pastoralist there needs to be a marked
price differential per kg favouring immature over mature animals. Such a differential
rarely exists in developing countries and past efforts at stratification have seldom proved
attractive to the primary producer 31/. Stratification also necessitates a more complex
marketing infrastructure to enable cattle to flow through the system. A change of this
nature is often strongly resisted where traditional marketing systems are firmly entrenched,
particularly so when stratification involves trade across international borders.

A number of studies have shown that traditional systems of livestock marketing in
Africa generally perform well in terms of distributing livestock and meat at low costs 32/.
They have also shown that expectations from the possibilities of marketing schemes alone -
and of stratification - are often exaggerated 33/. Both strategies undoubtedly have a
role to play but only as a part of a well planned and integrated development programme
which also has production components.

An approach to integration which seems to offer considerable potential in both arid
and semi-arid lands is the wider use of agro-forestry. This cannot only provide much
needed forage for livestock, particularly during lean periods, but can also supply fuel wood
and permanent soil cover which both improves soil fertility and inhibits erosion. One of
the attractions of integrated livestock production and forestry is that it can be a profitable venture for the small landowner, although it may call for a considerable degree of
management skill.

The grazing of sheep and cattle under trees has been pursued in the temperate developed
countries for centuries, with fire, tree thinning and harvesting being used to effect a
balanced level of production. In the tropical developing countries of Latin America, a

---

31/ Ferguson, D.S. A conceptual framework for the evaluation of livestock development
projects and programmes in sub-saharan West Africa, CRED, University of Michigan, 1979.

32/ SEDES, Coûts de trasport et législation du commerce du bétail et de la viande dans les
Etats de l'Entente, Paris, 1969.

33/ Jahnke, M.E. Livestock Production Systems and Livestock Development in Tropical Africa.
Kieler Wissenschaftsverlag Vauk, Kiel, 1982.

similar approach is often followed, although forest land does tend to be cleared to establish pastures rather than being linked in a sustainable wood and livestock production
system 34/.

In arid areas of the Sahel, India, Pakistan, Chile and Peru, fodder trees such as
species of Prosopis and Acacia provide the only dependable source of livestock feed and
help to stabilize the desert.  Some species, such as Prosopis, have a multi-use potential
because they can absorb atmospheric moisture through their leaves and grow on poor soils
in areas where the annual rainfall is as low as 75mm or less.

## Sheep Development in Syria

One of the most successful development schemes in the arid zone and one which involves
both stratification and integration with crop agriculture, occurs in Syria.  Here sheep
production is the major livestock activity, based largely on the grazing potential of the
steppe which covers about 11 million ha or 58% of the country's land area.  The Government
initiated a programme for the improvement of the steppe after the disastrous effects of
three consecutive years of drought (1958-1960) which had resulted in a reduction of the
sheep population from about 5.9 million to 2.9 million;  by 1980 it was about 8.8 million.
A special Steppe Department was set up and efforts were made to improve the situation for
the bedouins and their flocks.  Since 1964 this Department received continuous assistance
from the World Food Programme (WFP), while it also received help from a FAO/UNDP Project
and, since 1978, from a World Bank loan.

The general problem of improving the steppe and the lot of the bedouin has been tackled
on a broad front.  Grazing cooperatives were established to limit over-grazing and the
destruction of the ranges.  Each cooperative was given the sole right to graze certain
demarcated areas and each cooperative family received a licence for grazing a specified
number of sheep (usually 100-125).  Efforts were made to keep the sheep off at least a
part of the cooperative's range area during critical growing periods of the year.  The
approach was, in effect, a revival of the ancient hema system of range management which had
previously been applied by the bedouin tribes.  By 1981, 105 hema cooperatives with 2.5
million sheep on 6 million ha of rangeland had been established 35/.

There were considerable initial difficulties in getting cooperation from the bedouins
as they were afraid of losing their independence.  The programme started in small areas
from where it has expanded gradually as the pastoralists gained confidence in it.  Fattening
units were set up on a cooperative basis in cereal producing areas to limit the bedouin's
dependence on merchants for the purchase and fattening of animals and to reduce the grazing
pressure on the steppe.  In 1981, 55 such cooperatives were in existence with 4,400 members
fattening 1.5 million sheep.  Through research and experiments carried out as part of the
overall programme, efficient fattening rations, based on locally available products, have
been worked out for use by the cooperatives.

---

34/ See E.K. Byington  and R.D. Child, Forages from the World's Forested Lands and
    Ruminant Animal Production in Child, R.D. and E.K. Byington (eds), 'The Potential
    of the World's Forages for Ruminant Animal Production', Winrock, Morrilton, Ark., 1981.

35/ Draz, O.  The development of the arid and semi-arid rangelands of the Near East.
    Modernization of traditional systems based on experience in Syria.  World Anim. Rev.
    (in press).

In Syria, as in other countries in the Near East, the spread of cultivation to low rainfall rangeland has caused large areas of it to degenerate. In order to overcome this problem, a series of legislative orders were enforced which prohibited the ploughing and cultivation of rangelands within the Syrian steppe. Drought resistant shrubs such as Atriplex were planted to regenerate the range. So far, about 7 000 ha have been planted.

A further facet of the programme is the production of a forage crop on fallow lands to provide additional dry season feed for breeding stock. A programme for the introduction of a forage, usually a vetch, was started in 1967, again with WFP assistance, in the better rainfall areas at the same time as cultivation of irrigated alfalfa was promoted. The programme had a slow start, particularly in the rain-fed areas. However, from 1974 to 1979, the total area under forages and pulses increased nearly tenfold from 8 600 ha to 83 700 ha.

Finally, in order to improve water availability on the rangelands a number of programmes for establishing surface dams and deep wells have been initiated. No fewer than 2 800 ruined Roman water cisterns have been restored during the last four years.

The overall programme just described has tried to tackle a problem which, to varying degrees, is common to many countries in Africa, Asia and the Near East: how to integrate the nomadic or semi-nomadic pastoralists into the existing economic system and how to protect their basic resource, the rangeland, from degeneration and destruction by overgrazing or by cultivation. In general, the programme has met with success, although many of the results have taken much longer to achieve than originally planned. The programme is noteworthy: (a) for the way in which it has attempted to integrate change into the traditional culture, rather than forcefully attempting to settle the nomads; and (b) for the efforts to optimize the output of the range by integrating its production with cereal and forage crop use and water development.


## LIVESTOCK DEVELOPMENT ON HUMID AND SUB-HUMID LANDS

That livestock production on small farms should be regarded as part of a farming system which needs to be looked at in a holistic manner, rather than as a series of discreet activities, is particularly true in the humid and sub-humid tropics. Much of the land in these zones is capable of growing crops as well as feeding livestock. Priority is not always given by the livestock owner to obtaining a high rate of output of food products from his stock because other products and services derived from them are more important in his system. Improvement in the output of livestock products from small farms usually cannot take place without simultaneous improvement of water resources and/or feed supplies. Yet such changes may depend on agencies or programmes whose mandates or goals may have limited involvement with livestock production.

Large ruminant production in non-arid areas is heavily dependent upon fibrous residues and by-products produced on the farm, plus grass, weeds and tree trimmings which are cut and carried from roadsides and verges to tethered livestock. The availability of these feeds may be markedly influenced by crop production practices. For example, stubble burning to permit double or triple cropping may reduce the available straw; the use of herbicides may curtail the supply of weeds in the rainy season; and the production of high yielding varieties of rice, with short silicaceous straw, may reduce both the quality and the quantity of straw available as feed.

The relationship between crop and animal farming also concerns the use of draught animals and the efforts to introduce them to new areas, particularly tropical Africa.

Draught animal use is very widespread in Asia and is now firmly established in most of southern Africa and some parts of the East African highlands. In francophone West Africa, draught animals are widely used for crop cultivation in Mali and Senegal. However, in sub-humid and humid Africa, the use of livestock for draught pruposes is still very limited mainly because of the presence of trypanosomiasis and the difficulty of firmly integrating livestock, or at least draught animals, into the agricultural systems existing there.

A number of efforts have been made to use draught animals more extensively in West Africa on the grounds that this would increase both labour and land productivity. A review of the effects of ox ploughing in West Africa showed significant yield increases over hand cultivation of 21% to 157% for millet, sorghum, maize, rice and cotton 36/.

The impact of introducing draught animals is not, however, always straightforward especially if it leads to a higher demand for labour at times of the year when such labour is costly, if available at all 37/.

Most of the sheep and goats in the humid and sub-humid zones of developing countries belong to smallholders who typically own only a few animals which are looked after by children or the elderly. The small size of individual herds and the communal nature of the grazing make it very difficult to have any impact on this type of owner. The husbandry and management of small stock, as is the case of the buffalo in much of India, is often the prerogative of the women of the family. Their role in this area and in decision making at the household level is usually neglected or ignored by rural development planners. Indeed, institutional support directed at men in areas such as extension, credit and co-operative membership has sometimes reduced women's access to such support. It makes little sense if the end goal of the support is a commodity for whose production or marketing men have little responsibility.

This argument gains added relevance where countries place increasing emphasis on the rearing of non-traditional small animal species such as rabbits, guinea pigs and milk goats for increasing meat and milk production. These species are raised mainly on small farms and usually are managed by women and children.

The extent to which tree crops are used in conjunction with food crops and livestock provides a particularly interesting feature of integrated agriculture on small farms. Leguminous trees and bushes are cut extensively to feed livestock, the best known species being Leucaena leucocephala 38/. Another form of integration involves grazing livestock under tree crops. Various pasture legumes are grown under rubber in Malaysia and Sri Lanka and also in Malawi where, although the shade prevents good forage yields, it permits the growth of seed material. Forages are also grown successfully under coconuts in a number of countries of southeast Asia and the South Pacific 39/. In West Africa, sheep and cattle are grazed under oil plams and kola trees and under mangoes and cashews. However, in all

---

36/ Shapiro, K.H. Livestock Production and Marketing in the ENTENTE States of West Africa: Summary Report. Centre for Research on Economic Development, Univ. of Michigan and USAID, Ann Arbor, Michigan, 1979.

37/ See the section on "Animal and Tractor Power" in Chapter 1.

38/ Vietmeyer, N. and B. Cottom. Leucaena, promising forage and tree crop for the tropics, 155 pp. Nat. Acad. of Science, Washington, D.C., 1977.

39/ Thomas, D. Pastures and Livestock under tree crops in the humid tropics. Trop. Agric. (Trin) 55 39-44, 1978.

cases, once a dense canopy forms, insufficient light penetrates to permit a good stand of forage. From the development standpoint, the greater use of short season forage legumes and tree crops such as Leucaena and Glyricidia offer considerable prospects. These leguminous trees offer two other benefits: they add nitrogen to the soil, thus influencing crop yields, and they provide some fuel wood as a by-product. Intervention through the wider use of such multi-purpose trees is a measure that is wholly consistent with an overall strategy for small farms.

Integrated farming systems involving livestock, fish and poultry have existed in China for a long time. In most other Asian countries also there are many such systems of long tradition in popular use. Interest in and experimental work on them is rapidly gaining momentum. These systems, in which waste products from one sub-system become inputs to another, provide an attractive alternative to reliance on food production systems which need high inputs of fossil fuel.

China produces over 800 thousand tons of fish annually from ponds receiving organic matter such as waste, animal manure, rice bran, brewer's waste and various materials gathered in the vicinity of ponds including grass and snails 40/. In the future the recycling of organic wastes in this manner through fish may provide one of the cheapest sources of food of animal origin in tropical countries as well as a profitable way of overcoming the increasing problem of waste disposal in crowded cities 41/.

Different systems of integrated aquaculture are evolving for different purposes. For example, a system of cooperation has developed in the vicinity of Bangkok in Thailand. Small landowners with fishponds of about one hectare permit landless countrymen to build a home and pig pens over their ponds. The pig farmer buys restaurant swill and some concentrates plus rice bran and broken rice. These are mixed with water hyacinth and fed to the pigs. The pig manure and feed waste fall into the pond and provide additional nutrients for the fish. The system also relies on cooperation between the landowner and the pig farmer because the annual fish harvest is a joint effort. In addition, after the pond is drained, the bottom is dredged and the "compost" used for fertilizing crops. Related systems are found elsewhere in south east Asia and involve chickens and ducks.

## Dairy Development in India

An outstanding example of change involving small farmers has been carried out successfully in India where extraordinary progress has been made in a highly integrated system of dairy development. India has a long tradition of integrated livestock/crop production in smallholder systems. The average landholding per household is approximately 2 ha. Only 25 - 30% of grain production on these smallholdings is marketed and all livestock feed is in very short supply. Land cultivation is mainly carried out by draught animals.

The supply of milk to the big cities has long been of great concern to central and state governments. By tradition, milk distribution and sales were handled by private

40/ De-Shan, Z. A brief introduction to the fisheries of China. FAO Fisheries Circular No. 726, FAO, Rome, 1980. See also Wohlfarth, G. Utilization of fish farming. Proc. of the Conf. on fish farming and wastes, London, pp. 78-95, 1978.

41/ Cruz, E.M. and K.D. Hopkins. The ICLARM-CLSU integrated animal-fish farming project: Poultry-fish and pig-fish trials., ICLARM Technical Report No. 2, ICLARM, Philippines, 1981.

vendors, sometimes in close association with city cowkeepers. Milk was often adulterated on its way from the cow to the consumer. In order to secure supplies and to improve milk quality, the public sector built dairy plants and distribution networks within the major cities.

For more than a decade the Government of India has been involved in a large dairy development programme called Operation Flood. During the period 1970-81 this received assistance from the WFP in the form of skim milk powder and butter oil estimated to exceed $100 million in value 42/. These dairy commodities were reconstituted to milk in the city dairies. The sale proceeds were used to build up the dairy processing and distribution system in the country's four major cities (Bombay, Calcutta, Delhi and Madras), to construct dairy factories in the production areas, to erect feed factories, to establish producer cooperatives and to promote milk production in the rural areas. In the current phase of Operation Flood, the role of WFP has been taken over by the EEC, and the World Bank is also providing financial support.

Operation Flood aims at developing producer cooperatives, based on the so-called Anand model which has been developed and put into wide practice in the State of Gujarat during the last 30 years. Farmers in a village with surplus milk to sell, form a dairy cooperative society (DCS) with individual membership and elected executive officers. A union of village cooperative societies is formed at the district level. Each DCS arranges milk collection morning and evening. The amount of milk delivered per producer and per day varies between as little as one litre to usually no more than 10 to 20 litres. The milk at each village society is collected by a truck operated by the milk union and transported to the union's dairy plant.

A typical union collects between 100 and 300 thousand litres per day. The union provides concentrate feeds, minerals and other supplies which are transported to the villages by the milk truck and sold by the village DCS. It also arranges veterinary services, artificial insemination and advice on production matters. The unions in each area, usually a state, have linked together to form a federation of unions which enables member unions to benefit from shared processing, marketing and investment programmes managed by specialists employed by the federation. The cooperative movement has thus developed a three-tiered structure: the village cooperative (DCS); the union of village cooperatives; and the federation of unions.

Operation Flood has been successful in building up the infrastructure for milk collection, processing and distribution. About two-thirds of all funds generated from the sale of WFP commodities have been used for this purpose. The processing capacity in the four metropolitan cities increased from one million litres/day in 1969 to 2.9 million litres in 1980, while in the rural areas processing capacities were increased fivefold to 3.4 million litres/day. Feed manufacturing has received about 11% of the WFP generated funds. Sixteen new cattle feed plants, mostly with a daily capacity of 100 tons, had been completed by 1980. The network for milk collection has been enlarged considerably. No less than 27 district unions have been organized containing 10 thousand village cooperatives and 1.36 million milk producer members. These village cooperatives procured 800 thousand tons of milk in 1981.

A programme of such gigantic proportions as Operation Flood has naturally been subject to much discussion, praise and criticism. Questions have been raised, such as the

---

42/ WFP. Summary terminal evaluation report of Project No. India 618, WFP/CFA 12, 1981.

following: Who is benefitting from the programme, is it the already wealthy farmer or will also the small farmer and landless labourer profit? How will it influence the nutrition of the poor in the cities? Has the programme led to a real increase in milk production or is it just tapping milk from rural areas which could not previously be reached by milk collection, perhaps thereby diminishing milk consumption among producer families? Will profitable milk production cause a diversion of land to fodder production and diminish the area available for growing staple foods such as wheat and rice?

Studies of the composition of the membership of village societies in Gujarat where organized dairying is most advanced, indicate that farmers with less than 2.5 acres of land own 57% of the dairy animals. Furthermore, a study by the National Dairy Development Board showed that in a sample of producers 14% were landless, 38% were small farmers (less than 5 acres), while the rest had larger holdings. On the average, the 1.4 million members of all the cooperative societies had an income from milk sales of about Rs. 1 200 in 1980, an amount almost equal to the country's average GDP per head. In many cases an additional benefit to the villages has been the contribution through the profits of cooperative societies to the improvement of village facilities.

The programme has successfully circumvented caste and sex discrimination. Its benefits are available to all livestock owners, irrespective of caste and the village women, who are primarily responsible for the husbandry and management of the buffalo, participate in cooperative activities.

In the cities, dairy products are largely consumed by the wealthier part of the population. In 1980 households of the poorest income segments accounted for about a quarter of the total population in the four metropolitan cities but bought only between 7 and 16% of the total milk supplies. Thus, although Operation Flood may have helped somewhat in increasing the milk consumption of the city poor, the effect has probably been small. For some time to come milk and milk products in urban areas will probably continue to be mainly consumed by the higher and middle income groups. However, in developing countries, the majority of the poor people are generally found in the rural areas. Dairy development programmes such as Operation Flood can, therefore, assist in recycling some urban income to the rural areas where the poor will benefit either directly as small-scale milk producers, or indirectly through increased job opportunities. The importance of the programme in job creation is considerable. Not only are a range of new service and manufacturing industries dependent upon the milk plants but infrastructure for whole areas including better roads, clinics and houses has been constructed on funds derived from milk sales.

The possibility or likelihood that profitable milk production could cause a distortion in the land-use pattern with a reduction in the production and availability of staple foods has been raised as another major issue. Indian milk production is based on the use of agricultural by-products and is likely to continue to do so. There have been some slight increases in forage production in Operation Flood areas, but information on this is incomplete. However, experimental results and practical experience indicate that a small area of forage production can be introduced into the cereal rotation with a good impact on milk production and only a minor effect on total grain yield 43/. The concentrates used in the dairy development programmes are, furthermore, based mainly on broken grains, which are not generally used as human food, and on brans and oil cakes. Of the latter, India still exports about 1 million tons annually.

---

43/ Groenwold, H.H. and P.R. Crossing. The place of livestock in small farm development: an Indian example. World Animal Review 15: 2-6, 1975.

Although hard facts are lacking, it would appear that the effect of dairy development on grain production has been mainly positive. It has been regularly observed that in those villages where dairy societies are functioning well, marked increases in agricultural production are occurring. The reason for this is that the average farmer sells only 25-30% of his food grain production and so the sale of even one or two litres of milk each day markedly increases a small farmer's cash income. A substantial part of this increment, commonly as much as 50%, is spent on fertilizer, improved seed and the purchase of irrigation water 44/.

## Dairy Development in Kenya

Another example of dairy development based upon an integrated approach, although less centrally directed, has occurred in Kenya where smallholder dairy production has undergone a remarkable expansion and development in the short period since Independence 45/. Although increasing demand for milk has been a major force in this development, this is not the sole explanation.

The implementation of the Swynnerton Plan of 1954 laid the ground for an orderly land reform after independence. The Plan called for: (a) African landholdings to be consolidated and adjudicated under individual ownership; (b) small farms to be encouraged to grow cash crops such as coffee, tea and pyrethrum, the income of which was partly used to buy grade cattle; (c) credit to be provided for the purchase of dairy cattle; and (d) support services such as tick control, milk collection and artificial insemination, to be built up and made available for small-scale dairy production. Immediately after Independence, a number of additional development schemes were implemented. Through the Million Acre Settlement Scheme farmland previously owned by European farmers was distributed to 35 000 African families. By 1975 the area allocated to smallholders had doubled. In many cases, grade cattle were also distributed to them.

In 1960, the total number of grade dairy cattle kept by smallholders was about 80 thousand while by 1975 it had increased to about 550 thousand. During the same period, the number of dairy cattle on large farms decreased from 600 thousand to about 250 thousand head, since when it has remained relatively stable. In 1976 large dairy farms supplied about 20% of the total milk but supplied about 40% of the urban markets and they thus continued to play an important and stabilizing role for the supply of milk to the processing industry. At the same time, these farms continued to be an important source of dairy animals for small farmers who wanted to start dairying.

A major reason for the rapid expansion of smallholder dairy development has been and continues to be the increased demand caused by the rapid growth in population and urbanization, and increased incomes in both urban and rural areas. In higher altitude areas where dairy production with crossbred and grade cattle is concentrated, families have an income from cash crops such as coffee, tea and pyrethrum, and the local market for milk is expanding quickly. Important decisions influencing expansion were made including the abolition of the quota system which had previously restricted access by smallholder dairy

---

44/ Brumby, P.J. Milk production in India. Intensive animal production in developing countries. British Society of Animal Production, 4: 325-330, 1981.

45/ Stotz, D. Smallholder dairy development in the past, present and future in Kenya. University of Hohenheim, 1979.

producers to the Kenya Cooperative Creameries (KCC) and the establishment of a price system which did not discriminate against those farmers - typically small scale - who produced milk mainly from unirrigated pastures.

Milk collection is now organized so that the large producers deliver directly to the KCC, while the small producers (if they do not market all surplus milk locally) deliver their milk to cooperative collection societies of which about 300 existed in 1975, typically with about 250 members each. The societies, in turn, sell milk on the local markets and dispose of their surplus to the KCC. The direct on-the-farm sale of milk to neighbours is generally handled by housewives who also participate in or are responsible for the management of the cows. Although no data are available, the growth in small-scale dairying is assumed to have strengthened the economic power of women.

The income from smallholder milk production is good in comparison to alternate uses of family labour. A recent study of modernization in the Kenya dairy industry showed that for a herd of 2 to 4 milking cows kept on grass the income from dairying increased by a third with a shift from zebus and their crosses to European-type cattle, and by over a half following a shift from grazing to stall-feeding. Economic forces have thus accelerated the introduction of dairying: the change from zebu to grade cows; the increase in herd size; and lately, the cultivation of forage crops, particularly Napier grass and the use of stall-feeding based on green fodder and agricultural by-products. Dairying thus plays a role in the progressive intensification of smallholder agriculture.

One of the key factors in facilitating this process has been the role of the KCC in providing a stable market outlet for smallholders. Another factor of importance has been the control of tickborne disease. Without the introduction of dipping against ticks, smallholder dairy production with grade cattle would have been impossible. Artificial insemination services have been an important technical innovation in smallholder areas, making it possible to expand the numbers of grade cattle. In 1968, 162 thousand inseminations were performed. By 1980 the number had increased to 537 thousand. It is estimated that the services now cover about 400 thousand cows, of which about 10% are zebus 46/.

The examples given in this chapter all indicate change through a move towards intensification as well as integration. Such change always incurs costs that have to be funded in some way. The contribution of the WFP played a significant catalytic role in schemes such as Operation Flood and the Syrian sheep fattening programme. When the whole farming system is involved, such an approach involving food or feed aid may take time. But over the long term it may be one of the better ways of bringing about livestock development in a manner that also promotes equitable rural development.

---

46/ Oscarsson, G. and R. Israelsson. The Kenya National Insemination Service (KNAIS), Swedish University of Agricultural Sciences, Uppsala, 1981.

## CONCLUSIONS, POLICY ISSUES AND IMPLICATIONS FOR ACTION

Policy issues relating to the livestock sector can be differentiated between developing and developed countries. In the developing countries, the issues revolve around the apparent failure of the livestock sector to exploit its undeniable opportunities to promote development. Issues in developed country policies concern the adjustment of the sector to shifting demand patterns. The latter has implications for the developing countries as well. Failure to adjust to changes in demand results in the creation of surpluses of livestock products in developed countries which, in turn, creates problems for those developing countries whose domestic markets are open to competition from overseas.

The livestock industry in developing countries has a dual role. On the one hand, it is a means of satisfying the rising demand for livestock products; on the other it is an effective instrument of social and economic change. Improvements in livestock production in most situations can only come about within the context of the total farming system of which they are an integral part. An holistic approach can, of course, create administrative problems unless the agencies promoting livestock development possess interdisciplinary capability.

The relative importance of the various livestock policy issues, improvement approaches and technological challenges which have been discussed, will be tempered greatly by the particular setting provided by each country. While many gradients exist, both developed and developing countries often have contrasts that can usefully be noted.

### Pastoral Situations in Developing Countries

The major regions of the world where livelihoods centre on traditional, extensive animal grazing patterns are often characterized by nomadic life styles. The livestock in these areas are utilized in a variety of ways for basic living needs. Few, if any, purchased inputs are employed: market sales seldom occur except on an as needed basis and efforts to manage available grazing and water resources are often inadequate. There is strong dependency on the vicissitudes of nature, and human well-being is very fragile from season to season.

Such traditional pastoral systems are deceptively simple in appearance, but have deep social roots. The husbandry skills and human relationships evolved over the centuries are very intricate and functional in certain ways. In most situations, development undertakings would do well to build on these skills and relationships, rather than be too ready to remove them.

Efforts to help people in these pastoral settings can be attuned to either of two directions. One might be to help them improve their husbandry while continuing their pastoral way of life, either because of their own desire to do so or because no better alternative seems to be available. This development orientation may be very appropriate where the populations concerned are relatively stable and where intrusions of the modern world are unlikely to be significant in the foreseeable future. Some basic steps to improve animal health and productivity, as well as management of grazing lands and water supplies, should be included. Ideas for reducing the drudgery of their daily tasks and for meeting their fuel needs might be well received. Basic human rights and legal protections might be defined more clearly and enforced. Provision could be made to help prevent or buffer unusual hardships: emergency food and feed, temporary work, guaranteed markets in times of forced sales, access to new stock to replace depleted herds, animal disease monitoring and control, and breeding and selection to improve the tolerance of the animals to harsh conditions.

In working with tradition-oriented groups, it is important to consider carefully the delicate land-livestock balances, human relationships and intangible aspects of the quality of life that may be adversely affected by the proposed interventions. At the same time, it would be a disservice to these people if it were assumed that their lifestyle could continue indefinitely without change. The younger persons especially need to be prepared to meet the unaccustomed demands of the outside world.

The second path that pastoral people can take is to move toward a modernized set of husbandry practices, with emphasis on marketing and, perhaps, a more settled existence. This is already happening to some pastoral groups. Intensification may or may not be part of it because a modernized grazing livestock system may use broad expanses of range land and still be productive and scientific. But introduction of new feeding and health practices would probably need to be accompanied by more conscious management of land and water, together with a clear or revised definition of land, water and livestock ownership rights. New credit and finance arrangements may be called for to meet herd and land improvement costs. Especially if sales to distant cities or overseas markets are involved, help in evolving new marketing and processing arrangements will be important. These transitions will tend to break down traditional relationships with local leaders, traders and money-lenders. New concentrations of power are likely to emerge and needs may arise for the typical family or pastoral group to have help in maintaining its equitable bargaining position.

## Mixed Crop-Livestock Systems in Developing Countries

The emerging agricultures of many nations revolve around labour-intensive systems that combine crop and livestock production in closely integrated fashion. Often these are smallholdings that utilize animal power, produce crops for sale, domestic consumption and for animal feed, and have livestock products for home use and sale. Sometimes these are large collective, state-operated, or commercial units. Sometimes one would not find crops and livestock combined on any one unit but, in the locality as a whole, there would be a diversity of crop and livestock operations that add up to a highly self-contained system.

The animals are multi-purpose, making use of untillable land, cropping by-products and waste from local agro-processing operations. They in turn can provide power and manure for crop production. Having a combination of crops and livestock creates more flexibility when it comes to marketing, so that farmers are not completely dependent on the variations in prices for a single commodity. The combination is also a way to utilize labour more fully and evenly throughout the year.

From the regional or national viewpoint, a localized mixture of crops and livestock can lead to more self-sufficiency with respect to feed, fuel, fertilizer and human food needs. Also, there can be less need for infrastructure to transport these items over long distance.

Such crop-livestock combinations may be traditional and oriented to family living needs, or they may be very technologically advanced and sales oriented. But common to both extremes are some characteristics that carry important implications for policymakers, programme administrators and specialists.

When it comes to policy and programme design, integrated crop-livestock farming systems create special challenges. An action intended to affect certain crops, such as grain price subsidies, can have important indirect effects on farmers' livestock operations, and vice versa. Conventional research, extension and credit programmes that focus on single types of crops or livestock will not be appropriate. Interdisciplinary, interagency approaches that address needs in a broader context of resource use, farm management and consumer wants are required.

## Highly Commercialized Livestock Operations in Developing Countries

Whereas most rural people in developing countries are part of the nomadic or mixed farming systems just discussed, in some situations high-technology commercial livestock operations are being rapidly introduced. Broiler production and cattle fattening operations are examples. Often these are associated with large investors or multinational agribusiness. Characteristically they are mechanized and utilize relatively little labour, and they frequently depend on large imports of grain and feed supplements.

Such operations are beneficial from the viewpoint of certain consumer and business groups. They are a way to bring outside capital and managerial capacity into the economy. They can also help agricultural development by demonstrating that investment and scientific innovation in that sector is feasible and often has a high economic pay-off. But they may be at cross-purposes with some other concerns. If the products are mostly consumed domestically and are not substitutes for previously imported foods, the input needs associated with these commercial operations could create large drains on foreign exchange. Profits may be taken out of the country and not reinvested locally. The domestic multiplier effects on income and employment may also be low. Sometimes competition from these highly commercial operations may drive smallholder producers out of business. In addition, harmful environmental effects may result from large-scale land clearing, or from waste disposal problems associated with large feedlots and processing plants.

This does not necessarily imply that commercial operations should be discouraged by developing countries. Indeed, they can make valuable contributions to national development if ways can be found to link them more closely with the rural sector, local entrepreneurship and wise long-run natural resource use patterns. To catalyze such linking, it may be appropriate to consider such actions as: encouragement of joint-venture investment and managerial arrangements; incentives and organizational help to make it feasible to involve smallholders and other rural people in some of the input-supply and production steps; help to potential livestock investors in identifying needs and latent opportunities that would be complementary to development objectives; reasonable constraints to encourage better land-use and waste-disposal practices.

## Livestock System Adjustments in Developed Countries

The industrialized countries that already have their own livestock systems in place face challenges too. There is continual need to be responsive to changes in technology, domestic and foreign consumer demand patterns, competition from abroad and from substitutes for animal products, land availability in an urbanizing setting and access to labour and capital amidst competition from other seekers of these resources.

In at least two respects the task of forming policies is more difficult than that facing developing countries:

1)   There are many well organized interest groups to be reconciled - livestock pro-
     ducers, crop producers, small farmers, the grain trade, urban consumers, environ-
     mentalists and humanitarian groups concerned about nutrition problems of the
     poor in their own country and in others.

2)   Developed countries are not starting from the beginning:  changes in policies
     have to take into account the repercussions of making some groups worse off
     than before.

One of the major issues now confronting policy makers in the industrialized countries is to what extent to foster the continued existence of small livestock producers facing increasing competition from large agribusinesses. In animal husbandry it is not neces- sarily true that bigger is always better. Indeed, the careful daily attention that some livestock require puts large commercial operations at a disadvantage relative to the family farmer. Of course, it is true that some countries have artificially helped small livestock producers through such measures as price support and stabilization programmes, protective tariffs and export subsidies. These measures have benefited large-scale producers as well. An especially notable example is the extent to which dairy farmers in Western Europe and North America have been aided and the over-supply that has resulted from it.

These countries, being highly urbanized, face considerable pressure to take consumer and taxpayer interests into account. Resistance to costly producer subsidies and import protections that increase food prices is likely to be encountered, especially during times of recession and austerity.

Instead of high-cost supports and protections one answer is to help marginal live- stock producers adjust to these changes by finding new ways to achieve cost economies by cooperating together;   shifting to new crop or livestock enterprises;   moving into a part-time farm occupational pattern; or, in the case of some, shifting out of agriculture altogether.

Leaders in developing countries could well observe these problems and policy responses closely, for they too may be facing similar challenges as their own economies develop. On the one hand, they cannot afford to set in place farmer subsidies and protection that are costly and that lead to inefficient livestock systems. On the other, to go to extremes in yielding to consumer interest by holding down producer prices or permitting uncontrolled imports could jeopardize the development of their livestock sector.

Annex tables

ANNEX TABLE 1. VOLUME OF PRODUCTION OF MAJOR AGRICULTURAL, FISHERY AND FOREST PRODUCTS

| | 1967 | 1972 | 1973 | 1974 | 1975 | 1976 | 1977 | 1978 | 1979 | 1980 | 1981 | ANNUAL RATE OF CHANGE 1972-81 PERCENT |
|---|---|---|---|---|---|---|---|---|---|---|---|---|
| | | | | | | THOUSAND METRIC TONS | | | | | | |

**WORLD**

**AGRICULTURAL PRODUCTS**

| | 1967 | 1972 | 1973 | 1974 | 1975 | 1976 | 1977 | 1978 | 1979 | 1980 | 1981 | ANNUAL RATE |
|---|---|---|---|---|---|---|---|---|---|---|---|---|
| TOTAL CEREALS | 1134215 | 1271808 | 1380528 | 1342382 | 1372353 | 1480082 | 1470313 | 1600185 | 1553100 | 1561687 | 1650292 | 2.70 |
| WHEAT | 299029 | 348308 | 376196 | 364206 | 359392 | 425769 | 387571 | 451304 | 428704 | 444866 | 452389 | 3.03 |
| RICE PADDY | 277768 | 307988 | 335965 | 332981 | 358722 | 350428 | 371564 | 386925 | 376914 | 397684 | 412316 | 2.90 |
| BARLEY | 104683 | 135520 | 151066 | 152712 | 137464 | 172245 | 160330 | 179463 | 157722 | 159827 | 154615 | 1.51 |
| MAIZE | 272649 | 308821 | 326873 | 310046 | 343900 | 350214 | 370084 | 392594 | 418601 | 394049 | 450334 | 4.12 |
| MILLET AND SORGHUM | 86566 | 80260 | 95542 | 87207 | 89824 | 90852 | 94389 | 56189 | 92407 | 84207 | 101406 | 1.07 |
| ROOT CROPS | 541648 | 526173 | 566620 | 550872 | 541840 | 546572 | 568185 | 596274 | 583969 | 525548 | 545953 | .26 |
| POTATOES | 291292 | 261901 | 293886 | 273132 | 260882 | 264101 | 268179 | 278850 | 288630 | 229942 | 254215 | - .90 |
| CASSAVA | 88661 | 99856 | 100512 | 103446 | 107613 | 110778 | 115251 | 122339 | 116687 | 119381 | 126290 | 2.67 |
| TOTAL PULSES | 39997 | 41676 | 42138 | 42353 | 39738 | 44667 | 42339 | 43953 | 40055 | 39746 | 42679 | - .14 |
| CITRUS FRUIT | 33751 | 41945 | 45303 | 46220 | 48182 | 48905 | 51364 | 49952 | 50819 | 55727 | 55239 | 2.80 |
| BANANAS | 27029 | 31965 | 32408 | 33060 | 32856 | 35002 | 36563 | 37397 | 38161 | 39861 | 39933 | 2.83 |
| APPLES | 27187 | 26093 | 29802 | 28320 | 31917 | 32321 | 30769 | 32762 | 36312 | 34461 | 31955 | 2.52 |
| VEGETABLE OILS,OIL EQUIV | 135948 | 156823 | 170328 | 163512 | 180647 | 172047 | 195651 | 201870 | 217384 | 209858 | 223582 | 4.04 |
| SOYBEANS | 37442 | 47773 | 58175 | 52558 | 64401 | 57341 | 73780 | 75292 | 88945 | 81021 | 88466 | 7.03 |
| GROUNDNUTS IN SHELL | 17190 | 15709 | 16742 | 16995 | 18763 | 17058 | 17427 | 18303 | 18293 | 17129 | 19944 | 1.60 |
| SUNFLOWER SEED | 9993 | 9607 | 12080 | 10969 | 9613 | 10284 | 12155 | 13175 | 15317 | 13560 | 13879 | 4.27 |
| RAPESEED | 5380 | 6766 | 7204 | 7169 | 8641 | 7606 | 7914 | 10568 | 10536 | 10590 | 12340 | 6.68 |
| COTTONSEED | 21039 | 24589 | 25701 | 26149 | 22649 | 22079 | 25706 | 24377 | 26405 | 26572 | 28762 | 1.26 |
| COPRA | 3499 | 4553 | 3888 | 3483 | 4565 | 5286 | 4750 | 4892 | 4449 | 4683 | 4914 | 2.03 |
| PALM KERNELS | 967 | 1221 | 1189 | 1370 | 1397 | 1427 | 1507 | 1441 | 1714 | 1829 | 1890 | 5.10 |
| SUGAR (CENTRIFUGAL,RAW) | 65305 | 71827 | 76382 | 75681 | 79138 | 83705 | 89833 | 90427 | 88964 | 83951 | 92225 | 2.57 |
| COFFEE GREEN | 4341 | 4572 | 4198 | 4753 | 4611 | 3554 | 4418 | 4806 | 5067 | 4818 | 5983 | 2.48 |
| COCOA BEANS | 1388 | 1510 | 1401 | 1553 | 1556 | 1348 | 1438 | 1475 | 1656 | 1625 | 1652 | 1.26 |
| TEA | 1147 | 1394 | 1455 | 1490 | 1551 | 1591 | 1749 | 1791 | 1825 | 1863 | 1859 | 3.62 |
| COTTON LINT | 11311 | 13429 | 14017 | 13986 | 12340 | 11947 | 13977 | 13238 | 13935 | 13898 | 15148 | .84 |
| JUTE AND SIMILAR FIBRES | 3605 | 3489 | 3846 | 3030 | 3122 | 3373 | 3736 | 4522 | 4373 | 4024 | 4168 | 3.06 |
| SISAL | 634 | 672 | 638 | 692 | 614 | 420 | 457 | 404 | 431 | 450 | 451 | - 5.64 |
| TOBACCO | 4872 | 4858 | 4956 | 5291 | 5423 | 5702 | 5552 | 5980 | 5388 | 5299 | 5637 | 1.32 |
| NATURAL RUBBER | 2436 | 3032 | 3455 | 3458 | 3562 | 3795 | 3632 | 3713 | 3862 | 3840 | 3685 | 1.92 |
| TOTAL MEAT | 94450 | 111023 | 112223 | 118674 | 120802 | 124262 | 128973 | 132842 | 137101 | 140277 | 142359 | 2.98 |
| TOTAL MILK | 387476 | 409899 | 416113 | 424946 | 429986 | 438842 | 451299 | 457915 | 465431 | 469927 | 471798 | 1.70 |
| TOTAL EGGS | 19316 | 22726 | 22941 | 23642 | 24356 | 24746 | 25733 | 26939 | 27801 | 28651 | 29553 | 3.12 |
| WOOL GREASY | 2778 | 2792 | 2642 | 2615 | 2713 | 2667 | 2646 | 2641 | 2727 | 2800 | 2822 | .38 |

**FISHERY PRODUCTS 1/**

| | 1967 | 1972 | 1973 | 1974 | 1975 | 1976 | 1977 | 1978 | 1979 | 1980 | 1981 | ANNUAL RATE |
|---|---|---|---|---|---|---|---|---|---|---|---|---|
| FRESHWATER + DIADROMOUS | 6497 | 7046 | 7348 | 7301 | 7690 | 7475 | 7707 | 7452 | 7756 | 8111 | 5173 | - 1.11 |
| MARINE FISH | 46083 | 48928 | 48887 | 52858 | 51963 | 55134 | 53350 | 54858 | 54842 | 55193 | 25430 | - 2.82 |
| CRUST+ MOLLUS+ CEPHALOP | 5043 | 5965 | 6129 | 6280 | 6679 | 7045 | 7594 | 7866 | 8142 | 8541 | 3729 | - .03 |
| AQUATIC MAMMALS | 23 | 17 | 11 | 11 | 12 | 13 | 13 | 13 | 22 | 20 | | |
| AQUATIC ANIMALS | 111 | 154 | 257 | 140 | 139 | 143 | 232 | 211 | 200 | 186 | 98 | - 1.65 |
| AQUATIC PLANTS | 1392 | 2134 | 2177 | 2469 | 2331 | 2392 | 2936 | 3072 | 3093 | 3006 | 785 | - 2.74 |

**FOREST PRODUCTS 2/**

| | 1967 | 1972 | 1973 | 1974 | 1975 | 1976 | 1977 | 1978 | 1979 | 1980 | 1981 | ANNUAL RATE |
|---|---|---|---|---|---|---|---|---|---|---|---|---|
| SAWLOGS CONIFEROUS | 512411 | 565000 | 589834 | 566002 | 542523 | 597265 | 612579 | 628972 | 635142 | 611547 | 562081 | .76 |
| SAWLOGS NONCONIFEROUS | 192938 | 222391 | 240587 | 229414 | 213855 | 232463 | 241246 | 251356 | 250415 | 255219 | 241964 | 1.30 |
| PULPWOOD+PARTICLES | 267425 | 303542 | 326171 | 358182 | 322668 | 323349 | 313847 | 329291 | 355807 | 370435 | 372547 | 1.67 |
| FUELWOOD | 1247625 | 1335774 | 1352081 | 1387844 | 1414784 | 1452000 | 1481927 | 1525872 | 1568865 | 1634403 | 1673555 | 2.59 |
| SAWNWOOD CONIFEROUS | 292815 | 332487 | 339049 | 321531 | 304792 | 329492 | 338897 | 341195 | 337646 | 323525 | 307520 | - .25 |
| SAWNWOOD NONCONIFEROUS | 86595 | 97954 | 101854 | 100743 | 96880 | 103184 | 103085 | 105426 | 109123 | 113349 | 107729 | 1.38 |
| WOOD-BASED PANELS | 54533 | 87555 | 95322 | 88166 | 84614 | 95501 | 101679 | 104428 | 106081 | 101198 | 97515 | 1.84 |
| PULP FOR PAPER | 80701 | 103001 | 109310 | 112487 | 98093 | 110528 | 112044 | 116669 | 118654 | 121691 | 120673 | 1.82 |
| PAPER+PAPERBOARD | 106874 | 138895 | 148428 | 150854 | 132476 | 149087 | 153888 | 160743 | 173355 | 175145 | 174862 | 2.79 |

**WESTERN EUROPE**

**AGRICULTURAL PRODUCTS**

| | 1967 | 1972 | 1973 | 1974 | 1975 | 1976 | 1977 | 1978 | 1979 | 1980 | 1981 | ANNUAL RATE |
|---|---|---|---|---|---|---|---|---|---|---|---|---|
| TOTAL CEREALS | 131779 | 147969 | 150821 | 158844 | 146859 | 142300 | 153342 | 167814 | 164369 | 176838 | 165487 | 1.69 |
| WHEAT | 52170 | 56002 | 55355 | 62735 | 52959 | 57132 | 53568 | 63894 | 60271 | 69877 | 65098 | 2.00 |
| RICE PADDY | 1487 | 1411 | 1784 | 1729 | 1703 | 1533 | 1322 | 1650 | 1825 | 1702 | 1527 | .25 |
| BARLEY | 37950 | 44117 | 45046 | 47514 | 45665 | 42575 | 51206 | 55362 | 52830 | 56793 | 50529 | 2.54 |
| MAIZE | 17886 | 25442 | 28940 | 26299 | 27412 | 24098 | 29598 | 28202 | 32385 | 31155 | 32119 | 2.42 |
| MILLET AND SORGHUM | 265 | 453 | 523 | 497 | 498 | 475 | 602 | 761 | 644 | 614 | 686 | 4.76 |
| ROOT CROPS | 69502 | 56449 | 56385 | 58565 | 47536 | 45123 | 55026 | 53123 | 51961 | 49146 | 48303 | - 1.46 |
| POTATOES | 69342 | 56302 | 56245 | 58421 | 47397 | 44972 | 54875 | 52979 | 51816 | 48997 | 48160 | - 1.47 |
| TOTAL PULSES | 2674 | 2038 | 1962 | 2058 | 1903 | 1573 | 1676 | 1763 | 1722 | 1735 | 1722 | - 2.06 |
| CITRUS FRUIT | 4925 | 6480 | 6537 | 6666 | 6737 | 6799 | 6668 | 6211 | 6425 | 6565 | 6626 | - .13 |
| BANANAS | 409 | 406 | 480 | 426 | 385 | 362 | 422 | 430 | 435 | 505 | 475 | 1.42 |
| APPLES | 12155 | 8959 | 11591 | 9908 | 11473 | 10200 | 7695 | 10559 | 10629 | 10650 | 7737 | - 1.26 |
| VEGETABLE OILS,OIL EQUIV | 7760 | 8580 | 9337 | 8584 | 10300 | 8125 | 10256 | 10433 | 10035 | 11975 | 10723 | 2.95 |

1/ NOMINAL CATCH (LIVE WEIGHT) EXCLUDING WHALES
2/ EXCEPT FOR PULP FOR PAPER AND PAPER AND PAPERBOARD, ALL FOREST PRODUCTS ARE EXPRESSED IN THOUSAND CUBIC METRES

ANNEX TABLE 1. VOLUME OF PRODUCTION OF MAJOR AGRICULTURAL, FISHERY AND FOREST PRODUCTS

| | 1967 | 1972 | 1973 | 1974 | 1975 | 1976 | 1977 | 1978 | 1979 | 1980 | 1981 | ANNUAL RATE OF CHANGE 1972-81 PERCENT |
|---|---|---|---|---|---|---|---|---|---|---|---|---|
| | | | | | | ...THOUSAND METRIC TONS... | | | | | | |
| SOYBEANS | 9 | 9 | 26 | 59 | 47 | 58 | 78 | 85 | 102 | 65 | 119 | 23.45 |
| GROUNDNUTS IN SHELL | 20 | 16 | 18 | 16 | 19 | 17 | 19 | 20 | 21 | 19 | 19 | 1.95 |
| SUNFLOWER SEED | 299 | 666 | 842 | 692 | 858 | 774 | 1011 | 1150 | 1268 | 1125 | 1139 | 6.91 |
| RAPESEED | 937 | 1462 | 1456 | 1608 | 1334 | 1388 | 1329 | 1728 | 1688 | 2526 | 2566 | 6.18 |
| COTTONSEED | 318 | 379 | 333 | 365 | 335 | 303 | 341 | 330 | 272 | 294 | 346 | - 1.86 |
| SUGAR (CENTRIFUGAL,RAW) | 10162 | 11606 | 12262 | 11181 | 12923 | 13809 | 15435 | 15592 | 15826 | 15731 | 19048 | 5.36 |
| COTTON LINT | 167 | 192 | 171 | 187 | 169 | 152 | 178 | 170 | 142 | 164 | 191 | - .94 |
| TOBACCO | 369 | 333 | 350 | 329 | 401 | 446 | 391 | 409 | 446 | 403 | 418 | 2.76 |
| TOTAL MEAT | 19057 | 22171 | 22765 | 24682 | 24628 | 25116 | 25760 | 26653 | 27909 | 28771 | 28985 | 3.03 |
| TOTAL MILK | 117137 | 122551 | 124312 | 125486 | 126660 | 129261 | 132259 | 136242 | 139068 | 142465 | 143143 | 1.90 |
| TOTAL EGGS | 4154 | 4925 | 4826 | 4860 | 4988 | 5049 | 5142 | 5238 | 5286 | 5330 | 5428 | 1.31 |
| WOOL GREASY | 190 | 160 | 163 | 167 | 150 | 154 | 152 | 157 | 155 | 158 | 160 | - .28 |
| FISHERY PRODUCTS 1/ | | | | | | | | | | | | |
| FRESHWATER + DIADROMOUS | 170 | 165 | 172 | 175 | 178 | 179 | 178 | 193 | 201 | 244 | 170 | 2.26 |
| MARINE FISH | 10339 | 10009 | 10157 | 10142 | 9775 | 10881 | 10924 | 10264 | 10028 | 9886 | 5565 | - 3.21 |
| CRUST+ MOLLUS+ CEPHALOP | 709 | 961 | 1014 | 970 | 1034 | 960 | 967 | 974 | 919 | 1051 | 627 | - 2.41 |
| AQUATIC MAMMALS | 7 | 7 | 6 | 5 | 7 | 7 | 8 | 8 | 17 | 17 | | |
| AQUATIC ANIMALS | 4 | 2 | 5 | 5 | 2 | 4 | 3 | 5 | 2 | 1 | 1 | -12.28 |
| AQUATIC PLANTS | 119 | 134 | 120 | 147 | 117 | 109 | 185 | 190 | 180 | 176 | | |
| FOREST PRODUCTS 2/ | | | | | | | | | | | | |
| SAWLOGS CONIFEROUS | 74080 | 85502 | 96406 | 93756 | 74687 | 83972 | 87161 | 89561 | 96073 | 97713 | 90774 | .81 |
| SAWLOGS NONCONIFEROUS | 22797 | 22507 | 24973 | 23841 | 20797 | 20736 | 21885 | 24084 | 23882 | 24392 | 24456 | .66 |
| PULPWOOD+PARTICLES | 74315 | 77170 | 78597 | 88077 | 86604 | 79816 | 73403 | 75913 | 83932 | 83788 | 86010 | .43 |
| FUELWOOD | 59658 | 42338 | 38605 | 37713 | 36264 | 36247 | 34687 | 33285 | 34739 | 36353 | 37819 | - 1.29 |
| SAWNWOOD CONIFEROUS | 41923 | 49779 | 53441 | 51772 | 42943 | 47397 | 49022 | 48776 | 53617 | 54880 | 50702 | .57 |
| SAWNWOOD NONCONIFEROUS | 10905 | 12499 | 13173 | 12323 | 10525 | 11656 | 12385 | 12568 | 12724 | 12437 | 11563 | - .21 |
| WOOD-BASED PANELS | 13243 | 22404 | 25369 | 24365 | 22713 | 25170 | 25153 | 25578 | 26627 | 26845 | 25882 | 1.52 |
| PULP FOR PAPER | 19432 | 23914 | 25780 | 26442 | 22255 | 23201 | 22499 | 24268 | 26084 | 26098 | 26032 | .61 |
| PAPER+PAPERBOARD | 28143 | 36686 | 40032 | 41271 | 33366 | 38628 | 39223 | 41479 | 45174 | 44736 | 44654 | 2.25 |
| **USSR AND EASTERN EUROPE** | | | | | | | | | | | | |
| AGRICULTURAL PRODUCTS | | | | | | | | | | | | |
| TOTAL CEREALS | 200049 | 235182 | 287585 | 263322 | 208374 | 293762 | 265986 | 312619 | 250767 | 264083 | 233934 | .14 |
| WHEAT | 98063 | 111857 | 136681 | 111876 | 90542 | 126017 | 121253 | 151590 | 113476 | 127692 | 106366 | .39 |
| RICE PADDY | 1075 | 1826 | 1961 | 2096 | 2231 | 2129 | 2384 | 2271 | 2586 | 2938 | 2595 | 4.47 |
| BARLEY | 32385 | 47886 | 66993 | 68374 | 49605 | 83290 | 67038 | 78108 | 62925 | 59219 | 54330 | .61 |
| MAIZE | 22266 | 29089 | 29998 | 28228 | 27701 | 30859 | 30865 | 28977 | 32803 | 30592 | 29663 | .73 |
| MILLET AND SORGHUM | 3382 | 2229 | 4573 | 3180 | 1330 | 3514 | 2231 | 2408 | 1744 | 2078 | 1700 | - 5.67 |
| ROOT CROPS | 169233 | 149907 | 181029 | 153757 | 151141 | 152743 | 145245 | 154421 | 163134 | 111290 | 135260 | - 2.41 |
| POTATOES | 169229 | 149904 | 181025 | 153754 | 151137 | 152741 | 145242 | 154419 | 163131 | 111288 | 135256 | - 2.41 |
| TOTAL PULSES | 7954 | 7917 | 9202 | 9587 | 6153 | 9327 | 8227 | 8617 | 5048 | 7127 | 6421 | - 3.57 |
| CITRUS FRUIT | 38 | 56 | 58 | 126 | 158 | 132 | 231 | 200 | 335 | 150 | 279 | 17.92 |
| APPLES | 6139 | 6934 | 8196 | 7348 | 8744 | 10436 | 10946 | 8967 | 11301 | 8565 | 9499 | 3.34 |
| VEGETABLE OILS,OIL EQUIV | 14255 | 13113 | 16067 | 15592 | 14283 | 14824 | 15543 | 15039 | 15072 | 15328 | 15067 | .58 |
| SOYBEANS | 585 | 457 | 711 | 710 | 1111 | 834 | 862 | 1012 | 1042 | 1118 | 918 | 6.97 |
| GROUNDNUTS IN SHELL | 3 | 3 | 3 | 3 | 5 | 4 | 4 | 5 | 5 | 6 | 8 | 10.02 |
| SUNFLOWER SEED | 7903 | 6546 | 8768 | 7978 | 6328 | 6652 | 7385 | 6784 | 7196 | 6354 | 6566 | - 1.46 |
| RAPESEED | 1030 | 834 | 966 | 983 | 1312 | 1531 | 1285 | 1306 | 574 | 1224 | 1108 | .81 |
| COTTONSEED | 3693 | 4495 | 4714 | 5170 | 4843 | 5066 | 5364 | 5209 | 5617 | 6102 | 5905 | 3.05 |
| SUGAR (CENTRIFUGAL,RAW) | 13464 | 12746 | 13758 | 11817 | 12112 | 11597 | 13881 | 13641 | 12411 | 10974 | 10939 | - 1.31 |
| TEA | 57 | 71 | 75 | 81 | 86 | 92 | 106 | 111 | 118 | 130 | 135 | 7.79 |
| COTTON LINT | 2067 | 2382 | 2496 | 2497 | 2667 | 2597 | 2708 | 2743 | 2515 | 2817 | 2763 | 1.43 |
| JUTE AND SIMILAR FIBRES | 53 | 56 | 45 | 39 | 36 | 49 | 47 | 44 | 48 | 52 | 45 | .37 |
| TOBACCO | 540 | 611 | 616 | 606 | 646 | 712 | 608 | 567 | 622 | 544 | 595 | - .92 |
| TOTAL MEAT | 17694 | 21220 | 21517 | 23328 | 24150 | 22309 | 23869 | 25089 | 25444 | 25030 | 24835 | 1.89 |
| TOTAL MILK | 113017 | 119028 | 125523 | 129953 | 128577 | 127494 | 134455 | 135187 | 133979 | 131156 | 128039 | .80 |
| TOTAL EGGS | 3099 | 4105 | 4341 | 4642 | 4823 | 4768 | 5172 | 5395 | 5484 | 5601 | 5776 | 3.77 |
| WOOL GREASY | 483 | 513 | 527 | 558 | 566 | 534 | 567 | 578 | 588 | 578 | 571 | 1.21 |
| FISHERY PRODUCTS 1/ | | | | | | | | | | | | |
| FRESHWATER + DIADROMOUS | 1164 | 1177 | 1200 | 1072 | 1338 | 1068 | 1088 | 1037 | 1143 | 1085 | 82 | -14.10 |
| MARINE FISH | 5239 | 7597 | 8505 | 9393 | 9997 | 10333 | 9223 | 8725 | 8625 | 9044 | 323 | -16.09 |
| CRUST+ MOLLUS+ CEPHALOP | 136 | 102 | 105 | 131 | 158 | 109 | 248 | 219 | 491 | 512 | 2 | - 8.19 |
| AQUATIC ANIMALS | | 5 | 5 | | | | | | | | | |
| FOREST PRODUCTS 2/ | | | | | | | | | | | | |
| SAWLOGS CONIFEROUS | 154636 | 167416 | 164877 | 163360 | 171306 | 166669 | 164533 | 158643 | 154849 | 155724 | 155368 | - .95 |
| SAWLOGS NONCONIFEROUS | 33160 | 35650 | 35065 | 34896 | 36349 | 35247 | 35079 | 34599 | 33545 | 33594 | 33426 | - .74 |
| PULPWOOD+PARTICLES | 37373 | 47240 | 59446 | 62358 | 58856 | 57328 | 57068 | 55415 | 54820 | 55870 | 55658 | .13 |
| FUELWOOD | 113072 | 101333 | 98240 | 98601 | 95793 | 96373 | 94107 | 91309 | 90531 | 91647 | 92793 | - 1.13 |

1/ NOMINAL CATCH (LIVE WEIGHT) EXCLUDING WHALES
2/ EXCEPT FOR PULP FOR PAPER AND PAPER AND PAPERBOARD, ALL FOREST PRODUCTS ARE EXPRESSED IN THOUSAND CUBIC METRES

ANNEX TABLE 1. VOLUME OF PRODUCTION OF MAJOR AGRICULTURAL, FISHERY AND FOREST PRODUCTS

| | 1967 | 1972 | 1973 | 1974 | 1975 | 1976 | 1977 | 1978 | 1979 | 1980 | 1981 | ANNUAL RATE OF CHANGE 1972-81 PERCENT |
|---|---|---|---|---|---|---|---|---|---|---|---|---|
| | | | | | ......THOUSAND METRIC TONS...... | | | | | | | |
| SAWNWOOD CONIFEROUS | 110174 | 119356 | 117331 | 116371 | 117612 | 114640 | 110883 | 108564 | 102847 | 101476 | 100933 | - 2.05 |
| SAWNWOOD NONCONIFEROUS | 19267 | 20772 | 20524 | 20382 | 20492 | 20031 | 19507 | 19234 | 18543 | 18106 | 17904 | - 1.74 |
| WOOD-BASED PANELS | 7861 | 11274 | 12499 | 13731 | 14897 | 15565 | 16552 | 17125 | 17019 | 17476 | 16919 | 4.68 |
| PULP FOR PAPER | 7064 | 9048 | 9456 | 10192 | 10546 | 11094 | 11348 | 11654 | 11041 | 11105 | 11034 | 2.23 |
| PAPER+PAPERBOARD | 9115 | 11648 | 12288 | 12814 | 13495 | 14079 | 14428 | 14520 | 13989 | 14103 | 14041 | 2.04 |

**NORTH AMERICA DEVELOPED**

AGRICULTURAL PRODUCTS

| | 1967 | 1972 | 1973 | 1974 | 1975 | 1976 | 1977 | 1978 | 1979 | 1980 | 1981 | |
|---|---|---|---|---|---|---|---|---|---|---|---|---|
| TOTAL CEREALS | 238246 | 263644 | 274332 | 235557 | 286555 | 303124 | 308339 | 318215 | 338921 | 310954 | 384642 | 3.97 |
| WHEAT | 57168 | 56596 | 62720 | 61800 | 74967 | 82068 | 75533 | 69468 | 75265 | 83776 | 100828 | 4.90 |
| RICE PADDY | 4054 | 3875 | 4208 | 5098 | 5826 | 5246 | 4501 | 6040 | 5985 | 6629 | 8408 | 6.84 |
| BARLEY | 13644 | 20466 | 19312 | 15293 | 17765 | 18852 | 21112 | 20289 | 16794 | 19117 | 24138 | 1.46 |
| MAIZE | 125341 | 144262 | 146845 | 122040 | 152006 | 163522 | 169431 | 188646 | 206638 | 174221 | 215055 | 5.04 |
| MILLET AND SORGHUM | 19186 | 20355 | 23451 | 15817 | 19161 | 18055 | 19837 | 18575 | 20546 | 14712 | 22360 | - .67 |
| ROOT CROPS | 16618 | 15869 | 16220 | 18652 | 17398 | 19179 | 19181 | 19733 | 18905 | 16746 | 18574 | 1.27 |
| POTATOES | 16002 | 15312 | 15665 | 18042 | 16810 | 18573 | 18638 | 19134 | 18296 | 16247 | 17993 | 1.32 |
| TOTAL PULSES | 975 | 1115 | 1015 | 1303 | 1146 | 1115 | 946 | 1293 | 1278 | 1647 | 1848 | 4.99 |
| CITRUS FRUIT | 10374 | 11031 | 12604 | 12167 | 13237 | 13415 | 13827 | 12932 | 12092 | 14954 | 13754 | 1.90 |
| BANANAS | 4 | 3 | 3 | 3 | 3 | 2 | 3 | 3 | 3 | 2 | 3 | - 2.51 |
| APPLES | 2898 | 3059 | 3216 | 3391 | 3876 | 3345 | 3468 | 3898 | 4129 | 4557 | 3919 | 3.52 |
| VEGETABLE OILS,OIL EQUIV | 32654 | 44210 | 51539 | 41646 | 50733 | 42721 | 60074 | 63687 | 77924 | 59986 | 67687 | 5.64 |
| SOYBEANS | 26795 | 34956 | 42514 | 33383 | 42507 | 35293 | 48678 | 51375 | 62393 | 49485 | 55043 | 5.71 |
| GROUNDNUTS IN SHELL | 1124 | 1485 | 1576 | 1664 | 1745 | 1696 | 1690 | 1793 | 1800 | 1047 | 1809 | - .37 |
| SUNFLOWER SEED | 120 | 411 | 394 | 280 | 571 | 487 | 1409 | 1937 | 3627 | 1914 | 2273 | 30.55 |
| RAPESEED | 561 | 1300 | 1207 | 1164 | 1840 | 838 | 1974 | 3498 | 3412 | 2484 | 1838 | 10.40 |
| COTTONSEED | 2912 | 4892 | 4550 | 4091 | 2919 | 3739 | 5009 | 3873 | 5242 | 4056 | 5803 | 1.90 |
| SUGAR (CENTRIFUGAL,RAW) | 4934 | 5898 | 5329 | 5048 | 6443 | 6170 | 5403 | 5482 | 5167 | 5437 | 5748 | - .36 |
| COFFEE GREEN | 2 | 1 | 1 | 1 | 1 | 1 | 1 | 1 | 1 | 1 | 1 | - 4.78 |
| COTTON LINT | 1621 | 2984 | 2825 | 2513 | 1807 | 2304 | 3133 | 2364 | 3185 | 2422 | 3406 | 1.47 |
| TOBACCO | 989 | 878 | 907 | 1019 | 1096 | 1051 | 973 | 1034 | 771 | 917 | 1051 | .03 |
| TOTAL MEAT | 21766 | 23983 | 23000 | 24482 | 23870 | 25819 | 26015 | 25865 | 26152 | 27036 | 27434 | 1.79 |
| TOTAL MILK | 62123 | 62468 | 60052 | 60062 | 60095 | 62205 | 63376 | 62708 | 63828 | 66218 | 68186 | 1.17 |
| TOTAL EGGS | 4391 | 4404 | 4214 | 4191 | 4128 | 4115 | 4124 | 4289 | 4413 | 4459 | 4459 | .54 |
| WOOL GREASY | 105 | 81 | 73 | 65 | 55 | 51 | 50 | 48 | 49 | 50 | 52 | - 5.07 |

FISHERY PRODUCTS 1/

| | 1967 | 1972 | 1973 | 1974 | 1975 | 1976 | 1977 | 1978 | 1979 | 1980 | 1981 | |
|---|---|---|---|---|---|---|---|---|---|---|---|---|
| FRESHWATER + DIADROMOUS | 319 | 319 | 338 | 309 | 264 | 329 | 356 | 396 | 434 | 476 | 484 | 5.71 |
| MARINE FISH | 2270 | 2488 | 2485 | 2449 | 2491 | 2685 | 2579 | 3030 | 3102 | 3075 | 1037 | - 2.78 |
| CRUST+ MOLLUS+ CEPHALOP | 1057 | 1022 | 1013 | 1057 | 1075 | 1130 | 1272 | 1347 | 1376 | 1350 | 193 | - 6.36 |
| AQUATIC MAMMALS | 7 | 4 | | | | | | | | | | |
| AQUATIC ANIMALS | 8 | 2 | 4 | 6 | 6 | 9 | 9 | 11 | 10 | 2 | | |
| AQUATIC PLANTS | 47 | 182 | 180 | 224 | 198 | 189 | 195 | 196 | 195 | 191 | 28 | - 9.88 |

FOREST PRODUCTS 2/

| | 1967 | 1972 | 1973 | 1974 | 1975 | 1976 | 1977 | 1978 | 1979 | 1980 | 1981 | |
|---|---|---|---|---|---|---|---|---|---|---|---|---|
| SAWLOGS CONIFEROUS | 214821 | 239166 | 255365 | 237683 | 222108 | 267372 | 278553 | 299879 | 298266 | 263149 | 223000 | 1.01 |
| SAWLOGS NONCONIFEROUS | 39664 | 41002 | 41472 | 37932 | 32125 | 34953 | 36846 | 40908 | 42727 | 42586 | 40345 | .86 |
| PULPWOOD+PARTICLES | 126181 | 142366 | 149291 | 165000 | 132931 | 139779 | 135003 | 144889 | 157282 | 165353 | 165353 | 1.25 |
| FUELWOOD | 29202 | 18693 | 19551 | 20419 | 21790 | 22842 | 34520 | 49985 | 69950 | 93881 | 104445 | 24.03 |
| SAWNWOOD CONIFEROUS | 89130 | 104867 | 109561 | 96191 | 87609 | 106334 | 113629 | 116369 | 113841 | 100326 | 91596 | - .04 |
| SAWNWOOD NONCONIFEROUS | 18859 | 17346 | 17896 | 17626 | 14831 | 16373 | 16614 | 17282 | 18432 | 18650 | 17483 | .64 |
| WOOD-BASED PANELS | 23679 | 34656 | 36275 | 31038 | 28739 | 33860 | 37274 | 37288 | 36649 | 31026 | 29815 | - .45 |
| PULP FOR PAPER | 44493 | 55448 | 58004 | 59139 | 49977 | 59449 | 60716 | 63280 | 63106 | 64451 | 64451 | 1.92 |
| PAPER+PAPERBOARD | 50821 | 62859 | 64974 | 64617 | 54963 | 62913 | 64946 | 66682 | 72393 | 72847 | 72847 | 2.02 |

**OCEANIA DEVELOPED**

AGRICULTURAL PRODUCTS

| | 1967 | 1972 | 1973 | 1974 | 1975 | 1976 | 1977 | 1978 | 1979 | 1980 | 1981 | |
|---|---|---|---|---|---|---|---|---|---|---|---|---|
| TOTAL CEREALS | 10385 | 11672 | 17795 | 16974 | 18419 | 18374 | 15312 | 26084 | 24140 | 17163 | 24582 | 5.65 |
| WHEAT | 7894 | 6979 | 12363 | 11572 | 12162 | 12213 | 9724 | 18415 | 16483 | 11162 | 16740 | 6.21 |
| RICE PADDY | 214 | 248 | 309 | 409 | 388 | 417 | 530 | 490 | 692 | 613 | 728 | 11.56 |
| BARLEY | 969 | 2062 | 2655 | 2755 | 3442 | 3132 | 2655 | 4265 | 3967 | 2940 | 3834 | 5.35 |
| MAIZE | 208 | 330 | 257 | 194 | 291 | 316 | 355 | 305 | 348 | 307 | 360 | 3.21 |
| MILLET AND SORGHUM | 340 | 1254 | 1044 | 1096 | 923 | 1151 | 975 | 747 | 1162 | 936 | 1231 | - .87 |
| ROOT CROPS | 883 | 1074 | 1003 | 888 | 1007 | 984 | 1037 | 1099 | 1070 | 1196 | 1131 | 1.80 |
| POTATOES | 876 | 1064 | 991 | 876 | 997 | 975 | 1028 | 1081 | 1059 | 1177 | 1115 | 1.75 |
| TOTAL PULSES | 53 | 129 | 93 | 127 | 157 | 189 | 106 | 120 | 175 | 218 | 249 | 7.62 |
| CITRUS FRUIT | 274 | 435 | 401 | 434 | 458 | 428 | 461 | 495 | 510 | 564 | 504 | 2.97 |
| BANANAS | 131 | 124 | 125 | 118 | 103 | 115 | 98 | 113 | 125 | 124 | 125 | .26 |
| APPLES | 475 | 510 | 574 | 487 | 527 | 447 | 447 | 444 | 525 | 510 | 529 | - .39 |
| VEGETABLE OILS,OIL EQUIV | 109 | 355 | 278 | 308 | 332 | 246 | 289 | 455 | 530 | 442 | 474 | 6.04 |
| SOYBEANS | 1 | 34 | 38 | 64 | 74 | 45 | 55 | 77 | 99 | 82 | 73 | 9.45 |
| GROUNDNUTS IN SHELL | 42 | 46 | 38 | 29 | 32 | 35 | 32 | 39 | 62 | 39 | 43 | 2.32 |

1/ NOMINAL CATCH (LIVE WEIGHT) EXCLUDING WHALES
2/ EXCEPT FOR PULP FOR PAPER AND PAPER AND PAPERBOARD, ALL FOREST PRODUCTS ARE EXPRESSED IN THOUSAND CUBIC METRES

ANNEX TABLE 1. VOLUME OF PRODUCTION OF MAJOR AGRICULTURAL, FISHERY AND FOREST PRODUCTS

| | 1967 | 1972 | 1973 | 1974 | 1975 | 1976 | 1977 | 1978 | 1979 | 1980 | 1981 | ANNUAL RATE OF CHANGE 1972-81 PERCENT |
|---|---|---|---|---|---|---|---|---|---|---|---|---|
| | | | | | ...THOUSAND METRIC TONS... | | | | | | | |
| SUNFLOWER SEED | 2 | 148 | 102 | 84 | 113 | 80 | 75 | 158 | 186 | 142 | 139 | 4.11 |
| RAPESEED | | 25 | 11 | 9 | 12 | 9 | 16 | 24 | 41 | 18 | 18 | 6.61 |
| COTTONSEED | 30 | 73 | 53 | 50 | 54 | 41 | 46 | 72 | 87 | 136 | 161 | 11.22 |
| SUGAR (CENTRIFUGAL,RAW) | 2372 | 2835 | 2526 | 2848 | 2855 | 3296 | 3318 | 2902 | 2963 | 3329 | 3434 | 2.40 |
| COTTON LINT | 17 | 44 | 31 | 31 | 33 | 25 | 28 | 44 | 53 | 83 | 99 | 11.50 |
| TOBACCO | 17 | 19 | 20 | 20 | 18 | 18 | 19 | 19 | 18 | 19 | 17 | - 1.18 |
| TOTAL MEAT | 2584 | 3563 | 3638 | 3185 | 3519 | 4030 | 4089 | 4298 | 4096 | 3797 | 3823 | 1.71 |
| TOTAL MILK | 14033 | 13853 | 12973 | 12561 | 12819 | 13025 | 12476 | 11348 | 12232 | 12332 | 11904 | - 1.36 |
| TOTAL EGGS | 218 | 267 | 265 | 259 | 268 | 263 | 264 | 274 | 267 | 274 | 289 | .72 |
| WOOL GREASY | 1121 | 1202 | 1044 | 986 | 1088 | 1066 | 1005 | 988 | 1026 | 1066 | 1081 | - .58 |
| **FISHERY PRODUCTS 1/** | | | | | | | | | | | | |
| FRESHWATER + DIADROMOUS | 1 | 4 | 4 | 4 | 5 | 4 | 5 | 5 | 5 | 2 | 2 | - 4.05 |
| MARINE FISH | 80 | 93 | 116 | 122 | 97 | 110 | 131 | 146 | 152 | 156 | 62 | .58 |
| CRUST+ MOLLUS+ CEPHALOP | 70 | 79 | 70 | 77 | 70 | 72 | 74 | 72 | 83 | 75 | 65 | - .45 |
| AQUATIC PLANTS | | 6 | 6 | 4 | | 1 | | | | | | |
| **FOREST PRODUCTS 2/** | | | | | | | | | | | | |
| SAWLOGS CONIFEROUS | 6413 | 7912 | 8339 | 6537 | 6356 | 7595 | 7178 | 6913 | 7021 | 8443 | 8598 | .84 |
| SAWLOGS NONCONIFEROUS | 7553 | 6984 | 6902 | 7240 | 6490 | 6631 | 6518 | 6336 | 5846 | 5881 | 5986 | - 2.20 |
| PULPWOOD+PARTICLES | 2727 | 3640 | 5374 | 5006 | 7613 | 7191 | 8596 | 8335 | 8330 | 9890 | 10266 | 10.58 |
| FUELWOOD | 3050 | 2765 | 2447 | 2894 | 1912 | 1295 | 1292 | 1277 | 1077 | 1077 | 1227 | -10.99 |
| SAWNWOOD CONIFEROUS | 2307 | 2515 | 2836 | 2882 | 2821 | 3067 | 2917 | 2559 | 2743 | 3101 | 3371 | 1.63 |
| SAWNWOOD NONCONIFEROUS | 2505 | 2497 | 2482 | 2533 | 2505 | 2430 | 2340 | 2063 | 1986 | 4096 | 2144 | .18 |
| WOOD-BASED PANELS | 574 | 748 | 933 | 988 | 920 | 1054 | 1043 | 1059 | 1073 | 1166 | 1215 | 4.18 |
| PULP FOR PAPER | 842 | 1127 | 1326 | 1505 | 1524 | 1660 | 1712 | 1695 | 1693 | 1819 | 1909 | 4.90 |
| PAPER+PAPERBOARD | 1208 | 1546 | 1686 | 1732 | 1697 | 1761 | 1890 | 1867 | 1942 | 2104 | 2151 | 3.36 |

**AFRICA DEVELOPING**

**AGRICULTURAL PRODUCTS**

| | 1967 | 1972 | 1973 | 1974 | 1975 | 1976 | 1977 | 1978 | 1979 | 1980 | 1981 | ARC |
|---|---|---|---|---|---|---|---|---|---|---|---|---|
| TOTAL CEREALS | 40226 | 45293 | 39408 | 45930 | 44607 | 47987 | 43244 | 46678 | 44387 | 46242 | 46647 | .76 |
| WHEAT | 4265 | 5877 | 4672 | 4944 | 4705 | 5696 | 3817 | 4735 | 4556 | 5255 | 4341 | - 1.62 |
| RICE PADDY | 4410 | 4803 | 4977 | 5383 | 5561 | 5504 | 5495 | 5459 | 5752 | 6037 | 6189 | 2.40 |
| BARLEY | 2636 | 4133 | 2634 | 3611 | 2862 | 4646 | 2468 | 3660 | 3450 | 4182 | 2929 | .01 |
| MAIZE | 12191 | 13916 | 12013 | 14298 | 14492 | 14584 | 14097 | 14447 | 12850 | 12943 | 14757 | .29 |
| MILLET AND SORGHUM | 15279 | 15058 | 13512 | 16138 | 15732 | 16050 | 16015 | 16959 | 16296 | 16241 | 16827 | 1.56 |
| ROOT CROPS | 60797 | 68204 | 70374 | 73179 | 75019 | 75912 | 75712 | 77199 | 78217 | 80298 | 82012 | 1.83 |
| POTATOES | 1571 | 2065 | 2181 | 2314 | 2567 | 2577 | 2544 | 2890 | 3048 | 3162 | 3173 | 5.09 |
| CASSAVA | 36166 | 39228 | 39954 | 41310 | 42734 | 43466 | 43766 | 44382 | 44851 | 45840 | 47253 | 1.94 |
| TOTAL PULSES | 3675 | 4316 | 4102 | 4503 | 4779 | 5050 | 4396 | 4638 | 4579 | 4564 | 4497 | .59 |
| CITRUS FRUIT | 1989 | 2416 | 2599 | 2616 | 2402 | 2384 | 2475 | 2687 | 2493 | 2581 | 2647 | .55 |
| BANANAS | 3055 | 3334 | 3502 | 3801 | 3717 | 3942 | 3894 | 3941 | 3973 | 4067 | 4122 | 2.04 |
| APPLES | 41 | 43 | 47 | 49 | 56 | 53 | 58 | 57 | 61 | 68 | 68 | 4.88 |
| VEGETABLE OILS,OIL EQUIV | 10449 | 10555 | 10429 | 10864 | 11618 | 11182 | 10176 | 10336 | 10330 | 10666 | 11066 | - .07 |
| SOYBEANS | 65 | 81 | 83 | 85 | 95 | 112 | 135 | 136 | 166 | 182 | 208 | 11.95 |
| GROUNDNUTS IN SHELL | 4861 | 4095 | 3589 | 3971 | 4295 | 4479 | 3388 | 3830 | 3572 | 3328 | 3982 | - 1.16 |
| SUNFLOWER SEED | 31 | 79 | 78 | 84 | 100 | 122 | 148 | 156 | 149 | 148 | 145 | 9.08 |
| RAPESEED | 20 | 21 | 21 | 21 | 21 | 22 | 22 | 22 | 21 | 22 | 22 | .40 |
| COTTONSEED | 847 | 1050 | 1019 | 989 | 871 | 930 | 960 | 918 | 878 | 905 | 853 | - 1.86 |
| COPRA | 143 | 143 | 152 | 149 | 144 | 163 | 155 | 158 | 161 | 172 | 177 | 2.09 |
| PALM KERNELS | 620 | 691 | 637 | 744 | 730 | 706 | 703 | 599 | 707 | 731 | 735 | .41 |
| SUGAR (CENTRIFUGAL,RAW) | 2241 | 2883 | 2928 | 2934 | 2742 | 3122 | 3066 | 3390 | 3541 | 3613 | 3835 | 3.45 |
| COFFEE GREEN | 1085 | 1296 | 1384 | 1252 | 1312 | 1186 | 1236 | 1072 | 1175 | 1156 | 1254 | - 1.47 |
| COCOA BEANS | 981 | 1035 | 963 | 1021 | 998 | 854 | 917 | 890 | 1016 | 986 | 1015 | - .18 |
| TEA | 84 | 149 | 155 | 152 | 151 | 159 | 194 | 201 | 203 | 188 | 191 | 3.74 |
| COTTON LINT | 433 | 542 | 536 | 525 | 470 | 503 | 514 | 495 | 474 | 500 | 470 | - 1.27 |
| JUTE AND SIMILAR FIBRES | 16 | 12 | 12 | 11 | 11 | 8 | 7 | 8 | 8 | 8 | 8 | - 5.32 |
| SISAL | 392 | 332 | 330 | 350 | 256 | 218 | 204 | 175 | 168 | 184 | 176 | - 8.50 |
| TOBACCO | 175 | 185 | 193 | 195 | 221 | 250 | 229 | 224 | 260 | 282 | 219 | 3.45 |
| NATURAL RUBBER | 166 | 221 | 229 | 241 | 221 | 202 | 203 | 203 | 205 | 198 | 197 | - 1.88 |
| TOTAL MEAT | 3336 | 3662 | 3663 | 3660 | 3781 | 3924 | 4075 | 4232 | 4352 | 4479 | 4615 | 2.91 |
| TOTAL MILK | 6344 | 6768 | 6637 | 6649 | 7028 | 7292 | 7523 | 7832 | 7884 | 7909 | 8144 | 2.52 |
| TOTAL EGGS | 358 | 407 | 419 | 438 | 465 | 501 | 532 | 555 | 590 | 624 | 655 | 5.70 |
| WOOL GREASY | 57 | 60 | 66 | 63 | 63 | 67 | 58 | 60 | 62 | 64 | 65 | .16 |
| **FISHERY PRODUCTS 1/** | | | | | | | | | | | | |
| FRESHWATER + DIADROMOUS | 878 | 1221 | 1260 | 1255 | 1293 | 1322 | 1400 | 1352 | 1366 | 1421 | 519 | - 3.71 |
| MARINE FISH | 1228 | 2023 | 2012 | 1884 | 1623 | 1593 | 1658 | 1715 | 1609 | 1644 | 608 | - 7.48 |
| CRUST+ MOLLUS+ CEPHALOP | 23 | 43 | 44 | 57 | 56 | 63 | 57 | 71 | 62 | 81 | 17 | - 2.00 |
| AQUATIC ANIMALS | 1 | 1 | 1 | 1 | 1 | 1 | 1 | 1 | 1 | 1 | 1 | - 4.67 |
| AQUATIC PLANTS | 4 | 6 | 7 | 5 | 6 | 51 | 5 | 5 | 5 | 5 | | |

1/ NOMINAL CATCH (LIVE WEIGHT) EXCLUDING WHALES
2/ EXCEPT FOR PULP FOR PAPER AND PAPER AND PAPERBOARD, ALL FOREST PRODUCTS ARE EXPRESSED IN THOUSAND CUBIC METRES

ANNEX TABLE 1. VOLUME OF PRODUCTION OF MAJOR AGRICULTURAL, FISHERY AND FOREST PRODUCTS

| | 1967 | 1972 | 1973 | 1974 | 1975 | 1976 | 1977 | 1978 | 1979 | 1980 | 1981 | ANNUAL RATE OF CHANGE 1972-81 PERCENT |
|---|---|---|---|---|---|---|---|---|---|---|---|---|
| | | | | | ....THOUSAND METRIC TONS.... | | | | | | | |
| **FOREST PRODUCTS 2/** | | | | | | | | | | | | |
| SAWLOGS CONIFEROUS | 737 | 1014 | 1042 | 1051 | 1046 | 1085 | 1240 | 1169 | 913 | 1252 | 1271 | 1.88 |
| SAWLOGS NONCONIFEROUS | 11672 | 14982 | 16703 | 14409 | 13707 | 15513 | 16474 | 17240 | 17974 | 19322 | 19461 | 3.22 |
| PULPWOOD+PARTICLES | 785 | 1428 | 1375 | 1498 | 2137 | 2213 | 2255 | 2402 | 1934 | 1900 | 1909 | 4.03 |
| FUELWOOD | 220865 | 251744 | 259501 | 266597 | 273916 | 281728 | 290509 | 298964 | 307380 | 316829 | 326147 | 2.91 |
| SAWNWOOD CONIFEROUS | 338 | 411 | 405 | 431 | 456 | 517 | 542 | 482 | 508 | 537 | 568 | 3.66 |
| SAWNWOOD NONCONIFEROUS | 2127 | 2586 | 3048 | 3391 | 3537 | 3465 | 3677 | 4437 | 4627 | 5408 | 5395 | 8.15 |
| WOOD-BASED PANELS | 368 | 695 | 776 | 796 | 648 | 740 | 822 | 845 | 861 | 910 | 894 | 2.87 |
| PULP FOR PAPER | 150 | 211 | 244 | 251 | 262 | 292 | 281 | 297 | 322 | 611 | 652 | 11.64 |
| PAPER+PAPERBOARD | 128 | 184 | 186 | 196 | 217 | 219 | 258 | 273 | 333 | 339 | 344 | 8.43 |
| **LATIN AMERICA** | | | | | | | | | | | | |
| **AGRICULTURAL PRODUCTS** | | | | | | | | | | | | |
| TOTAL CEREALS | 64186 | 67892 | 74854 | 78388 | 80593 | 86263 | 86143 | 85360 | 84299 | 89161 | 103777 | 3.44 |
| WHEAT | 11804 | 12433 | 12094 | 13474 | 14971 | 19336 | 11541 | 14969 | 15084 | 14840 | 14779 | 1.86 |
| RICE PADDY | 10408 | 10917 | 11792 | 12241 | 14059 | 15426 | 15108 | 13426 | 14415 | 16444 | 15491 | 3.79 |
| BARLEY | 1358 | 1778 | 1665 | 1249 | 1556 | 1883 | 1376 | 1716 | 1330 | 1395 | 1263 | - 2.41 |
| MAIZE | 35127 | 35121 | 37842 | 39561 | 38298 | 37386 | 43738 | 40360 | 40277 | 45475 | 55213 | 3.55 |
| MILLET AND SORGHUM | 4100 | 6035 | 9891 | 10780 | 10510 | 10984 | 13242 | 13582 | 11974 | 9919 | 16006 | 6.43 |
| ROOT CROPS | 44845 | 48751 | 45060 | 44973 | 45598 | 45053 | 45920 | 46434 | 45482 | 43648 | 46590 | - .30 |
| POTATOES | 8263 | 8385 | 8583 | 9969 | 9260 | 9741 | 10140 | 10935 | 11013 | 10256 | 11669 | 3.24 |
| CASSAVA | 31888 | 35528 | 32034 | 30928 | 32106 | 31325 | 31985 | 31641 | 30970 | 29964 | 31369 | - .97 |
| TOTAL PULSES | 4785 | 4886 | 4547 | 4653 | 4712 | 3913 | 4600 | 4722 | 4592 | 4501 | 5526 | .69 |
| CITRUS FRUIT | 7368 | 9227 | 10422 | 11117 | 11883 | 12796 | 13419 | 13859 | 14366 | 16882 | 17559 | 6.87 |
| BANANAS | 13840 | 17623 | 17254 | 17402 | 17030 | 17701 | 18454 | 18249 | 17890 | 18737 | 19016 | 1.00 |
| APPLES | 908 | 978 | 680 | 1297 | 1090 | 1207 | 1328 | 1439 | 1630 | 1686 | 1744 | 8.61 |
| VEGETABLE OILS,OIL EQUIV | 10469 | 13497 | 15716 | 18970 | 20295 | 21507 | 25289 | 23662 | 26488 | 30549 | 29931 | 8.93 |
| SOYBEANS | 969 | 3886 | 6100 | 9180 | 11410 | 12643 | 14960 | 12927 | 15476 | 20000 | 20320 | 17.32 |
| GROUNDNUTS IN SHELL | 1293 | 1445 | 1244 | 979 | 1049 | 1058 | 1159 | 1014 | 1387 | 1052 | 888 | - 2.29 |
| SUNFLOWER SEED | 1229 | 923 | 970 | 1033 | 804 | 1192 | 955 | 1717 | 1550 | 1777 | 1378 | 7.50 |
| RAPESEED | 67 | 85 | 46 | 41 | 68 | 111 | 91 | 61 | 75 | 93 | 59 | 2.51 |
| COTTONSEED | 2774 | 2927 | 3246 | 3428 | 2771 | 2356 | 3375 | 3220 | 3116 | 2910 | 2804 | - .50 |
| COPRA | 264 | 236 | 232 | 220 | 224 | 229 | 239 | 242 | 212 | 243 | 236 | .26 |
| PALM KERNELS | 242 | 280 | 277 | 291 | 279 | 303 | 321 | 314 | 349 | 348 | 356 | 3.14 |
| SUGAR (CENTRIFUGAL,RAW) | 20047 | 21032 | 23281 | 24518 | 23817 | 25966 | 27282 | 26934 | 26668 | 26435 | 26622 | 2.36 |
| COFFEE GREEN | 2909 | 2909 | 2446 | 3136 | 2858 | 1918 | 2680 | 3103 | 3271 | 2946 | 4020 | 3.08 |
| COCOA BEANS | 373 | 431 | 397 | 476 | 497 | 434 | 459 | 519 | 569 | 555 | 544 | 3.41 |
| TEA | 23 | 41 | 40 | 44 | 51 | 44 | 52 | 39 | 44 | 51 | 39 | .36 |
| COTTON LINT | 1585 | 1661 | 1839 | 1954 | 1565 | 1339 | 1893 | 1809 | 1740 | 1598 | 1566 | - .79 |
| JUTE AND SIMILAR FIBRES | 70 | 81 | 113 | 90 | 108 | 127 | 114 | 100 | 108 | 107 | 123 | 2.42 |
| SISAL | 220 | 328 | 293 | 323 | 340 | 187 | 241 | 218 | 251 | 254 | 263 | - 3.18 |
| TOBACCO | 519 | 573 | 567 | 670 | 677 | 727 | 740 | 768 | 796 | 724 | 663 | 2.62 |
| NATURAL RUBBER | 27 | 32 | 28 | 24 | 25 | 26 | 30 | 31 | 33 | 36 | 38 | 3.50 |
| TOTAL MEAT | 9413 | 10661 | 10881 | 11189 | 11736 | 12542 | 13169 | 13700 | 13905 | 14236 | 14749 | 3.96 |
| TOTAL MILK | 23170 | 27039 | 27203 | 28856 | 31061 | 32874 | 32163 | 33178 | 34191 | 33789 | 34105 | 2.85 |
| TOTAL EGGS | 1178 | 1529 | 1627 | 1696 | 1805 | 1877 | 1953 | 2129 | 2304 | 2549 | 2671 | 6.40 |
| WOOL GREASY | 358 | 309 | 303 | 300 | 300 | 298 | 315 | 301 | 317 | 323 | 326 | .77 |
| **FISHERY PRODUCTS 1/** | | | | | | | | | | | | |
| FRESHWATER + DIADROMOUS | 235 | 199 | 200 | 257 | 272 | 247 | 267 | 297 | 264 | 311 | 239 | 3.20 |
| MARINE FISH | 12053 | 6843 | 4559 | 6806 | 5940 | 7528 | 6074 | 7993 | 9049 | 8691 | 5387 | 2.74 |
| CRUST+ MOLLUS+ CEPHALOP | 352 | 457 | 438 | 421 | 427 | 488 | 475 | 580 | 633 | 552 | 299 | .42 |
| AQUATIC MAMMALS | 7 | | | | | | | | | | | |
| AQUATIC ANIMALS | 24 | 60 | 49 | 38 | 51 | 25 | 61 | 52 | 54 | 50 | 20 | - 4.20 |
| AQUATIC PLANTS | 93 | 79 | 81 | 90 | 80 | 92 | 112 | 90 | 128 | 124 | 57 | 1.50 |
| **FOREST PRODUCTS 2/** | | | | | | | | | | | | |
| SAWLOGS CONIFEROUS | 12991 | 16815 | 16359 | 16315 | 19171 | 21673 | 23837 | 22865 | 25661 | 31745 | 30343 | 8.09 |
| SAWLOGS NONCONIFEROUS | 15499 | 18706 | 19604 | 19933 | 21948 | 23044 | 23700 | 23913 | 26142 | 29061 | 28579 | 5.10 |
| PULPWOOD+PARTICLES | 6223 | 9056 | 9080 | 9866 | 11556 | 12913 | 13667 | 19804 | 26631 | 29264 | 29115 | 16.60 |
| FUELWOOD | 182345 | 206814 | 212354 | 217000 | 221721 | 228279 | 234433 | 241014 | 249046 | 254566 | 260207 | 2.64 |
| SAWNWOOD CONIFEROUS | 6229 | 7692 | 7063 | 7430 | 9059 | 9748 | 10541 | 11289 | 12149 | 11443 | 10989 | 6.11 |
| SAWNWOOD NONCONIFEROUS | 7271 | 8110 | 8477 | 8807 | 9747 | 10854 | 11725 | 11770 | 12340 | 13832 | 13832 | 6.61 |
| WOOD-BASED PANELS | 1199 | 2400 | 2536 | 2629 | 2795 | 3132 | 3377 | 3521 | 3723 | 4316 | 4403 | 7.34 |
| PULP FOR PAPER | 1336 | 1977 | 2185 | 2423 | 2299 | 2701 | 3068 | 3520 | 3695 | 5017 | 4999 | 11.31 |
| PAPER+PAPERBOARD | 2897 | 4246 | 4700 | 5231 | 4818 | 5276 | 5654 | 6243 | 6934 | 7300 | 7326 | 6.41 |

1/ NOMINAL CATCH (LIVE WEIGHT) EXCLUDING WHALES
2/ EXCEPT FOR PULP FOR PAPER AND PAPER AND PAPERBOARD, ALL FOREST PRODUCTS ARE EXPRESSED IN THOUSAND CUBIC METRES

## ANNEX TABLE 1. VOLUME OF PRODUCTION OF MAJOR AGRICULTURAL, FISHERY AND FOREST PRODUCTS

| | 1967 | 1972 | 1973 | 1974 | 1975 | 1976 | 1977 | 1978 | 1979 | 1980 | 1981 | ANNUAL RATE OF CHANGE 1972-81 PERCENT |
|---|---|---|---|---|---|---|---|---|---|---|---|---|
| | | | | | | THOUSAND METRIC TONS | | | | | | |
| **NEAR EAST DEVELOPING** | | | | | | | | | | | | |
| **AGRICULTURAL PRODUCTS** | | | | | | | | | | | | |
| TOTAL CEREALS | 42047 | 46926 | 40690 | 44852 | 51879 | 56212 | 51513 | 53985 | 55172 | 56006 | 58225 | 3.23 |
| WHEAT | 20118 | 25956 | 21221 | 24341 | 28405 | 31335 | 29200 | 30513 | 30995 | 31128 | 32437 | 3.73 |
| RICE PADDY | 4189 | 4583 | 4447 | 4304 | 4602 | 4741 | 4564 | 4557 | 5033 | 4559 | 4800 | .79 |
| BARLEY | 7223 | 7275 | 5197 | 6271 | 7859 | 8952 | 7415 | 7932 | 7965 | 9312 | 9937 | 4.92 |
| MAIZE | 4069 | 4265 | 4536 | 4842 | 5026 | 5441 | 5097 | 5563 | 5400 | 5632 | 5073 | 2.37 |
| MILLET AND SORGHUM | 4726 | 3403 | 3950 | 3920 | 4588 | 4360 | 3947 | 4209 | 4580 | 4303 | 4943 | 2.69 |
| ROOT CROPS | 3458 | 4372 | 4634 | 4628 | 4855 | 5683 | 5821 | 5646 | 6211 | 6665 | 6597 | 5.09 |
| POTATOES | 3015 | 3956 | 4250 | 4252 | 4426 | 5276 | 5428 | 5238 | 5734 | 6207 | 6132 | 5.37 |
| CASSAVA | 160 | 134 | 140 | 92 | 130 | 99 | 95 | 103 | 127 | 122 | 122 | - .57 |
| TOTAL PULSES | 1554 | 1804 | 1493 | 1718 | 1604 | 1852 | 1872 | 1707 | 1663 | 1827 | 1865 | 1.06 |
| CITRUS FRUIT | 2077 | 2750 | 2884 | 3123 | 3104 | 3157 | 3328 | 3448 | 3742 | 3670 | 3669 | 3.42 |
| BANANAS | 221 | 275 | 276 | 296 | 296 | 290 | 314 | 292 | 290 | 321 | 328 | 1.56 |
| APPLES | 960 | 1286 | 1245 | 1335 | 1393 | 1626 | 1585 | 1850 | 2162 | 2227 | 2050 | 7.22 |
| VEGETABLE OILS,OIL EQUIV | 4339 | 6262 | 5181 | 6413 | 5458 | 6081 | 5655 | 6287 | 5467 | 6721 | 5360 | - .01 |
| SOYBEANS | 8 | 24 | 30 | 47 | 82 | 123 | 119 | 199 | 195 | 145 | 258 | 29.10 |
| GROUNDNUTS IN SHELL | 415 | 684 | 656 | 1039 | 905 | 878 | 1151 | 911 | 1004 | 924 | 928 | 3.24 |
| SUNFLOWER SEED | 235 | 613 | 616 | 487 | 541 | 612 | 506 | 524 | 628 | 786 | 618 | 1.69 |
| RAPESEED | 8 | 1 | 1 | 1 | | 6 | 14 | 13 | 43 | 12 | 15 | |
| COTTONSEED | 2229 | 2941 | 2780 | 3037 | 2523 | 2339 | 2627 | 2446 | 2320 | 2277 | 2210 | - 3.16 |
| SUGAR (CENTRIFUGAL,RAW) | 1729 | 2193 | 2221 | 2323 | 2455 | 2846 | 2667 | 2592 | 2546 | 2193 | 2922 | 1.86 |
| COFFEE GREEN | 5 | 5 | 5 | 5 | 4 | 4 | 4 | 5 | 5 | 5 | 5 | - .62 |
| TEA | 38 | 69 | 66 | 67 | 77 | 82 | 98 | 113 | 130 | 115 | 62 | 4.74 |
| COTTON LINT | 1299 | 1699 | 1608 | 1763 | 1453 | 1363 | 1521 | 1446 | 1376 | 1353 | 1327 | - 2.74 |
| JUTE AND SIMILAR FIBRES | 7 | 15 | 15 | 12 | 14 | 14 | 13 | 13 | 13 | 13 | 13 | - 1.24 |
| TOBACCO | 246 | 242 | 215 | 240 | 245 | 379 | 300 | 345 | 273 | 300 | 211 | 1.52 |
| TOTAL MEAT | 2088 | 2471 | 2584 | 2712 | 2820 | 2950 | 3113 | 3223 | 3451 | 3555 | 3736 | 4.72 |
| TOTAL MILK | 10857 | 11598 | 12008 | 12448 | 12885 | 13316 | 13421 | 14166 | 14627 | 14962 | 15531 | 3.24 |
| TOTAL EGGS | 286 | 383 | 401 | 469 | 543 | 595 | 679 | 721 | 674 | 703 | 764 | 8.16 |
| WOOL GREASY | 144 | 143 | 148 | 158 | 163 | 165 | 166 | 169 | 174 | 179 | 179 | 2.39 |
| **FISHERY PRODUCTS 1/** | | | | | | | | | | | | |
| FRESHWATER + DIADROMOUS | 127 | 130 | 130 | 128 | 135 | 134 | 133 | 139 | 159 | 168 | 100 | .37 |
| MARINE FISH | 405 | 443 | 410 | 674 | 634 | 606 | 487 | 491 | 629 | 695 | 107 | - 6.14 |
| CRUST+ MOLLUS+ CEPHALOP | 30 | 29 | 35 | 27 | 26 | 42 | 38 | 25 | 31 | 34 | 10 | - 5.40 |
| AQUATIC MAMMALS | | 3 | 3 | 2 | 2 | 2 | 2 | 2 | 2 | 2 | | |
| AQUATIC PLANTS | 1 | | | | | | | | | | | |
| **FOREST PRODUCTS 2/** | | | | | | | | | | | | |
| SAWLOGS CONIFEROUS | 2858 | 3624 | 4259 | 4569 | 4770 | 4796 | 5265 | 5216 | 4718 | 4965 | 5218 | 3.00 |
| SAWLOGS NONCONIFEROUS | 1047 | 1775 | 1626 | 1805 | 1287 | 1314 | 1442 | 1859 | 1523 | 1315 | 1366 | - 2.10 |
| PULPWOOD+PARTICLES | 207 | 960 | 1133 | 1363 | 869 | 907 | 1004 | 1003 | 1043 | 672 | 714 | - 4.23 |
| FUELWOOD | 52386 | 60395 | 55094 | 62587 | 64730 | 70501 | 61145 | 62003 | 50483 | 57429 | 56531 | - 1.00 |
| SAWNWOOD CONIFEROUS | 1781 | 2163 | 2297 | 2281 | 2278 | 2916 | 2932 | 2959 | 2968 | 2982 | 2963 | 4.19 |
| SAWNWOOD NONCONIFEROUS | 557 | 711 | 750 | 733 | 693 | 646 | 816 | 824 | 822 | 1126 | 1116 | 5.12 |
| WOOD-BASED PANELS | 223 | 391 | 409 | 430 | 512 | 615 | 761 | 798 | 844 | 845 | 740 | 10.01 |
| PULP FOR PAPER | 77 | 234 | 311 | 268 | 247 | 228 | 252 | 166 | 276 | 272 | 277 | - .22 |
| PAPER+PAPERBOARD | 258 | 515 | 595 | 606 | 671 | 582 | 623 | 554 | 732 | 592 | 655 | 1.58 |
| **FAR EAST DEVELOPING** | | | | | | | | | | | | |
| **AGRICULTURAL PRODUCTS** | | | | | | | | | | | | |
| TOTAL CEREALS | 175958 | 199877 | 224940 | 211254 | 238597 | 233608 | 251790 | 266829 | 250347 | 273505 | 291171 | 3.71 |
| WHEAT | 16213 | 33840 | 32734 | 29942 | 32405 | 38298 | 38914 | 41023 | 46470 | 44085 | 49491 | 5.24 |
| RICE PADDY | 122538 | 132623 | 150725 | 143459 | 162660 | 152730 | 171296 | 181096 | 162277 | 186718 | 194795 | 3.71 |
| BARLEY | 4036 | 4334 | 3979 | 3947 | 5021 | 5219 | 3373 | 3864 | 3871 | 2694 | 3315 | - 3.84 |
| MAIZE | 13114 | 13691 | 15465 | 15175 | 17374 | 16163 | 15445 | 17667 | 16994 | 19085 | 20468 | 3.49 |
| MILLET AND SORGHUM | 19988 | 15320 | 21779 | 18482 | 21055 | 21131 | 22689 | 23114 | 20673 | 20861 | 23037 | 2.63 |
| ROOT CROPS | 31645 | 38137 | 41149 | 43733 | 46814 | 49965 | 51888 | 58524 | 55123 | 55238 | 60544 | 5.02 |
| POTATOES | 5317 | 6837 | 6533 | 6927 | 8667 | 9750 | 9443 | 10272 | 12444 | 10835 | 12265 | 7.68 |
| CASSAVA | 17769 | 21497 | 24734 | 27411 | 28811 | 31281 | 33942 | 39819 | 34207 | 36605 | 40517 | 6.64 |
| TOTAL PULSES | 10533 | 12732 | 12725 | 11485 | 12443 | 14628 | 13780 | 13909 | 13637 | 10856 | 13046 | .15 |
| CITRUS FRUIT | 2204 | 2207 | 2331 | 2446 | 2604 | 2674 | 3526 | 3019 | 3026 | 3124 | 3212 | 4.47 |
| BANANAS | 7236 | 8262 | 8707 | 9001 | 9445 | 10616 | 11292 | 12271 | 13200 | 13699 | 13469 | 6.46 |
| APPLES | 339 | 676 | 763 | 805 | 827 | 889 | 987 | 1068 | 1206 | 1230 | 1447 | 8.25 |
| VEGETABLE OILS,OIL EQUIV | 34843 | 40788 | 40889 | 39666 | 46419 | 47824 | 47718 | 49034 | 47601 | 47636 | 52070 | 2.67 |
| SOYBEANS | 685 | 843 | 931 | 1107 | 1158 | 1077 | 1119 | 1317 | 1417 | 1450 | 1612 | 6.64 |
| GROUNDNUTS IN SHELL | 6801 | 5240 | 7127 | 6409 | 8126 | 6574 | 7480 | 7698 | 7148 | 6460 | 7855 | 2.12 |
| SUNFLOWER SEED | 1 | 1 | 1 | 1 | 1 | 1 | 3 | 13 | 47 | 76 | 97 | 73.70 |
| RAPESEED | 1553 | 1869 | 2221 | 2131 | 2651 | 2351 | 1996 | 2042 | 2273 | 1822 | 2643 | .67 |

1/ NOMINAL CATCH (LIVE WEIGHT) EXCLUDING WHALES
2/ EXCEPT FOR PULP FOR PAPER AND PAPER AND PAPERBOARD, ALL FOREST PRODUCTS ARE EXPRESSED IN THOUSAND CUBIC METRES

ANNEX TABLE 1. VOLUME OF PRODUCTION OF MAJOR AGRICULTURAL, FISHERY AND FOREST PRODUCTS

| | 1967 | 1972 | 1973 | 1974 | 1975 | 1976 | 1977 | 1978 | 1979 | 1980 | 1981 | ANNUAL RATE OF CHANGE 1972-81 PERCENT |
|---|---|---|---|---|---|---|---|---|---|---|---|---|
| | | | | | ..........THOUSAND METRIC TONS.......... | | | | | | | |
| COTTONSEED | 3445 | 3813 | 3780 | 3933 | 3405 | 3072 | 3711 | 3739 | 4229 | 4224 | 4415 | 1.79 |
| COPRA | 2783 | 3863 | 3203 | 2788 | 3849 | 4566 | 4000 | 4121 | 3690 | 3897 | 4108 | 2.08 |
| PALM KERNELS | 87 | 212 | 234 | 293 | 341 | 365 | 431 | 472 | 595 | 686 | 730 | 15.21 |
| SUGAR (CENTRIFUGAL,RAW) | 5365 | 7199 | 8596 | 9585 | 10535 | 11178 | 12507 | 13442 | 12826 | 9664 | 12199 | 4.88 |
| COFFEE GREEN | 311 | 321 | 314 | 312 | 385 | 387 | 438 | 566 | 551 | 643 | 631 | 9.67 |
| COCOA BEANS | 9 | 12 | 16 | 20 | 22 | 25 | 30 | 34 | 40 | 49 | 57 | 17.57 |
| TEA | 709 | 767 | 790 | 807 | 813 | 827 | 891 | 896 | 894 | 912 | 925 | 2.18 |
| COTTON LINT | 1722 | 1908 | 1891 | 1966 | 1704 | 1539 | 1856 | 1870 | 2115 | 2113 | 2208 | 1.78 |
| JUTE AND SIMILAR FIBRES | 3145 | 2890 | 3137 | 2283 | 2262 | 2409 | 2660 | 3234 | 3077 | 2710 | 2679 | .58 |
| SISAL | 8 | | | | | | | | | | | |
| TOBACCO | 847 | 922 | 873 | 961 | 886 | 849 | 1000 | 1059 | 973 | 938 | 944 | .90 |
| NATURAL RUBBER | 2137 | 2705 | 3115 | 3092 | 3211 | 3443 | 3253 | 3317 | 3470 | 3446 | 3258 | 1.83 |
| TOTAL MEAT | 3156 | 3673 | 3769 | 3864 | 4015 | 4167 | 4312 | 4584 | 4894 | 5173 | 5304 | 4.42 |
| TOTAL MILK | 29476 | 32822 | 33427 | 35021 | 36565 | 38350 | 39801 | 40824 | 42101 | 43332 | 44643 | 3.62 |
| TOTAL EGGS | 713 | 1067 | 1145 | 1275 | 1371 | 1436 | 1563 | 1717 | 1819 | 1926 | 2009 | 7.46 |
| WOOL GREASY | 61 | 60 | 60 | 62 | 65 | 69 | 73 | 75 | 79 | 83 | 88 | 4.69 |
| **FISHERY PRODUCTS 1/** | | | | | | | | | | | | |
| FRESHWATER + DIADROMOUS | 2179 | 2376 | 2422 | 2474 | 2493 | 2506 | 2569 | 2378 | 2419 | 2536 | 2173 | - .43 |
| MARINE FISH | 4000 | 5640 | 6203 | 6761 | 6910 | 6931 | 7709 | 7814 | 7554 | 7503 | 5402 | 1.20 |
| CRUST+ MOLLUS+ CEPHALOP | 689 | 1133 | 1241 | 1219 | 1437 | 1681 | 1810 | 1815 | 1929 | 2043 | 1499 | 5.66 |
| AQUATIC MAMMALS | 1 | | | | | | | | | | | |
| AQUATIC ANIMALS | 8 | 26 | 89 | 28 | 25 | 50 | 106 | 87 | 74 | 76 | 26 | 5.18 |
| AQUATIC PLANTS | 89 | 144 | 238 | 351 | 260 | 297 | 347 | 354 | 372 | 258 | | |
| **FOREST PRODUCTS 2/** | | | | | | | | | | | | |
| SAWLOGS CONIFEROUS | 1952 | 2707 | 2096 | 2771 | 3116 | 3091 | 4035 | 2975 | 3960 | 4191 | 4172 | 6.67 |
| SAWLOGS NONCONIFEROUS | 44658 | 63461 | 76599 | 71210 | 63440 | 76064 | 80003 | 82468 | 78084 | 78641 | 68591 | 1.33 |
| PULPWOOD+PARTICLES | 602 | 1847 | 2623 | 3058 | 2810 | 2851 | 3033 | 3027 | 2957 | 2988 | 2882 | 3.10 |
| FUELWOOD | 392028 | 443285 | 455035 | 466536 | 478685 | 490465 | 502476 | 514720 | 527582 | 539863 | 549959 | 2.45 |
| SAWNWOOD CONIFEROUS | 1263 | 1638 | 1547 | 1972 | 1857 | 1953 | 2810 | 3006 | 3454 | 3148 | 3704 | 10.80 |
| SAWNWOOD NONCONIFEROUS | 11462 | 15641 | 16404 | 16817 | 17990 | 20634 | 22073 | 22791 | 22330 | 23793 | 22453 | 5.00 |
| WOOD-BASED PANELS | 1747 | 3554 | 4027 | 3372 | 3864 | 4424 | 5340 | 6002 | 6130 | 5751 | 6205 | 7.55 |
| PULP FOR PAPER | 160 | 291 | 470 | 503 | 457 | 543 | 588 | 650 | 720 | 691 | 730 | 8.78 |
| PAPER+PAPERBOARD | 1107 | 1912 | 2023 | 2116 | 2081 | 2215 | 2760 | 3700 | 4399 | 4574 | 4716 | 12.50 |
| **ASIAN CENT PLANNED ECON** | | | | | | | | | | | | |
| **AGRICULTURAL PRODUCTS** | | | | | | | | | | | | |
| TOTAL CEREALS | 198163 | 224864 | 246882 | 256796 | 266970 | 272388 | 264803 | 293420 | 313624 | 301100 | 309919 | 3.41 |
| WHEAT | 29038 | 36436 | 35861 | 41421 | 45999 | 51006 | 41704 | 54471 | 63343 | 54745 | 59166 | 6.09 |
| RICE PADDY | 110592 | 132227 | 139964 | 142276 | 144566 | 147385 | 149330 | 156172 | 163368 | 159817 | 164922 | 2.36 |
| BARLEY | 3342 | 3078 | 3319 | 3385 | 3395 | 3404 | 3391 | 3799 | 4035 | 3712 | 3830 | 2.43 |
| MAIZE | 32617 | 33182 | 46582 | 48272 | 52127 | 50501 | 51803 | 58472 | 62644 | 63823 | 62939 | 6.02 |
| MILLET AND SORGHUM | 18512 | 15580 | 16544 | 16558 | 15572 | 14820 | 14434 | 15198 | 14414 | 13820 | 14038 | - 1.80 |
| ROOT CROPS | 134382 | 134814 | 142920 | 145170 | 144801 | 143867 | 160197 | 172274 | 155888 | 153402 | 139145 | 1.08 |
| POTATOES | 13455 | 13717 | 14264 | 14829 | 15481 | 14890 | 16343 | 17657 | 17792 | 17487 | 14430 | 2.01 |
| CASSAVA | 2504 | 3273 | 3451 | 3503 | 3626 | 4398 | 5250 | 6178 | 6313 | 6625 | 6801 | 10.09 |
| TOTAL PULSES | 7342 | 6358 | 6668 | 6572 | 6574 | 6757 | 6436 | 6905 | 7131 | 7066 | 7283 | 1.30 |
| CITRUS FRUIT | 883 | 1073 | 1140 | 1180 | 1157 | 1196 | 1191 | 1222 | 1256 | 1272 | 1310 | 1.86 |
| BANANAS | 1254 | 974 | 1063 | 999 | 837 | 923 | 1019 | 1010 | 1128 | 1252 | 1232 | 2.79 |
| APPLES | 1892 | 2303 | 2159 | 2494 | 2579 | 2771 | 2911 | 3148 | 3331 | 3480 | 3600 | 5.90 |
| VEGETABLE OILS,OIL EQUIV | 17938 | 16443 | 18104 | 17981 | 18046 | 16546 | 17144 | 19136 | 20382 | 22859 | 27195 | 4.33 |
| SOYBEANS | 8131 | 7353 | 7620 | 7771 | 7771 | 7029 | 7636 | 7938 | 7835 | 8281 | 9677 | 1.98 |
| GROUNDNUTS IN SHELL | 2036 | 2136 | 2172 | 2196 | 2224 | 2070 | 2154 | 2576 | 3000 | 3798 | 4002 | 7.28 |
| SUNFLOWER SEED | 70 | 65 | 70 | 70 | 80 | 100 | 170 | 279 | 340 | 900 | 1000 | 39.26 |
| RAPESEED | 1125 | 1152 | 1262 | 1201 | 1394 | 1345 | 1183 | 1871 | 2404 | 2386 | 4068 | 12.91 |
| COTTONSEED | 4721 | 3927 | 5135 | 4933 | 4772 | 4120 | 4112 | 4347 | 4425 | 5426 | 6012 | 2.08 |
| COPRA | 29 | 30 | 32 | 31 | 30 | 32 | 40 | 43 | 44 | 45 | 45 | 5.66 |
| PALM KERNELS | 18 | 37 | 38 | 39 | 39 | 41 | 40 | 42 | 46 | 48 | 46 | 2.84 |
| SUGAR (CENTRIFUGAL,RAW) | 2231 | 2535 | 2767 | 2777 | 2678 | 2781 | 3150 | 3300 | 3689 | 3745 | 4151 | 5.43 |
| COFFEE GREEN | 11 | 9 | 12 | 12 | 13 | 18 | 21 | 14 | 14 | 16 | 19 | 6.07 |
| TEA | 148 | 197 | 221 | 237 | 259 | 277 | 295 | 313 | 325 | 350 | 391 | 7.28 |
| COTTON LINT | 2360 | 1963 | 2567 | 2466 | 2386 | 2060 | 2055 | 2173 | 2213 | 2713 | 2975 | 2.02 |
| JUTE AND SIMILAR FIBRES | 313 | 433 | 523 | 594 | 690 | 766 | 893 | 1122 | 1118 | 1133 | 1299 | 12.94 |
| SISAL | 10 | 8 | 8 | 10 | 9 | 9 | 8 | 9 | 8 | 8 | 8 | - 1.04 |
| TOBACCO | 930 | 918 | 1027 | 1064 | 1039 | 1060 | 1077 | 1338 | 1026 | 995 | 1350 | 2.36 |
| NATURAL RUBBER | 100 | 68 | 77 | 95 | 99 | 120 | 142 | 159 | 151 | 157 | 187 | 11.49 |
| TOTAL MEAT | 13265 | 16555 | 17274 | 18172 | 18871 | 19937 | 20782 | 21127 | 22547 | 23801 | 24545 | 4.49 |
| TOTAL MILK | 4641 | 5359 | 5639 | 5900 | 6154 | 6441 | 6759 | 7040 | 7712 | 7939 | 8145 | 4.94 |
| TOTAL EGGS | 3388 | 3633 | 3687 | 3788 | 3906 | 4038 | 4156 | 4393 | 4713 | 4923 | 5235 | 4.20 |
| WOOL GREASY | 125 | 144 | 148 | 151 | 154 | 155 | 156 | 157 | 174 | 196 | 200 | 3.49 |

1/ NOMINAL CATCH (LIVE WEIGHT) EXCLUDING WHALES
2/ EXCEPT FOR PULP FOR PAPER AND PAPER AND PAPERBOARD, ALL FOREST PRODUCTS ARE EXPRESSED IN THOUSAND CUBIC METRES

ANNEX TABLE 1.  VOLUME OF PRODUCTION OF MAJOR AGRICULTURAL, FISHERY AND FOREST PRODUCTS

| | 1967 | 1972 | 1973 | 1974 | 1975 | 1976 | 1977 | 1978 | 1979 | 1980 | 1981 | ANNUAL RATE OF CHANGE 1972-81 PERCENT |
|---|---|---|---|---|---|---|---|---|---|---|---|---|
| | | | | | | ......THOUSAND METRIC TONS..... | | | | | | |
| **FISHERY PRODUCTS 1/** | | | | | | | | | | | | |
| FRESHWATER + DIADROMOUS | 1155 | 1205 | 1343 | 1349 | 1392 | 1398 | 1424 | 1370 | 1446 | 1555 | 1390 | 1.60 |
| MARINE FISH | 3112 | 4353 | 4280 | 4592 | 4749 | 4855 | 4952 | 4922 | 4713 | 4812 | 3694 | - .24 |
| CRUST+ MOLLUS+ CEPHALOP | 535 | 711 | 872 | 937 | 1007 | 1082 | 1207 | 1280 | 1162 | 1211 | 975 | 4.37 |
| AQUATIC MAMMALS | | | 1 | 1 | 1 | 2 | 2 | 2 | 2 | | | |
| AQUATIC ANIMALS | | 17 | 59 | 22 | 17 | 16 | 13 | 14 | 14 | 14 | 15 | - 8.45 |
| AQUATIC PLANTS | 502 | 978 | 833 | 899 | 997 | 943 | 1397 | 1572 | 1555 | 1543 | | |
| **FOREST PRODUCTS 2/** | | | | | | | | | | | | |
| SAWLOGS CONIFEROUS | 14269 | 16133 | 16725 | 18340 | 19145 | 19993 | 20768 | 21717 | 22706 | 23744 | 23744 | 4.60 |
| SAWLOGS NONCONIFEROUS | 9197 | 10160 | 10531 | 11702 | 12088 | 12999 | 13546 | 14108 | 14708 | 15308 | 15308 | 4.94 |
| PULPWOOD+PARTICLES | 1920 | 2810 | 2930 | 4000 | 4291 | 4476 | 4671 | 4876 | 5089 | 5313 | 5313 | 7.24 |
| FUELWOOD | 176628 | 195262 | 198541 | 202753 | 207186 | 211490 | 215913 | 220451 | 225089 | 229645 | 231142 | 2.00 |
| SAWNWOOD CONIFEROUS | 8637 | 10354 | 10604 | 11074 | 11166 | 11697 | 12256 | 12814 | 13400 | 14016 | 11089 | 2.44 |
| SAWNWOOD NONCONIFEROUS | 5588 | 6571 | 6753 | 6734 | 6739 | 7039 | 7354 | 7685 | 8032 | 8396 | 8396 | 3.11 |
| WOOD-BASED PANELS | 656 | 1572 | 1579 | 1328 | 1340 | 1510 | 1531 | 1896 | 1922 | 2095 | 1875 | 4.00 |
| PULP FOR PAPER | 988 | 1348 | 1403 | 1649 | 1691 | 1795 | 1926 | 2047 | 2199 | 2364 | 2364 | 6.76 |
| PAPER+PAPERBOARD | 3616 | 4817 | 5027 | 5619 | 6638 | 7010 | 7308 | 7792 | 8359 | 8976 | 8976 | 7.65 |

1/ NOMINAL CATCH (LIVE WEIGHT) EXCLUDING WHALES
2/ EXCEPT FOR PULP FOR PAPER AND PAPER AND PAPERBOARD, ALL FOREST PRODUCTS ARE EXPRESSED IN THOUSAND CUBIC METRES

ANNEX TABLE 2.  INDICES OF FOOD PRODUCTION

| | TOTAL | | | | | CHANGE 1980 TO 1981 | PER CAPUT | | | | | CHANGE 1980 TO 1981 |
|---|---|---|---|---|---|---|---|---|---|---|---|---|
| | 1977 | 1978 | 1979 | 1980 | 1981 | | 1977 | 1978 | 1979 | 1980 | 1981 | |
| | ..............1969-71=100............... | | | | | PERCENT | ..............1969-71=100............... | | | | | PERCENT |
| **FOOD PRODUCTION** | | | | | | | | | | | | |
| WORLD | 119 | 124 | 125 | 125 | 129 | 2.75 | 104 | 107 | 106 | 104 | 105 | 1.02 |
| DEVELOPED COUNTRIES | 116 | 120 | 120 | 119 | 121 | 1.78 | 109 | 112 | 111 | 109 | 110 | 1.04 |
| WESTERN EUROPE | 111 | 115 | 118 | 123 | 121 | - 1.51 | 107 | 111 | 113 | 117 | 115 | - 1.88 |
| EUROPEAN ECON COMMUNITY | 109 | 113 | 117 | 121 | 121 | - .64 | 106 | 110 | 113 | 117 | 116 | - .92 |
| BELGIUM-LUXEMBOURG | 105 | 106 | 109 | 110 | 115 | 5.09 | 103 | 104 | 107 | 107 | 113 | 5.02 |
| DENMARK | 110 | 109 | 115 | 116 | 117 | 1.55 | 107 | 105 | 110 | 111 | 113 | 1.57 |
| FRANCE | 106 | 114 | 121 | 125 | 124 | - .82 | 102 | 109 | 115 | 118 | 117 | - 1.28 |
| GERMANY FED.REP. OF | 106 | 110 | 110 | 113 | 111 | - 2.14 | 105 | 110 | 109 | 112 | 109 | - 2.30 |
| GREECE | 121 | 132 | 127 | 137 | 140 | 2.19 | 115 | 124 | 118 | 125 | 127 | 1.48 |
| IRELAND | 134 | 136 | 129 | 140 | 118 | - 15.71 | 124 | 124 | 117 | 125 | 104 | - 16.65 |
| ITALY | 107 | 110 | 115 | 122 | 120 | - 1.09 | 102 | 104 | 109 | 114 | 113 | - 1.36 |
| NETHERLANDS | 116 | 118 | 121 | 122 | 132 | 7.90 | 109 | 110 | 113 | 113 | 121 | 7.12 |
| UNITED KINGDOM | 114 | 116 | 119 | 126 | 124 | - 1.81 | 113 | 115 | 119 | 125 | 122 | - 1.87 |
| OTHER WESTERN EUROPE | 117 | 122 | 124 | 127 | 121 | - 4.31 | 111 | 114 | 115 | 117 | 111 | - 4.92 |
| AUSTRIA | 108 | 110 | 111 | 119 | 113 | - 5.07 | 107 | 109 | 109 | 117 | 111 | - 5.08 |
| FINLAND | 99 | 102 | 107 | 110 | 104 | - 4.85 | 97 | 99 | 104 | 106 | 100 | - 5.24 |
| ICELAND | 109 | 124 | 117 | 121 | 126 | 3.35 | 100 | 112 | 105 | 107 | 110 | 2.47 |
| MALTA | 127 | 144 | 117 | 120 | 120 | .42 | 124 | 139 | 112 | 113 | 113 | - .44 |
| NORWAY | 117 | 124 | 119 | 122 | 129 | 6.50 | 113 | 119 | 114 | 115 | 122 | 6.14 |
| PORTUGAL | 80 | 80 | 93 | 86 | 71 | - 16.78 | 72 | 72 | 83 | 76 | 63 | - 17.38 |
| SPAIN | 127 | 140 | 138 | 144 | 133 | - 7.78 | 118 | 129 | 126 | 130 | 119 | - 8.61 |
| SWEDEN | 118 | 120 | 118 | 120 | 124 | 3.20 | 115 | 117 | 114 | 116 | 120 | 3.10 |
| SWITZERLAND | 112 | 114 | 120 | 123 | 119 | - 2.65 | 111 | 113 | 119 | 121 | 117 | - 2.87 |
| YUGOSLAVIA | 127 | 120 | 127 | 128 | 129 | .78 | 119 | 112 | 117 | 117 | 117 | - .01 |
| USSR AND EASTERN EUROPE | 116 | 124 | 118 | 115 | 113 | - 1.36 | 109 | 116 | 110 | 106 | 104 | - 2.10 |
| EASTERN EUROPE | 120 | 125 | 124 | 122 | 121 | - .65 | 115 | 119 | 117 | 115 | 113 | - 1.22 |
| ALBANIA | 131 | 129 | 134 | 133 | 136 | 2.50 | 111 | 106 | 108 | 104 | 105 | .20 |
| BULGARIA | 110 | 115 | 123 | 118 | 121 | 3.21 | 106 | 110 | 118 | 113 | 116 | 2.89 |
| CZECHOSLOVAKIA | 125 | 130 | 115 | 127 | 121 | - 4.73 | 120 | 123 | 109 | 119 | 113 | - 4.93 |
| GERMAN DEMOCRATIC REP. | 117 | 121 | 125 | 125 | 131 | 4.61 | 120 | 124 | 127 | 127 | 133 | 4.62 |
| HUNGARY | 129 | 132 | 130 | 141 | 139 | - 1.48 | 126 | 128 | 126 | 136 | 134 | - 1.49 |
| POLAND | 108 | 116 | 114 | 102 | 99 | - 3.09 | 102 | 108 | 105 | 93 | 90 | - 3.96 |
| ROMANIA | 155 | 157 | 164 | 158 | 158 | .01 | 145 | 146 | 150 | 144 | 143 | - .83 |
| USSR | 113 | 124 | 115 | 111 | 109 | - 1.79 | 106 | 115 | 106 | 101 | 99 | - 2.60 |
| NORTH AMERICA DEVELOPED | 122 | 121 | 126 | 123 | 134 | 8.84 | 114 | 112 | 115 | 111 | 120 | 7.80 |
| CANADA | 122 | 125 | 116 | 123 | 132 | 7.31 | 112 | 114 | 104 | 109 | 115 | 6.09 |
| UNITED STATES | 122 | 121 | 127 | 123 | 134 | 8.96 | 114 | 112 | 116 | 111 | 120 | 7.96 |
| OCEANIA DEVELOPED | 125 | 141 | 138 | 123 | 132 | 7.15 | 112 | 125 | 121 | 107 | 114 | 5.96 |
| AUSTRALIA | 127 | 152 | 147 | 124 | 135 | 8.85 | 114 | 135 | 128 | 108 | 116 | 7.59 |
| NEW ZEALAND | 118 | 112 | 115 | 119 | 122 | 2.53 | 107 | 102 | 104 | 108 | 110 | 1.71 |
| DEVELOPING COUNTRIES | 123 | 129 | 131 | 134 | 139 | 3.92 | 105 | 108 | 108 | 108 | 110 | 1.82 |
| AFRICA DEVELOPING | 109 | 113 | 115 | 119 | 122 | 2.01 | 89 | 90 | 89 | 90 | 89 | - 1.05 |
| NORTH WESTERN AFRICA | 99 | 113 | 114 | 125 | 113 | - 9.44 | 82 | 90 | 88 | 93 | 82 | - 12.32 |
| ALGERIA | 90 | 97 | 103 | 119 | 116 | - 2.46 | 73 | 76 | 77 | 86 | 81 | - 5.80 |
| MOROCCO | 91 | 114 | 115 | 116 | 95 | - 17.88 | 75 | 91 | 89 | 86 | 69 | - 20.53 |
| TUNISIA | 142 | 140 | 134 | 164 | 161 | - 1.73 | 124 | 119 | 111 | 133 | 127 | - 4.13 |
| WESTERN AFRICA | 108 | 113 | 117 | 123 | 127 | 3.32 | 88 | 89 | 89 | 91 | 91 | - .12 |
| BENIN | 116 | 125 | 130 | 129 | 126 | - 2.19 | 95 | 100 | 100 | 97 | 92 | - 5.16 |
| GAMBIA | 86 | 105 | 85 | 83 | 103 | 23.80 | 69 | 82 | 65 | 62 | 75 | 20.60 |
| GHANA | 91 | 92 | 99 | 100 | 100 | .81 | 74 | 72 | 76 | 74 | 72 | - 2.39 |
| GUINEA | 111 | 110 | 108 | 112 | 113 | 1.48 | 94 | 91 | 87 | 87 | 86 | - 1.16 |
| IVORY COAST | 136 | 144 | 154 | 166 | 178 | 7.30 | 100 | 103 | 106 | 110 | 115 | 3.90 |
| LIBERIA | 129 | 130 | 133 | 135 | 133 | - 1.46 | 102 | 99 | 98 | 95 | 91 | - 4.90 |
| MALI | 105 | 116 | 114 | 108 | 120 | 11.80 | 88 | 95 | 91 | 83 | 90 | 8.71 |
| MAURITANIA | 88 | 92 | 99 | 99 | 107 | 8.96 | 73 | 74 | 78 | 75 | 79 | 5.92 |
| NIGER | 111 | 118 | 123 | 127 | 122 | - 3.70 | 91 | 94 | 95 | 95 | 89 | - 6.53 |
| NIGERIA | 110 | 114 | 119 | 126 | 130 | 2.62 | 89 | 89 | 90 | 92 | 92 | - .74 |
| SENEGAL | 83 | 130 | 95 | 85 | 123 | 44.92 | 67 | 103 | 74 | 64 | 90 | 41.19 |
| SIERRA LEONE | 109 | 103 | 105 | 109 | 101 | - 7.73 | 92 | 84 | 83 | 84 | 76 | - 10.25 |
| TOGO | 100 | 114 | 116 | 119 | 119 | - .34 | 83 | 93 | 92 | 91 | 88 | - 3.30 |
| UPPER VOLTA | 104 | 116 | 119 | 114 | 127 | 11.02 | 88 | 96 | 96 | 89 | 97 | 8.09 |
| CENTRAL AFRICA | 113 | 110 | 112 | 115 | 117 | 2.41 | 96 | 91 | 90 | 90 | 90 | - .26 |
| ANGOLA | 100 | 101 | 101 | 102 | 102 | - .31 | 85 | 84 | 82 | 81 | 79 | - 2.83 |
| CAMEROON | 129 | 118 | 121 | 128 | 130 | 1.96 | 111 | 100 | 99 | 103 | 102 | - .49 |
| CENTRAL AFRICAN REP | 117 | 118 | 122 | 126 | 129 | 2.54 | 101 | 100 | 101 | 102 | 102 | .17 |
| CHAD | 103 | 111 | 116 | 117 | 119 | 1.69 | 89 | 95 | 97 | 96 | 95 | - .40 |
| CONGO | 107 | 104 | 103 | 104 | 107 | 2.75 | 90 | 85 | 83 | 81 | 81 | .09 |
| GABON | 96 | 100 | 103 | 103 | 104 | .64 | 90 | 94 | 95 | 94 | 94 | - .63 |
| ZAIRE | 113 | 109 | 111 | 113 | 116 | 3.53 | 94 | 89 | 88 | 86 | 87 | .62 |
| EASTERN AFRICA | 113 | 114 | 112 | 114 | 119 | 4.62 | 93 | 91 | 87 | 86 | 87 | 1.47 |
| BURUNDI | 118 | 119 | 119 | 122 | 123 | .74 | 104 | 103 | 100 | 101 | 99 | - 1.75 |
| ETHIOPIA | 101 | 100 | 103 | 105 | 106 | .90 | 86 | 84 | 85 | 85 | 84 | - 1.25 |
| KENYA | 126 | 125 | 121 | 121 | 129 | 6.87 | 97 | 92 | 86 | 83 | 85 | 2.63 |
| MADAGASCAR | 115 | 113 | 118 | 121 | 124 | 2.94 | 96 | 92 | 95 | 94 | 94 | .17 |
| MALAWI | 122 | 133 | 127 | 130 | 136 | 4.96 | 98 | 104 | 97 | 95 | 97 | 1.57 |
| MAURITIUS | 113 | 116 | 117 | 90 | 107 | 19.23 | 102 | 103 | 103 | 78 | 91 | 17.16 |

ANNEX TABLE 2. INDICES OF FOOD PRODUCTION

| | TOTAL | | | | | CHANGE 1980 TO 1981 | PER CAPUT | | | | | CHANGE 1980 TO 1981 |
|---|---|---|---|---|---|---|---|---|---|---|---|---|
| | 1977 | 1978 | 1979 | 1980 | 1981 | | 1977 | 1978 | 1979 | 1980 | 1981 | |
| | ............1969-71=100................ | | | | | PERCENT | ...............1969-71=100................ | | | | | PERCENT |

**FOOD PRODUCTION**

| | 1977 | 1978 | 1979 | 1980 | 1981 | CHANGE | 1977 | 1978 | 1979 | 1980 | 1981 | CHANGE |
|---|---|---|---|---|---|---|---|---|---|---|---|---|
| MOZAMBIQUE | 94 | 92 | 93 | 93 | 94 | 1.02 | 79 | 76 | 74 | 73 | 71 | - 1.65 |
| RWANDA | 128 | 136 | 136 | 140 | 144 | 2.73 | 105 | 108 | 105 | 104 | 104 | - .43 |
| SOMALIA | 107 | 108 | 104 | 107 | 108 | .75 | 81 | 75 | 67 | 65 | 62 | - 4.58 |
| TANZANIA | 118 | 121 | 122 | 122 | 124 | 1.71 | 96 | 95 | 93 | 90 | 89 | - 1.45 |
| UGANDA | 111 | 120 | 115 | 115 | 118 | 2.91 | 90 | 95 | 88 | 85 | 85 | - .28 |
| ZAMBIA | 130 | 130 | 117 | 123 | 134 | 9.08 | 106 | 102 | 89 | 91 | 96 | 5.52 |
| ZIMBABWE | 137 | 134 | 112 | 117 | 157 | 33.84 | 109 | 103 | 83 | 84 | 109 | 29.29 |
| SOUTHERN AFRICA | 104 | 106 | 105 | 104 | 118 | 13.20 | 88 | 87 | 84 | 81 | 89 | 10.09 |
| BOTSWANA | 96 | 78 | 88 | 70 | 93 | 33.00 | 81 | 64 | 70 | 54 | 70 | 29.03 |
| LESOTHO | 112 | 119 | 107 | 103 | 116 | 11.95 | 95 | 99 | 87 | 82 | 90 | 9.25 |
| SWAZILAND | 115 | 129 | 122 | 139 | 148 | 6.45 | 97 | 106 | 97 | 107 | 111 | 3.29 |
| SOUTH AFRICA | 125 | 132 | 128 | 132 | 149 | 12.80 | 104 | 106 | 101 | 101 | 111 | 9.63 |
| LATIN AMERICA | 127 | 132 | 136 | 138 | 144 | 4.19 | 107 | 108 | 108 | 108 | 110 | 1.71 |
| CENTRAL AMERICA | 128 | 139 | 136 | 142 | 149 | 4.94 | 103 | 109 | 103 | 105 | 107 | 1.92 |
| COSTA RICA | 138 | 135 | 142 | 139 | 140 | - .86 | 116 | 114 | 114 | 109 | 107 | - 1.50 |
| EL SALVADOR | 126 | 144 | 146 | 139 | 134 | - 3.44 | 102 | 114 | 112 | 104 | 97 | - 6.22 |
| GUATEMALA | 138 | 141 | 153 | 157 | 162 | 2.74 | 111 | 110 | 116 | 116 | 116 | - .27 |
| HONDURAS | 104 | 112 | 107 | 112 | 116 | 3.63 | 83 | 86 | 80 | 80 | 80 | .08 |
| MEXICO | 128 | 140 | 135 | 145 | 153 | 5.70 | 103 | 109 | 102 | 107 | 109 | 2.66 |
| NICARAGUA | 131 | 144 | 142 | 105 | 112 | 6.78 | 104 | 111 | 106 | 76 | 78 | 3.33 |
| PANAMA | 125 | 128 | 125 | 129 | 137 | 6.47 | 104 | 105 | 100 | 101 | 105 | 4.16 |
| CARIBBEAN | 109 | 118 | 119 | 111 | 114 | 2.51 | 95 | 101 | 100 | 92 | 92 | - .67 |
| BARBADOS | 93 | 91 | 98 | 112 | 94 | - 16.15 | 88 | 85 | 91 | 102 | 85 | - 17.10 |
| CUBA | 106 | 119 | 128 | 115 | 119 | 3.80 | 96 | 107 | 113 | 101 | 104 | 3.18 |
| DOMINICAN REPUBLIC | 122 | 125 | 126 | 131 | 135 | 2.67 | 100 | 100 | 98 | 100 | 100 | .18 |
| HAITI | 107 | 113 | 115 | 109 | 112 | 2.07 | 92 | 94 | 93 | 87 | 86 | - .40 |
| JAMAICA | 114 | 131 | 109 | 105 | 104 | - 1.68 | 101 | 115 | 94 | 90 | 87 | - 3.11 |
| SOUTH AMERICA | 130 | 132 | 139 | 141 | 147 | 4.11 | 110 | 109 | 112 | 112 | 114 | 1.75 |
| ARGENTINA | 118 | 131 | 136 | 127 | 134 | 6.12 | 108 | 118 | 121 | 111 | 117 | 4.84 |
| BOLIVIA | 128 | 130 | 129 | 135 | 131 | - 2.92 | 107 | 106 | 103 | 105 | 99 | - 5.46 |
| BRAZIL | 147 | 141 | 149 | 164 | 168 | 2.49 | 123 | 115 | 119 | 128 | 128 | .13 |
| CHILE | 112 | 105 | 113 | 112 | 119 | 6.46 | 100 | 91 | 97 | 95 | 99 | 4.66 |
| COLOMBIA | 131 | 143 | 150 | 148 | 157 | 6.38 | 113 | 120 | 123 | 119 | 124 | 4.11 |
| ECUADOR | 122 | 119 | 121 | 133 | 139 | 4.48 | 99 | 94 | 93 | 99 | 100 | 1.27 |
| GUYANA | 110 | 117 | 113 | 113 | 114 | .39 | 95 | 98 | 92 | 91 | 89 | - 1.83 |
| PARAGUAY | 131 | 128 | 146 | 159 | 155 | - 2.63 | 105 | 99 | 109 | 115 | 109 | - 5.63 |
| PERU | 111 | 106 | 109 | 102 | 118 | 15.11 | 92 | 86 | 86 | 78 | 87 | 12.00 |
| URUGUAY | 99 | 99 | 96 | 105 | 122 | 15.85 | 98 | 96 | 94 | 101 | 116 | 15.02 |
| VENEZUELA | 130 | 136 | 149 | 151 | 142 | - 5.81 | 101 | 102 | 108 | 106 | 97 | - 8.94 |
| NEAR EAST DEVELOPING | 125 | 131 | 134 | 138 | 140 | 1.14 | 103 | 105 | 105 | 104 | 103 | - 1.68 |
| NEAR EAST IN AFRICA | 115 | 118 | 122 | 123 | 124 | .87 | 96 | 96 | 97 | 95 | 94 | - 1.77 |
| EGYPT | 108 | 112 | 114 | 116 | 115 | - .96 | 91 | 92 | 91 | 91 | 88 | - 3.36 |
| LIBYA | 161 | 158 | 221 | 213 | 202 | - 5.09 | 121 | 113 | 152 | 141 | 129 | - 8.77 |
| SUDAN | 127 | 128 | 131 | 131 | 139 | 6.47 | 106 | 104 | 103 | 100 | 104 | 3.48 |
| NEAR EAST IN ASIA | 128 | 135 | 138 | 142 | 143 | 1.21 | 104 | 107 | 106 | 106 | 105 | - 1.70 |
| AFGHANISTAN | 109 | 117 | 120 | 125 | 130 | 3.65 | 91 | 95 | 95 | 97 | 98 | 1.07 |
| CYPRUS | 98 | 96 | 99 | 107 | 106 | - .84 | 97 | 94 | 97 | 104 | 103 | - 1.32 |
| IRAN | 142 | 150 | 147 | 144 | 161 | 11.93 | 116 | 119 | 113 | 107 | 116 | 8.52 |
| IRAQ | 107 | 110 | 125 | 127 | 122 | - 3.89 | 85 | 85 | 93 | 91 | 84 | - 7.13 |
| JORDAN | 97 | 110 | 81 | 131 | 104 | - 20.62 | 76 | 84 | 59 | 93 | 71 | - 23.44 |
| LEBANON | 76 | 106 | 105 | 133 | 115 | - 13.02 | 68 | 97 | 97 | 123 | 106 | - 13.89 |
| SAUDI ARABIA | 135 | 128 | 92 | 39 | | | 99 | 90 | 62 | 25 | | |
| SYRIA | 170 | 203 | 191 | 262 | 251 | - 4.34 | 132 | 153 | 138 | 182 | 168 | - 7.96 |
| TURKEY | 129 | 135 | 142 | 144 | 145 | .60 | 109 | 111 | 113 | 113 | 111 | - 1.83 |
| YEMEN ARAB REPUBLIC | 109 | 109 | 114 | 116 | 118 | 2.25 | 97 | 95 | 97 | 96 | 96 | .04 |
| YEMEN DEMOCRATIC | 126 | 124 | 125 | 129 | 126 | - 2.00 | 109 | 105 | 103 | 104 | 99 | - 4.46 |
| ISRAEL | 132 | 133 | 137 | 134 | 130 | - 3.28 | 109 | 107 | 108 | 103 | 98 | - 5.06 |
| FAR EAST DEVELOPING | 127 | 132 | 129 | 134 | 142 | 6.15 | 109 | 111 | 106 | 107 | 111 | 3.96 |
| SOUTH ASIA | 123 | 127 | 122 | 128 | 135 | 5.91 | 105 | 106 | 100 | 102 | 106 | 3.67 |
| BANGLADESH | 112 | 116 | 115 | 124 | 123 | - .32 | 94 | 95 | 92 | 96 | 93 | - 3.10 |
| INDIA | 125 | 129 | 121 | 126 | 135 | 7.24 | 107 | 108 | 100 | 102 | 107 | 5.15 |
| NEPAL | 105 | 108 | 100 | 111 | 105 | - 5.49 | 90 | 90 | 82 | 89 | 82 | - 7.62 |
| PAKISTAN | 127 | 127 | 134 | 137 | 144 | 4.73 | 104 | 102 | 104 | 104 | 106 | 1.76 |
| SRI LANKA | 126 | 136 | 163 | 179 | 183 | 2.11 | 112 | 119 | 141 | 152 | 152 | .11 |
| EAST SOUTH-EAST ASIA | 138 | 147 | 148 | 150 | 160 | 6.74 | 118 | 123 | 121 | 121 | 126 | 4.60 |
| BURMA | 114 | 121 | 122 | 131 | 141 | 7.56 | 96 | 99 | 98 | 102 | 107 | 4.98 |
| INDONESIA | 127 | 131 | 133 | 144 | 151 | 4.71 | 110 | 112 | 112 | 119 | 122 | 2.98 |
| KOREA REP | 152 | 161 | 164 | 138 | 152 | 9.90 | 132 | 138 | 138 | 115 | 124 | 8.06 |
| LAO | 88 | 106 | 123 | 140 | 153 | 8.72 | 75 | 89 | 100 | 112 | 119 | 6.15 |
| MALAYSIA | 151 | 151 | 170 | 180 | 188 | 4.31 | 126 | 122 | 135 | 139 | 142 | 1.80 |
| PHILIPPINES | 148 | 154 | 154 | 160 | 167 | 4.45 | 123 | 124 | 121 | 122 | 124 | 1.73 |
| THAILAND | 146 | 172 | 154 | 163 | 181 | 10.60 | 121 | 139 | 122 | 127 | 137 | 8.17 |
| JAPAN | 110 | 107 | 108 | 98 | 100 | 1.78 | 101 | 97 | 97 | 88 | 88 | 1.03 |
| ASIAN CENT PLANNED ECON | 122 | 130 | 136 | 136 | 141 | 3.07 | 107 | 112 | 116 | 115 | 117 | 1.69 |
| CHINA | 121 | 130 | 137 | 136 | 140 | 3.08 | 106 | 113 | 117 | 115 | 117 | 1.77 |
| KAMPUCHEA,DEMOCRATIC | 68 | 58 | 38 | 45 | 49 | 8.31 | 68 | 59 | 39 | 47 | 50 | 7.01 |
| KOREA DPR | 160 | 161 | 170 | 171 | 176 | 2.74 | 134 | 131 | 135 | 133 | 133 | .35 |
| MONGOLIA | 114 | 128 | 127 | 121 | 122 | .25 | 93 | 101 | 97 | 91 | 89 | - 2.50 |
| VIET NAM | 122 | 127 | 133 | 140 | 145 | 3.08 | 105 | 107 | 110 | 113 | 114 | .78 |
| OTHER DEVELOPING MRKT | 116 | 119 | 125 | 124 | 131 | 5.15 | 97 | 97 | 100 | 97 | 100 | 2.66 |

ANNEX TABLE 3.  INDICES OF AGRICULTURAL PRODUCTION

| | TOTAL | | | | | CHANGE | PER CAPUT | | | | | CHANGE |
|---|---|---|---|---|---|---|---|---|---|---|---|---|
| | 1977 | 1978 | 1979 | 1980 | 1981 | 1980 TO 1981 | 1977 | 1978 | 1979 | 1980 | 1981 | 1980 TO 1981 |
| | ·················1969-71=100················ | | | | | PERCENT | ·················1969-71=100················ | | | | | PERCENT |

AGRICULTURAL PRODUCTION

| | | | | | | | | | | | | |
|---|---|---|---|---|---|---|---|---|---|---|---|---|
| WORLD | 118 | 123 | 124 | 124 | 128 | 2.99 | 104 | 106 | 105 | 104 | 105 | 1.25 |
| DEVELOPED COUNTRIES | 115 | 119 | 119 | 118 | 120 | 2.08 | 109 | 111 | 111 | 108 | 110 | 1.33 |
| WESTERN EUROPE | 111 | 115 | 119 | 123 | 121 | - 1.44 | 107 | 111 | 113 | 117 | 115 | - 1.80 |
| EUROPEAN ECON COMMUNITY | 109 | 113 | 117 | 122 | 121 | - .60 | 106 | 110 | 113 | 117 | 116 | - .87 |
| BELGIUM-LUXEMBOURG | 105 | 105 | 109 | 109 | 115 | 5.29 | 103 | 103 | 107 | 107 | 112 | 5.21 |
| DENMARK | 110 | 109 | 115 | 116 | 117 | 1.62 | 107 | 105 | 110 | 111 | 113 | 1.64 |
| FRANCE | 106 | 114 | 122 | 125 | 124 | - .81 | 102 | 109 | 115 | 118 | 117 | - 1.27 |
| GERMANY FED.REP. OF | 106 | 110 | 110 | 113 | 111 | - 2.13 | 105 | 110 | 109 | 112 | 109 | - 2.29 |
| GREECE | 121 | 132 | 126 | 135 | 139 | 2.90 | 115 | 124 | 117 | 123 | 126 | 2.19 |
| IRELAND | 133 | 136 | 129 | 140 | 118 | - 15.62 | 123 | 124 | 117 | 125 | 104 | - 16.54 |
| ITALY | 107 | 110 | 116 | 122 | 121 | - 1.13 | 102 | 104 | 109 | 115 | 113 | - 1.39 |
| NETHERLANDS | 116 | 118 | 122 | 123 | 133 | 8.04 | 109 | 110 | 113 | 113 | 122 | 7.26 |
| UNITED KINGDOM | 113 | 115 | 119 | 126 | 123 | - 1.81 | 113 | 115 | 118 | 125 | 122 | - 1.87 |
| OTHER WESTERN EUROPE | 117 | 121 | 123 | 126 | 121 | - 4.17 | 110 | 114 | 115 | 117 | 111 | - 4.78 |
| AUSTRIA | 108 | 110 | 111 | 119 | 113 | - 5.06 | 107 | 109 | 109 | 117 | 111 | - 5.06 |
| FINLAND | 99 | 102 | 107 | 110 | 104 | - 4.87 | 97 | 99 | 104 | 106 | 100 | - 5.26 |
| ICELAND | 109 | 122 | 116 | 120 | 124 | 3.54 | 99 | 111 | 104 | 106 | 109 | 2.65 |
| MALTA | 127 | 143 | 117 | 120 | 120 | .42 | 124 | 139 | 111 | 113 | 113 | - .46 |
| NORWAY | 117 | 124 | 119 | 121 | 129 | 6.47 | 112 | 118 | 113 | 115 | 122 | 6.11 |
| PORTUGAL | 80 | 81 | 93 | 86 | 72 | - 16.45 | 73 | 73 | 83 | 76 | 63 | - 17.04 |
| SPAIN | 127 | 139 | 137 | 144 | 133 | - 7.56 | 118 | 128 | 125 | 130 | 119 | - 8.39 |
| SWEDEN | 118 | 120 | 118 | 120 | 124 | 3.21 | 115 | 117 | 114 | 116 | 120 | 3.11 |
| SWITZERLAND | 112 | 114 | 120 | 122 | 119 | - 2.65 | 111 | 113 | 119 | 121 | 117 | - 2.87 |
| YUGOSLAVIA | 127 | 120 | 127 | 127 | 128 | .95 | 119 | 112 | 117 | 116 | 116 | .16 |
| USSR AND EASTERN EUROPE | 116 | 124 | 118 | 115 | 113 | - 1.28 | 109 | 116 | 109 | 106 | 104 | - 2.01 |
| EASTERN EUROPE | 119 | 125 | 124 | 121 | 121 | - .48 | 114 | 118 | 117 | 114 | 113 | - 1.04 |
| ALBANIA | 129 | 128 | 133 | 132 | 135 | 2.46 | 109 | 105 | 107 | 104 | 104 | .13 |
| BULGARIA | 109 | 115 | 124 | 116 | 120 | 3.58 | 105 | 111 | 119 | 111 | 114 | 3.25 |
| CZECHOSLOVAKIA | 124 | 129 | 115 | 126 | 120 | - 4.70 | 119 | 123 | 108 | 119 | 113 | - 4.89 |
| GERMAN DEMOCRATIC REP. | 118 | 122 | 125 | 125 | 131 | 4.59 | 120 | 124 | 128 | 128 | 134 | 4.59 |
| HUNGARY | 129 | 132 | 130 | 140 | 138 | - 1.30 | 125 | 127 | 125 | 135 | 133 | - 1.30 |
| POLAND | 108 | 115 | 113 | 102 | 99 | - 2.74 | 101 | 107 | 104 | 93 | 89 | - 3.62 |
| ROMANIA | 155 | 157 | 163 | 158 | 157 | - .15 | 145 | 145 | 149 | 144 | 142 | - .99 |
| USSR | 113 | 123 | 114 | 111 | 109 | - 1.74 | 106 | 115 | 105 | 102 | 99 | - 2.55 |
| NORTH AMERICA DEVELOPED | 122 | 120 | 125 | 122 | 134 | 9.78 | 113 | 111 | 114 | 110 | 119 | 8.74 |
| CANADA | 120 | 124 | 114 | 121 | 130 | 7.23 | 110 | 113 | 102 | 107 | 114 | 6.00 |
| UNITED STATES | 122 | 120 | 126 | 122 | 134 | 10.01 | 114 | 111 | 115 | 110 | 120 | 8.97 |
| OCEANIA DEVELOPED | 116 | 128 | 126 | 116 | 123 | 6.22 | 104 | 114 | 111 | 101 | 106 | 5.06 |
| AUSTRALIA | 116 | 135 | 132 | 115 | 124 | 7.40 | 104 | 119 | 115 | 99 | 106 | 6.16 |
| NEW ZEALAND | 114 | 109 | 112 | 117 | 121 | 2.96 | 103 | 99 | 101 | 106 | 109 | 2.14 |
| DEVELOPING COUNTRIES | 122 | 128 | 130 | 133 | 138 | 4.07 | 104 | 107 | 107 | 106 | 108 | 1.95 |
| AFRICA DEVELOPING | 109 | 112 | 114 | 118 | 120 | 1.88 | 89 | 89 | 88 | 89 | 88 | - 1.18 |
| NORTH WESTERN AFRICA | 99 | 113 | 114 | 125 | 113 | - 9.27 | 82 | 90 | 88 | 93 | 82 | - 12.16 |
| ALGERIA | 90 | 98 | 103 | 119 | 116 | - 2.39 | 73 | 76 | 77 | 86 | 82 | - 5.71 |
| MOROCCO | 91 | 113 | 115 | 115 | 95 | - 17.67 | 75 | 90 | 88 | 86 | 69 | - 20.33 |
| TUNISIA | 143 | 141 | 135 | 164 | 162 | - 1.59 | 125 | 120 | 112 | 133 | 128 | - 4.00 |
| WESTERN AFRICA | 109 | 113 | 117 | 122 | 126 | 3.49 | 88 | 88 | 89 | 90 | 91 | .29 |
| BENIN | 114 | 122 | 128 | 126 | 125 | - .71 | 93 | 98 | 99 | 94 | 91 | - 3.71 |
| GAMBIA | 86 | 105 | 85 | 83 | 103 | 23.82 | 70 | 83 | 65 | 62 | 75 | 20.61 |
| GHANA | 91 | 92 | 99 | 100 | 100 | .82 | 74 | 72 | 76 | 74 | 72 | - 2.39 |
| GUINEA | 111 | 111 | 108 | 112 | 114 | 1.46 | 94 | 91 | 87 | 88 | 87 | - 1.16 |
| IVORY COAST | 133 | 131 | 147 | 154 | 171 | 10.84 | 98 | 93 | 101 | 103 | 110 | 7.32 |
| LIBERIA | 122 | 122 | 125 | 129 | 125 | - 2.57 | 96 | 93 | 92 | 91 | 86 | - 5.96 |
| MALI | 110 | 119 | 119 | 114 | 123 | 8.46 | 92 | 97 | 94 | 88 | 93 | 5.48 |
| MAURITANIA | 88 | 92 | 99 | 99 | 107 | 8.96 | 73 | 74 | 78 | 75 | 79 | 5.92 |
| NIGER | 110 | 117 | 122 | 126 | 121 | - 3.65 | 90 | 93 | 94 | 95 | 88 | - 6.49 |
| NIGERIA | 110 | 113 | 118 | 125 | 129 | 2.56 | 89 | 88 | 89 | 92 | 91 | - .78 |
| SENEGAL | 84 | 131 | 96 | 85 | 123 | 45.04 | 68 | 104 | 74 | 64 | 91 | 41.26 |
| SIERRA LEONE | 110 | 102 | 107 | 109 | 101 | - 7.75 | 92 | 84 | 85 | 85 | 76 | - 10.26 |
| TOGO | 100 | 112 | 115 | 119 | 118 | - .65 | 83 | 91 | 91 | 92 | 88 | - 3.58 |
| UPPER VOLTA | 106 | 116 | 121 | 117 | 129 | 9.70 | 90 | 96 | 97 | 92 | 98 | 6.80 |
| CENTRAL AFRICA | 108 | 105 | 107 | 109 | 110 | 1.28 | 91 | 87 | 86 | 85 | 84 | - 1.36 |
| ANGOLA | 76 | 74 | 76 | 74 | 72 | - 2.68 | 64 | 62 | 61 | 59 | 56 | - 5.17 |
| CAMEROON | 124 | 118 | 120 | 126 | 127 | .34 | 107 | 100 | 99 | 102 | 100 | - 2.05 |
| CENTRAL AFRICAN REP | 116 | 116 | 120 | 123 | 125 | 1.56 | 100 | 99 | 99 | 99 | 99 | - .82 |
| CHAD | 104 | 113 | 113 | 114 | 115 | .86 | 90 | 96 | 95 | 93 | 92 | - 1.19 |
| CONGO | 108 | 104 | 104 | 105 | 108 | 2.99 | 91 | 86 | 83 | 82 | 82 | .32 |
| GABON | 95 | 100 | 102 | 103 | 104 | .76 | 90 | 93 | 94 | 94 | 94 | - .51 |
| ZAIRE | 113 | 109 | 110 | 112 | 115 | 2.79 | 94 | 88 | 87 | 86 | 86 | - .07 |
| EASTERN AFRICA | 113 | 113 | 112 | 114 | 118 | 3.87 | 93 | 90 | 87 | 86 | 86 | .77 |
| BURUNDI | 116 | 119 | 121 | 122 | 125 | 2.81 | 103 | 103 | 102 | 100 | 100 | - .28 |
| ETHIOPIA | 102 | 101 | 103 | 105 | 107 | 1.31 | 87 | 85 | 85 | 85 | 85 | - .87 |
| KENYA | 139 | 135 | 132 | 134 | 141 | 5.12 | 107 | 100 | 94 | 92 | 93 | .95 |
| MADAGASCAR | 117 | 113 | 118 | 121 | 124 | 2.98 | 99 | 93 | 95 | 94 | 94 | .21 |
| MALAWI | 131 | 141 | 137 | 139 | 144 | 4.08 | 106 | 111 | 104 | 102 | 102 | .70 |
| MAURITIUS | 113 | 117 | 118 | 92 | 108 | 17.00 | 103 | 104 | 104 | 80 | 92 | 14.97 |

ANNEX TABLE 3. INDICES OF AGRICULTURAL PRODUCTION

| | TOTAL | | | | | CHANGE 1980 TO 1981 | PER CAPUT | | | | | CHANGE 1980 TO 1981 |
|---|---|---|---|---|---|---|---|---|---|---|---|---|
| | 1977 | 1978 | 1979 | 1980 | 1981 | | 1977 | 1978 | 1979 | 1980 | 1981 | |
| | ..............1969-71=100................ | | | | | PERCENT | ...............1969-71=100............... | | | | | PERCENT |
| **AGRICULTURAL PRODUCTION** | | | | | | | | | | | | |
| MOZAMBIQUE | 90 | 89 | 89 | 90 | 91 | .78 | 76 | 73 | 71 | 70 | 69 | - 1.86 |
| RWANDA | 129 | 135 | 141 | 144 | 147 | 1.75 | 105 | 107 | 109 | 108 | 106 | - 1.38 |
| SOMALIA | 107 | 108 | 104 | 107 | 108 | .74 | 81 | 75 | 67 | 65 | 62 | - 4.58 |
| TANZANIA | 113 | 115 | 116 | 116 | 119 | 2.92 | 92 | 91 | 89 | 86 | 86 | - .27 |
| UGANDA | 97 | 101 | 95 | 95 | 99 | 4.15 | 79 | 79 | 72 | 70 | 71 | .95 |
| ZAMBIA | 129 | 128 | 116 | 123 | 134 | 8.39 | 105 | 101 | 89 | 91 | 95 | 4.83 |
| ZIMBABWE | 137 | 137 | 126 | 133 | 152 | 13.86 | 109 | 105 | 94 | 96 | 105 | 9.99 |
| SOUTHERN AFRICA | 105 | 107 | 105 | 106 | 119 | 12.25 | 88 | 88 | 84 | 82 | 90 | 9.16 |
| BOTSWANA | 96 | 78 | 89 | 70 | 93 | 32.33 | 81 | 64 | 70 | 54 | 70 | 28.35 |
| LESOTHO | 105 | 111 | 101 | 98 | 109 | 11.13 | 89 | 93 | 82 | 78 | 84 | 8.43 |
| SWAZILAND | 121 | 138 | 127 | 149 | 157 | 5.15 | 102 | 113 | 101 | 115 | 117 | 2.03 |
| SOUTH AFRICA | 122 | 130 | 126 | 130 | 145 | 11.41 | 102 | 105 | 99 | 99 | 107 | 8.28 |
| LATIN AMERICA | 125 | 130 | 134 | 135 | 142 | 5.25 | 105 | 106 | 107 | 105 | 108 | 2.74 |
| CENTRAL AMERICA | 127 | 137 | 134 | 138 | 144 | 4.49 | 102 | 107 | 102 | 101 | 103 | 1.47 |
| COSTA RICA | 133 | 135 | 137 | 138 | 142 | 2.95 | 112 | 111 | 110 | 108 | 108 | .55 |
| EL SALVADOR | 120 | 135 | 140 | 132 | 116 | - 11.84 | 98 | 107 | 108 | 98 | 84 | - 14.35 |
| GUATEMALA | 141 | 145 | 153 | 155 | 159 | 2.43 | 114 | 114 | 116 | 114 | 114 | - .57 |
| HONDURAS | 108 | 118 | 119 | 123 | 127 | 3.58 | 86 | 91 | 89 | 88 | 88 | .03 |
| MEXICO | 126 | 137 | 132 | 140 | 148 | 5.45 | 101 | 107 | 100 | 103 | 105 | 2.43 |
| NICARAGUA | 135 | 149 | 143 | 96 | 112 | 16.14 | 108 | 115 | 107 | 69 | 78 | 12.40 |
| PANAMA | 124 | 128 | 125 | 129 | 138 | 6.68 | 104 | 105 | 100 | 101 | 105 | 4.35 |
| CARIBBEAN | 110 | 118 | 119 | 111 | 114 | 3.12 | 95 | 101 | 100 | 91 | 92 | 1.26 |
| BARBADOS | 93 | 91 | 99 | 112 | 94 | - 16.17 | 88 | 85 | 91 | 102 | 85 | - 17.12 |
| CUBA | 106 | 119 | 127 | 113 | 119 | 5.17 | 96 | 106 | 113 | 99 | 104 | 4.53 |
| DOMINICAN REPUBLIC | 124 | 128 | 130 | 133 | 136 | 1.99 | 102 | 103 | 101 | 101 | 101 | - .49 |
| HAITI | 107 | 111 | 115 | 108 | 110 | 2.72 | 91 | 93 | 93 | 85 | 86 | .21 |
| JAMAICA | 113 | 130 | 109 | 105 | 104 | - 1.39 | 101 | 114 | 95 | 90 | 87 | - 2.81 |
| SOUTH AMERICA | 127 | 129 | 136 | 137 | 145 | 5.82 | 107 | 107 | 110 | 108 | 112 | 3.42 |
| ARGENTINA | 119 | 130 | 135 | 125 | 131 | 4.79 | 109 | 117 | 120 | 110 | 114 | 3.52 |
| BOLIVIA | 130 | 133 | 132 | 135 | 131 | - 2.77 | 110 | 109 | 106 | 105 | 99 | - 5.33 |
| BRAZIL | 136 | 133 | 141 | 151 | 162 | 7.76 | 114 | 109 | 113 | 117 | 123 | 5.27 |
| CHILE | 112 | 104 | 112 | 112 | 119 | 6.35 | 99 | 91 | 96 | 95 | 99 | 4.56 |
| COLOMBIA | 132 | 140 | 146 | 146 | 155 | 6.43 | 113 | 118 | 120 | 118 | 122 | 4.15 |
| ECUADOR | 123 | 120 | 124 | 133 | 140 | 5.58 | 100 | 95 | 95 | 99 | 101 | 2.34 |
| GUYANA | 111 | 117 | 113 | 114 | 114 | .38 | 95 | 98 | 93 | 91 | 90 | - 1.85 |
| PARAGUAY | 140 | 135 | 150 | 162 | 159 | - 1.74 | 112 | 105 | 112 | 117 | 112 | - 4.78 |
| PERU | 109 | 106 | 111 | 104 | 117 | 12.76 | 90 | 86 | 87 | 79 | 87 | 9.68 |
| URUGUAY | 96 | 95 | 94 | 102 | 116 | 13.69 | 95 | 93 | 91 | 99 | 112 | 12.88 |
| VENEZUELA | 128 | 133 | 146 | 149 | 138 | - 7.13 | 100 | 100 | 106 | 104 | 94 | - 10.20 |
| NEAR EAST DEVELOPING | 123 | 129 | 131 | 134 | 134 | .49 | 101 | 103 | 102 | 101 | 99 | - 2.31 |
| NEAR EAST IN AFRICA | 107 | 112 | 115 | 116 | 116 | - .15 | 90 | 91 | 91 | 90 | 87 | - 2.76 |
| EGYPT | 102 | 107 | 110 | 114 | 112 | - 1.65 | 86 | 88 | 88 | 89 | 85 | - 4.06 |
| LIBYA | 161 | 155 | 217 | 209 | 199 | - 4.80 | 120 | 111 | 150 | 139 | 127 | - 8.49 |
| SUDAN | 114 | 118 | 115 | 113 | 118 | 4.54 | 95 | 96 | 91 | 86 | 88 | - 1.61 |
| NEAR EAST IN ASIA | 127 | 133 | 135 | 139 | 140 | .65 | 104 | 106 | 104 | 104 | 102 | - 2.24 |
| AFGHANISTAN | 110 | 117 | 119 | 122 | 127 | 3.92 | 92 | 95 | 95 | 95 | 96 | 1.33 |
| CYPRUS | 98 | 96 | 99 | 106 | 106 | - .81 | 96 | 94 | 97 | 104 | 102 | - 1.29 |
| IRAN | 139 | 145 | 141 | 137 | 153 | 11.88 | 114 | 115 | 108 | 102 | 110 | 8.47 |
| IRAQ | 106 | 109 | 123 | 125 | 120 | - 3.74 | 84 | 83 | 91 | 89 | 83 | - 6.97 |
| JORDAN | 97 | 110 | 81 | 131 | 105 | - 20.12 | 76 | 84 | 59 | 93 | 71 | - 22.94 |
| LEBANON | 74 | 102 | 102 | 127 | 112 | - 12.38 | 67 | 94 | 95 | 118 | 103 | - 13.26 |
| SAUDI ARABIA | 135 | 128 | 93 | 41 | | | 99 | 90 | 63 | 26 | | |
| SYRIA | 157 | 184 | 172 | 228 | 220 | - 3.68 | 122 | 138 | 124 | 159 | 147 | - 7.32 |
| TURKEY | 130 | 135 | 140 | 143 | 142 | - .58 | 109 | 111 | 112 | 112 | 108 | - 2.98 |
| YEMEN ARAB REPUBLIC | 109 | 110 | 114 | 116 | 118 | 2.16 | 97 | 95 | 97 | 97 | 96 | - .05 |
| YEMEN DEMOCRATIC | 122 | 121 | 122 | 125 | 123 | - 1.88 | 106 | 102 | 101 | 101 | 96 | - 4.33 |
| ISRAEL | 135 | 138 | 142 | 139 | 138 | - 1.38 | 111 | 111 | 111 | 107 | 104 | - 3.20 |
| FAR EAST DEVELOPING | 126 | 131 | 129 | 133 | 140 | 5.66 | 108 | 110 | 105 | 106 | 110 | 3.46 |
| SOUTH ASIA | 122 | 126 | 122 | 127 | 134 | 5.67 | 104 | 105 | 100 | 101 | 105 | 3.45 |
| BANGLADESH | 111 | 116 | 115 | 121 | 120 | - .23 | 94 | 95 | 91 | 93 | 91 | - 3.01 |
| INDIA | 124 | 129 | 121 | 126 | 135 | 6.93 | 106 | 108 | 100 | 102 | 107 | 4.86 |
| NEPAL | 105 | 108 | 100 | 111 | 105 | - 5.83 | 90 | 90 | 82 | 89 | 82 | - 7.94 |
| PAKISTAN | 123 | 122 | 132 | 135 | 141 | 4.63 | 101 | 98 | 103 | 102 | 104 | 1.69 |
| SRI LANKA | 112 | 118 | 136 | 144 | 148 | 2.77 | 100 | 103 | 117 | 122 | 123 | .77 |
| EAST SOUTH-EAST ASIA | 137 | 145 | 146 | 148 | 156 | 5.66 | 117 | 121 | 120 | 119 | 123 | 3.52 |
| BURMA | 114 | 121 | 123 | 131 | 139 | 6.32 | 96 | 100 | 99 | 103 | 107 | 3.75 |
| INDONESIA | 124 | 129 | 132 | 142 | 147 | 3.08 | 108 | 111 | 111 | 118 | 119 | 1.39 |
| KOREA REP | 153 | 161 | 163 | 138 | 151 | 9.54 | 134 | 138 | 138 | 114 | 123 | 7.70 |
| LAO | 90 | 105 | 123 | 139 | 151 | 8.79 | 77 | 87 | 100 | 111 | 118 | 6.21 |
| MALAYSIA | 142 | 142 | 155 | 159 | 164 | 2.71 | 118 | 115 | 122 | 123 | 123 | - .24 |
| PHILIPPINES | 149 | 155 | 156 | 162 | 169 | 4.51 | 123 | 125 | 122 | 124 | 126 | 1.78 |
| THAILAND | 142 | 166 | 152 | 160 | 175 | 9.20 | 118 | 135 | 120 | 124 | 132 | 6.77 |
| JAPAN | 109 | 106 | 107 | 97 | 98 | 1.39 | 100 | 96 | 96 | 87 | 87 | .64 |
| ASIAN CENT PLANNED ECON | 121 | 130 | 136 | 136 | 141 | 3.65 | 106 | 112 | 116 | 115 | 117 | 2.24 |
| CHINA | 121 | 130 | 136 | 136 | 141 | 3.71 | 106 | 112 | 116 | 115 | 118 | 2.40 |
| KAMPUCHEA,DEMOCRATIC | 68 | 59 | 38 | 45 | 49 | 8.23 | 68 | 60 | 39 | 46 | 50 | 6.91 |
| KOREA DPR | 158 | 159 | 168 | 169 | 174 | 2.81 | 132 | 130 | 133 | 132 | 132 | .43 |
| MONGOLIA | 112 | 124 | 124 | 119 | 120 | .57 | 92 | 99 | 95 | 89 | 87 | - 2.17 |
| VIET NAM | 122 | 128 | 134 | 141 | 146 | 3.18 | 105 | 108 | 110 | 113 | 114 | .87 |
| OTHER DEVELOPING MRKT | 117 | 121 | 127 | 127 | 133 | 4.92 | 99 | 99 | 102 | 99 | 102 | 2.44 |

ANNEX TABLE 4. VOLUME OF EXPORTS OF MAJOR AGRICULTURAL, FISHERY AND FOREST PRODUCTS

| | 1967 | 1972 | 1973 | 1974 | 1975 | 1976 | 1977 | 1978 | 1979 | 1980 | 1981 | ANNUAL RATE OF CHANGE 1972-81 PERCENT |
|---|---|---|---|---|---|---|---|---|---|---|---|---|
| | ......................................................THOUSAND METRIC TONS.................................................... | | | | | | | | | | | |

**WORLD**

**AGRICULTURAL PRODUCTS**

| | 1967 | 1972 | 1973 | 1974 | 1975 | 1976 | 1977 | 1978 | 1979 | 1980 | 1981 | % |
|---|---|---|---|---|---|---|---|---|---|---|---|---|
| WHEAT+FLOUR,WHEAT EQUIV. | 51215 | 63462 | 79879 | 63657 | 72054 | 67293 | 72298 | 82373 | 78784 | 96459 | 102292 | 4.43 |
| RICE MILLED | 8246 | 8652 | 8583 | 8349 | 7800 | 9124 | 11044 | 9765 | 11876 | 13136 | 13519 | 6.01 |
| BARLEY | 7272 | 13989 | 12445 | 11693 | 12604 | 13927 | 13112 | 14586 | 14111 | 16215 | 19299 | 3.75 |
| MAIZE | 27714 | 37582 | 48352 | 49753 | 52051 | 62377 | 57764 | 68743 | 76087 | 80280 | 78930 | 8.27 |
| MILLET | 330 | 168 | 226 | 216 | 207 | 303 | 273 | 318 | 286 | 204 | 226 | 2.77 |
| SORGHUM | 7314 | 6168 | 9050 | 10766 | 10155 | 11161 | 11954 | 10923 | 11389 | 11152 | 14421 | 6.04 |
| POTATOES | 3362 | 5128 | 3912 | 3877 | 3931 | 4406 | 4697 | 4035 | 4626 | 4920 | 4909 | 1.36 |
| SUGAR,TOTAL (RAW EQUIV.) | 19798 | 21730 | 22762 | 22969 | 21484 | 22680 | 28417 | 25537 | 25858 | 26768 | 28937 | 3.11 |
| PULSES | 1670 | 1936 | 2013 | 1655 | 1788 | 1906 | 1976 | 2120 | 2366 | 2770 | 3103 | 5.49 |
| SOYBEANS | 8142 | 13794 | 15629 | 17233 | 16479 | 19766 | 20025 | 24058 | 25488 | 26875 | 26569 | 8.07 |
| SOYBEAN OIL | 670 | 1103 | 1053 | 1546 | 1365 | 1839 | 2106 | 2610 | 2953 | 3196 | 3483 | 15.26 |
| GROUNDNUTS SHELLED BASIS | 1528 | 966 | 1000 | 884 | 935 | 1077 | 886 | 800 | 794 | 749 | 881 | - 2.42 |
| GROUNDNUT OIL | 422 | 522 | 498 | 368 | 395 | 561 | 581 | 421 | 501 | 482 | 329 | - 1.57 |
| COPRA | 1213 | 1355 | 1043 | 527 | 1082 | 1147 | 941 | 685 | 434 | 450 | 404 | -11.04 |
| COCONUT OIL | 473 | 867 | 737 | 667 | 1043 | 1374 | 1110 | 1337 | 1142 | 1216 | 1356 | 6.74 |
| PALM NUTS KERNELS | 366 | 397 | 302 | 360 | 308 | 391 | 279 | 181 | 168 | 204 | 139 | -10.31 |
| PALM OIL | 574 | 1382 | 1514 | 1691 | 2043 | 2188 | 2332 | 2401 | 2839 | 3590 | 3323 | 10.90 |
| OILSEED CAKE AND MEAL | 9300 | 13168 | 14573 | 14719 | 14487 | 18817 | 19105 | 21883 | 23343 | 25802 | 27613 | 9.00 |
| BANANAS | 5217 | 6749 | 6786 | 6626 | 6371 | 6343 | 6660 | 6981 | 7097 | 7050 | 6782 | .59 |
| ORANGES+TANGER+CLEMEN | 3871 | 4631 | 5036 | 4999 | 5194 | 5210 | 5410 | 5204 | 4949 | 5106 | 5158 | .64 |
| LEMONS AND LIMES | 663 | 733 | 782 | 832 | 814 | 964 | 894 | 985 | 930 | 998 | 986 | 3.34 |
| COFFEE GREEN+ROASTED | 3188 | 3579 | 3804 | 3410 | 3575 | 3659 | 2938 | 3443 | 3800 | 3717 | 3763 | .30 |
| COCOA BEANS | 1094 | 1250 | 1109 | 1194 | 1161 | 1153 | 969 | 1088 | 1017 | 1090 | 1171 | - 1.13 |
| TEA | 696 | 781 | 803 | 812 | 828 | 865 | 913 | 886 | 927 | 968 | 958 | 2.50 |
| COTTON LINT | 3858 | 4096 | 4728 | 3818 | 3994 | 4049 | 3929 | 4458 | 4374 | 4815 | 4296 | .94 |
| JUTE AND SIMILAR FIBRES | 1093 | 757 | 906 | 890 | 590 | 670 | 569 | 515 | 571 | 524 | 592 | - 5.22 |
| TOBACCO UNMANUFACTURED | 1004 | 1213 | 1240 | 1389 | 1252 | 1317 | 1289 | 1440 | 1372 | 1355 | 1490 | 1.71 |
| NATURAL RUBBER | 2393 | 2849 | 3359 | 3191 | 3006 | 3249 | 3292 | 3317 | 3422 | 3327 | 3129 | .87 |
| WOOL GREASY | 1169 | 1204 | 1119 | 834 | 853 | 1010 | 1103 | 891 | 938 | 908 | 957 | - 1.64 |
| BOVINE CATTLE 1/ | 5505 | 7742 | 6860 | 6018 | 6839 | 6890 | 6687 | 7592 | 7437 | 6933 | 7202 | .47 |
| SHEEP AND GOATS 1/ | 8964 | 10999 | 10825 | 10397 | 11874 | 10775 | 12472 | 14853 | 15142 | 18165 | 19440 | 7.18 |
| PIGS 1/ | 3193 | 6096 | 5927 | 6071 | 6428 | 6943 | 6940 | 7945 | 8416 | 10736 | 9929 | 6.78 |
| TOTAL MEAT | 3853 | 5389 | 5681 | 5191 | 5502 | 6258 | 6809 | 7070 | 7838 | 8128 | 8772 | 6.11 |
| MILK DRY | 161 | 294 | 381 | 358 | 376 | 442 | 571 | 585 | 657 | 877 | 891 | 13.19 |
| TOTAL EGGS IN SHELL | 333 | 437 | 461 | 514 | 543 | 518 | 573 | 605 | 655 | 753 | 786 | 6.48 |

**FISHERY PRODUCTS**

| | 1967 | 1972 | 1973 | 1974 | 1975 | 1976 | 1977 | 1978 | 1979 | 1980 | 1981 | % |
|---|---|---|---|---|---|---|---|---|---|---|---|---|
| FISH FRESH FROZEN | 1741 | 2498 | 2855 | 2788 | 2967 | 3025 | 3460 | 3827 | 4226 | 3938 | 3175 | 4.58 |
| FISH CURED | 549 | 557 | 531 | 459 | 449 | 456 | 443 | 428 | 464 | 469 | 432 | - 1.96 |
| SHELLFISH | 343 | 690 | 712 | 706 | 761 | 879 | 844 | 990 | 1128 | 973 | 725 | 3.53 |
| FISH CANNED AND PREPARED | 540 | 677 | 739 | 747 | 721 | 831 | 792 | 839 | 872 | 941 | 846 | 3.00 |
| SHELLFISH CANNED+PREPAR | 67 | 91 | 93 | 89 | 88 | 94 | 102 | 116 | 117 | 99 | 78 | .84 |
| FISH BODY AND LIVER OIL | 812 | 749 | 550 | 558 | 597 | 565 | 566 | 694 | 743 | 752 | 673 | 1.89 |
| FISH MEAL | 3020 | 3008 | 1631 | 1951 | 2188 | 2113 | 2041 | 2107 | 2464 | 2340 | 2160 | .34 |

**FOREST PRODUCTS 2/**

| | 1967 | 1972 | 1973 | 1974 | 1975 | 1976 | 1977 | 1978 | 1979 | 1980 | 1981 | % |
|---|---|---|---|---|---|---|---|---|---|---|---|---|
| SAWLOGS CONIFEROUS | 16778 | 25489 | 28793 | 26238 | 23898 | 28411 | 28657 | 29893 | 31870 | 28072 | 22968 | .33 |
| SAWLOGS NONCONIFEROUS | 25216 | 42618 | 51864 | 44885 | 36366 | 45481 | 47174 | 48449 | 46058 | 42140 | 33361 | - 1.58 |
| PULPWOOD+PARTICLE | 19537 | 23071 | 29208 | 32980 | 31876 | 33851 | 35120 | 32665 | 36412 | 40914 | 41575 | 5.14 |
| FUELWOOD | 1283 | 1049 | 1291 | 1288 | 1040 | 783 | 1066 | 632 | 720 | 865 | 594 | - 7.02 |
| SAWNWOOD CONIFEROUS | 42830 | 57094 | 60913 | 51822 | 43250 | 56294 | 61793 | 65962 | 68826 | 66058 | 60789 | 2.40 |
| SAWNWOOD NONCONIFEROUS | 5691 | 8413 | 10648 | 8928 | 7956 | 11461 | 11240 | 12046 | 13438 | 12616 | 10970 | 4.24 |
| WOOD-BASED PANELS | 7140 | 12700 | 14674 | 12963 | 12436 | 14383 | 14690 | 16132 | 16303 | 15732 | 15940 | 2.75 |
| PULP FOR PAPER | 11811 | 14580 | 16666 | 17192 | 13525 | 15309 | 15401 | 17311 | 18491 | 19634 | 18763 | 2.78 |
| PAPER AND PAPERBOARD | 18214 | 25247 | 27522 | 29962 | 22867 | 27092 | 28294 | 30327 | 33328 | 35114 | 35567 | 3.84 |

**WESTERN EUROPE**

**AGRICULTURAL PRODUCTS**

| | 1967 | 1972 | 1973 | 1974 | 1975 | 1976 | 1977 | 1978 | 1979 | 1980 | 1981 | % |
|---|---|---|---|---|---|---|---|---|---|---|---|---|
| WHEAT+FLOUR,WHEAT EQUIV. | 5431 | 9457 | 11857 | 11587 | 13472 | 13635 | 11782 | 12485 | 14505 | 18221 | 21927 | 7.10 |
| RICE MILLED | 359 | 525 | 405 | 616 | 625 | 670 | 751 | 850 | 889 | 968 | 1000 | 9.36 |
| BARLEY | 4085 | 5311 | 5586 | 5966 | 5686 | 5075 | 4408 | 8634 | 7199 | 8057 | 9880 | 6.38 |
| MAIZE | 2782 | 4593 | 5613 | 6012 | 5666 | 5876 | 4458 | 4869 | 5050 | 5474 | 4821 | - .81 |
| MILLET | 2 | 5 | 9 | 7 | 15 | 11 | 12 | 12 | 13 | 14 | 19 | 10.53 |
| SORGHUM | 176 | 195 | 276 | 711 | 736 | 771 | 384 | 262 | 308 | 206 | 241 | - 4.79 |
| POTATOES | 1864 | 2763 | 2485 | 2358 | 2589 | 2337 | 2708 | 2798 | 3016 | 3455 | 3557 | 3.82 |
| SUGAR,TOTAL (RAW EQUIV.) | 1079 | 2604 | 2615 | 2439 | 2082 | 2839 | 3628 | 4124 | 4280 | 5210 | 5680 | 10.82 |
| PULSES | 238 | 291 | 288 | 253 | 323 | 226 | 302 | 353 | 450 | 457 | 436 | 6.45 |
| SOYBEANS | | 269 | 113 | 16 | 111 | 189 | 120 | 237 | 353 | 327 | 160 | 12.99 |
| SOYBEAN OIL | 123 | 395 | 470 | 720 | 719 | 744 | 767 | 1099 | 1208 | 1204 | 1272 | 13.58 |
| GROUNDNUTS SHELLED BASIS | 17 | 18 | 18 | 18 | 14 | 24 | 22 | 29 | 15 | 19 | 23 | 2.18 |
| GROUNDNUT OIL | 35 | 32 | 54 | 51 | 74 | 49 | 44 | 45 | 64 | 79 | 68 | 5.62 |
| COPRA | 3 | 7 | 6 | | 1 | 17 | 3 | 4 | 1 | | | |

1/ THOUSAND HEAD
2/ EXCEPT FOR PULP FOR PAPER AND PAPER AND PAPERBOARD, ALL FOREST PRODUCTS ARE EXPRESSED IN THOUSAND CUBIC METRES

ANNEX TABLE 4. VOLUME OF EXPORTS OF MAJOR AGRICULTURAL, FISHERY AND FOREST PRODUCTS

| | 1967 | 1972 | 1973 | 1974 | 1975 | 1976 | 1977 | 1978 | 1979 | 1980 | 1981 | ANNUAL RATE OF CHANGE 1972-81 PERCENT |
|---|---|---|---|---|---|---|---|---|---|---|---|---|
| | | | | | ....THOUSAND METRIC TONS.... | | | | | | | |
| COCONUT OIL | 50 | 143 | 117 | 78 | 203 | 269 | 163 | 119 | 61 | 43 | 56 | -10.69 |
| PALM NUTS KERNELS | | 1 | 1 | 5 | 1 | 1 | 1 | 1 | 2 | 1 | 1 | - .17 |
| PALM OIL | 18 | 77 | 80 | 68 | 86 | 98 | 111 | 97 | 92 | 123 | 112 | 5.23 |
| OILSEED CAKE AND MEAL | 1254 | 2150 | 2710 | 2875 | 2257 | 2630 | 2519 | 3437 | 3957 | 4247 | 4925 | 8.47 |
| BANANAS | 76 | 30 | 23 | 27 | 35 | 25 | 31 | 41 | 43 | 43 | 48 | 7.29 |
| ORANGES+TANGER+CLEMEN | 1506 | 1837 | 1943 | 1933 | 1999 | 2056 | 2113 | 1921 | 1906 | 1799 | 1808 | - .51 |
| LEMONS AND LIMES | 431 | 424 | 384 | 444 | 461 | 525 | 464 | 505 | 483 | 512 | 486 | 2.34 |
| COFFEE GREEN+ROASTED | 21 | 47 | 62 | 76 | 86 | 92 | 78 | 102 | 124 | 106 | 120 | 9.53 |
| COCOA BEANS | 4 | 2 | 3 | 6 | 11 | 15 | 30 | 34 | 32 | 44 | 48 | 44.27 |
| TEA | 40 | 47 | 58 | 61 | 43 | 46 | 60 | 50 | 46 | 43 | 44 | - 1.99 |
| COTTON LINT | 126 | 74 | 101 | 79 | 65 | 89 | 70 | 71 | 60 | 57 | 55 | - 4.81 |
| JUTE AND SIMILAR FIBRES | 42 | 29 | 28 | 25 | 21 | 18 | 17 | 19 | 16 | 17 | 16 | - 6.69 |
| TOBACCO UNMANUFACTURED | 129 | 148 | 141 | 196 | 177 | 179 | 153 | 223 | 234 | 197 | 208 | 4.23 |
| NATURAL RUBBER | 21 | 24 | 30 | 40 | 29 | 32 | 27 | 21 | 21 | 16 | 16 | - 7.32 |
| WOOL GREASY | 57 | 66 | 55 | 43 | 55 | 64 | 57 | 60 | 65 | 69 | 63 | 2.16 |
| BOVINE CATTLE 1/ | 2003 | 3094 | 2566 | 2312 | 3416 | 3121 | 2979 | 3322 | 3340 | 3412 | 3544 | 3.03 |
| SHEEP AND GOATS 1/ | 724 | 790 | 619 | 575 | 1152 | 1183 | 1318 | 1732 | 1384 | 1418 | 1079 | 9.08 |
| PIGS 1/ | 881 | 2445 | 2552 | 2576 | 2596 | 3112 | 3106 | 3421 | 4004 | 4777 | 4763 | 8.47 |
| TOTAL MEAT | 1224 | 1823 | 1933 | 2215 | 2434 | 2394 | 2652 | 2825 | 3173 | 3673 | 3868 | 8.60 |
| MILK DRY | 133 | 221 | 289 | 272 | 285 | 334 | 432 | 450 | 514 | 660 | 681 | 13.37 |
| TOTAL EGGS IN SHELL | 125 | 237 | 262 | 308 | 326 | 335 | 349 | 382 | 445 | 505 | 539 | 9.06 |

FISHERY PRODUCTS

| | 1967 | 1972 | 1973 | 1974 | 1975 | 1976 | 1977 | 1978 | 1979 | 1980 | 1981 | PERCENT |
|---|---|---|---|---|---|---|---|---|---|---|---|---|
| FISH FRESH FROZEN | 863 | 1061 | 1095 | 1017 | 1054 | 1115 | 1151 | 1394 | 1685 | 1622 | 1293 | 4.92 |
| FISH CURED | 330 | 349 | 327 | 283 | 278 | 288 | 267 | 255 | 276 | 281 | 258 | - 2.54 |
| SHELLFISH | 115 | 243 | 196 | 225 | 250 | 274 | 232 | 263 | 277 | 311 | 200 | 1.51 |
| FISH CANNED AND PREPARED | 181 | 198 | 235 | 226 | 207 | 243 | 240 | 259 | 261 | 258 | 237 | 2.24 |
| SHELLFISH CANNED+PREPAR | 12 | 26 | 28 | 24 | 27 | 32 | 34 | 36 | 38 | 40 | 36 | 5.27 |
| FISH BODY AND LIVER OIL | 391 | 196 | 271 | 196 | 249 | 319 | 328 | 270 | 295 | 330 | 331 | 5.23 |
| FISH MEAL | 811 | 840 | 797 | 803 | 864 | 948 | 1019 | 882 | 951 | 924 | 903 | 1.63 |

FOREST PRODUCTS 2/

| | 1967 | 1972 | 1973 | 1974 | 1975 | 1976 | 1977 | 1978 | 1979 | 1980 | 1981 | PERCENT |
|---|---|---|---|---|---|---|---|---|---|---|---|---|
| SAWLOGS CONIFEROUS | 1549 | 1380 | 2236 | 2784 | 1704 | 2428 | 2590 | 1899 | 2395 | 2937 | 2737 | 4.78 |
| SAWLOGS NONCONIFEROUS | 1166 | 1549 | 1850 | 1943 | 1665 | 1833 | 2077 | 2017 | 2055 | 2262 | 2149 | 3.29 |
| PULPWOOD+PARTICLE | 4930 | 6089 | 7114 | 7920 | 8627 | 8166 | 7573 | 6843 | 8457 | 10717 | 11102 | 4.86 |
| FUELWOOD | 727 | 604 | 881 | 888 | 735 | 512 | 740 | 314 | 442 | 554 | 342 | - 8.16 |
| SAWNWOOD CONIFEROUS | 12836 | 17929 | 20295 | 17248 | 12640 | 17061 | 16554 | 18051 | 20349 | 19783 | 17144 | .78 |
| SAWNWOOD NONCONIFEROUS | 1232 | 1766 | 2274 | 1858 | 1607 | 2801 | 2494 | 2756 | 2514 | 2395 | 2039 | 2.87 |
| WOOD-BASED PANELS | 3220 | 5270 | 6337 | 5854 | 5171 | 6151 | 6194 | 6737 | 7386 | 7057 | 6730 | 3.02 |
| PULP FOR PAPER | 6400 | 6623 | 8036 | 7436 | 5179 | 5670 | 5559 | 6689 | 6837 | 6635 | 6218 | - .95 |
| PAPER AND PAPERBOARD | 7788 | 12032 | 13708 | 14964 | 10655 | 13098 | 13753 | 15658 | 17387 | 17427 | 18199 | 4.56 |

USSR AND EASTERN EUROPE

AGRICULTURAL PRODUCTS

| | 1967 | 1972 | 1973 | 1974 | 1975 | 1976 | 1977 | 1978 | 1979 | 1980 | 1981 | PERCENT |
|---|---|---|---|---|---|---|---|---|---|---|---|---|
| WHEAT+FLOUR,WHEAT EQUIV. | 7568 | 5801 | 6852 | 8008 | 5109 | 3912 | 5149 | 3659 | 4691 | 3916 | 4131 | - 6.09 |
| RICE MILLED | 6 | 92 | 90 | 149 | 16 | 11 | 11 | 14 | 25 | 36 | 28 | -14.91 |
| BARLEY | 608 | 847 | 570 | 1158 | 1040 | 943 | 1725 | 222 | 232 | 308 | 238 | -15.50 |
| MAIZE | 1595 | 946 | 1570 | 1727 | 983 | 1536 | 1318 | 1493 | 554 | 1325 | 1367 | - 1.48 |
| POTATOES | 704 | 1510 | 534 | 648 | 490 | 442 | 682 | 371 | 655 | 322 | 310 | -10.41 |
| SUGAR,TOTAL (RAW EQUIV.) | 2241 | 888 | 754 | 724 | 403 | 527 | 743 | 877 | 660 | 679 | 794 | .28 |
| PULSES | 213 | 127 | 118 | 115 | 119 | 112 | 117 | 135 | 145 | 122 | 120 | .76 |
| SOYBEANS | 4 | 10 | 34 | 31 | 11 | 10 | 32 | 6 | 30 | 5 | 4 | -12.71 |
| SOYBEAN OIL | 1 | 3 | 6 | 8 | 2 | 12 | 13 | 7 | 10 | 17 | 14 | 16.23 |
| GROUNDNUTS SHELLED BASIS | 2 | 1 | | 1 | | | | | 1 | 1 | | |
| OILSEED CAKE AND MEAL | 404 | 79 | 75 | 47 | 49 | 14 | 61 | 53 | 20 | 27 | 8 | -16.79 |
| ORANGES+TANGER+CLEMEN | 5 | | | | | | | | | 1 | 1 | |
| TEA | 10 | 12 | 13 | 14 | 17 | 15 | 22 | 17 | 17 | 20 | 18 | 5.15 |
| COTTON LINT | 566 | 662 | 734 | 740 | 801 | 887 | 976 | 865 | 807 | 863 | 927 | 3.03 |
| JUTE AND SIMILAR FIBRES | 1 | 2 | 3 | | | | | | | | | |
| TOBACCO UNMANUFACTURED | 118 | 88 | 97 | 100 | 102 | 101 | 99 | 89 | 102 | 103 | 93 | .31 |
| NATURAL RUBBER | 25 | | | | | | | | | | | |
| WOOL GREASY | 3 | 1 | 1 | 1 | 1 | 1 | 1 | 2 | 3 | 3 | 2 | 15.70 |
| BOVINE CATTLE 1/ | 525 | 817 | 783 | 630 | 686 | 498 | 540 | 544 | 676 | 577 | 446 | - 4.64 |
| SHEEP AND GOATS 1/ | 1596 | 3183 | 3168 | 2875 | 3457 | 3025 | 3504 | 3800 | 4609 | 4522 | 4602 | 5.35 |
| PIGS 1/ | 366 | 787 | 412 | 628 | 944 | 720 | 720 | 1158 | 1152 | 1143 | 1818 | 11.74 |
| TOTAL MEAT | 492 | 395 | 433 | 527 | 627 | 547 | 658 | 620 | 744 | 736 | 777 | 7.33 |
| TOTAL EGGS IN SHELL | 112 | 108 | 103 | 111 | 121 | 101 | 120 | 114 | 104 | 90 | 66 | - 3.46 |

FISHERY PRODUCTS

| | 1967 | 1972 | 1973 | 1974 | 1975 | 1976 | 1977 | 1978 | 1979 | 1980 | 1981 | PERCENT |
|---|---|---|---|---|---|---|---|---|---|---|---|---|
| FISH FRESH FROZEN | 209 | 345 | 379 | 494 | 606 | 607 | 540 | 569 | 605 | 619 | 556 | 5.25 |
| FISH CURED | 36 | 16 | 15 | 13 | 19 | 12 | 11 | 15 | 21 | 16 | 16 | 1.31 |
| SHELLFISH | 11 | 4 | 7 | 3 | 1 | 1 | 1 | 2 | 1 | 2 | 1 | -12.41 |
| FISH CANNED AND PREPARED | 24 | 29 | 31 | 32 | 45 | 47 | 48 | 40 | 36 | 39 | 37 | 2.50 |
| SHELLFISH CANNED+PREPAR | 5 | 3 | 2 | 2 | 3 | 2 | 1 | 1 | 1 | 2 | 2 | - 7.07 |
| FISH BODY AND LIVER OIL | 58 | 17 | 6 | 6 | 4 | 2 | 1 | 1 | 1 | 1 | 1 | -25.77 |
| FISH MEAL | 38 | 18 | 13 | 11 | 19 | 18 | 14 | 21 | 20 | 22 | 23 | 5.46 |

1/ THOUSAND HEAD
2/ EXCEPT FOR PULP FOR PAPER AND PAPER AND PAPERBOARD, ALL FOREST PRODUCTS ARE EXPRESSED IN THOUSAND CUBIC METRES

ANNEX TABLE 4. VOLUME OF EXPORTS OF MAJOR AGRICULTURAL, FISHERY AND FOREST PRODUCTS

| | 1967 | 1972 | 1973 | 1974 | 1975 | 1976 | 1977 | 1978 | 1979 | 1980 | 1981 | ANNUAL RATE OF CHANGE 1972-81 PERCENT |
|---|---|---|---|---|---|---|---|---|---|---|---|---|
| | | | | | | THOUSAND METRIC TONS | | | | | | |
| **FOREST PRODUCTS 2/** | | | | | | | | | | | | |
| SAWLOGS CONIFEROUS | 5005 | 7982 | 10195 | 9829 | 8884 | 9534 | 9919 | 10281 | 8763 | 7445 | 7110 | - 2.00 |
| SAWLOGS NONCONIFEROUS | 176 | 290 | 334 | 397 | 354 | 201 | 315 | 296 | 404 | 384 | 285 | .48 |
| PULPWOOD+PARTICLE | 8432 | 8021 | 11019 | 12480 | 12146 | 12401 | 12155 | 11375 | 12066 | 12206 | 12128 | 2.49 |
| FUELWOOD | 254 | 108 | 141 | 127 | 95 | 40 | 63 | 92 | 46 | 31 | 18 | -17.29 |
| SAWNWOOD CONIFEROUS | 10882 | 11059 | 11085 | 9865 | 10362 | 11009 | 10592 | 10782 | 9956 | 9513 | 9370 | - 1.47 |
| SAWNWOOD NONCONIFEROUS | 793 | 827 | 825 | 767 | 749 | 714 | 702 | 752 | 600 | 597 | 539 | - 4.35 |
| WOOD-BASED PANELS | 906 | 1247 | 1476 | 1457 | 1588 | 1702 | 1791 | 1875 | 1842 | 1827 | 1673 | 3.61 |
| PULP FOR PAPER | 472 | 599 | 618 | 592 | 601 | 728 | 754 | 851 | 753 | 889 | 892 | 5.23 |
| PAPER AND PAPERBOARD | 634 | 1180 | 1264 | 1304 | 1095 | 1480 | 1653 | 1779 | 1664 | 1715 | 1755 | 5.28 |
| **NORTH AMERICA DEVELOPED** | | | | | | | | | | | | |
| **AGRICULTURAL PRODUCTS** | | | | | | | | | | | | |
| WHEAT+FLOUR,WHEAT EQUIV. | 28523 | 36693 | 50900 | 36371 | 43188 | 38493 | 40151 | 50193 | 46586 | 53756 | 60776 | 4.12 |
| RICE MILLED | 1851 | 2038 | 1630 | 1726 | 2139 | 2107 | 2345 | 2342 | 2323 | 3065 | 3197 | 6.47 |
| BARLEY | 2017 | 5749 | 5168 | 3547 | 4068 | 5432 | 4343 | 4249 | 4654 | 4195 | 6831 | .83 |
| MAIZE | 12938 | 22409 | 33215 | 29875 | 33526 | 44692 | 40580 | 50550 | 59414 | 63923 | 56063 | 11.13 |
| SORGHUM | 5832 | 3858 | 5629 | 5722 | 5848 | 5797 | 6139 | 5184 | 5950 | 8050 | 8032 | 5.60 |
| POTATOES | 292 | 300 | 313 | 356 | 369 | 857 | 503 | 282 | 289 | 344 | 395 | .47 |
| SUGAR,TOTAL (RAW EQUIV.) | 21 | 18 | 65 | 97 | 268 | 112 | 153 | 137 | 124 | 602 | 1092 | 36.93 |
| PULSES | 295 | 359 | 416 | 339 | 390 | 400 | 374 | 390 | 470 | 912 | 1141 | 11.17 |
| SOYBEANS | 7234 | 12034 | 13250 | 13953 | 12506 | 15361 | 16234 | 20794 | 20952 | 21882 | 21980 | 7.90 |
| SOYBEAN OIL | 532 | 618 | 439 | 766 | 355 | 506 | 768 | 916 | 1110 | 1081 | 809 | 8.75 |
| GROUNDNUTS SHELLED BASIS | 78 | 196 | 192 | 262 | 244 | 132 | 306 | 393 | 368 | 292 | 153 | 2.85 |
| GROUNDNUT OIL | 3 | 28 | 47 | 21 | 12 | 48 | 45 | 40 | 5 | 18 | 20 | - 7.67 |
| COCONUT OIL | 5 | 6 | 11 | 5 | 8 | 26 | 17 | 9 | 5 | 19 | 14 | 7.36 |
| OILSEED CAKE AND MEAL | 3082 | 4084 | 5075 | 5260 | 4113 | 5370 | 4740 | 6793 | 6845 | 8009 | 7472 | 7.11 |
| BANANAS | 61 | 188 | 188 | 195 | 187 | 201 | 199 | 201 | 197 | 205 | 217 | 1.33 |
| ORANGES+TANGER+CLEMEN | 303 | 303 | 292 | 328 | 481 | 461 | 410 | 356 | 318 | 482 | 443 | 3.56 |
| LEMONS AND LIMES | 117 | 157 | 201 | 202 | 183 | 225 | 236 | 237 | 173 | 171 | 176 | - .01 |
| COFFEE GREEN+ROASTED | 28 | 34 | 72 | 85 | 55 | 69 | 106 | 59 | 79 | 79 | 70 | 4.62 |
| COCOA BEANS | 7 | 4 | 9 | 23 | 9 | 10 | 14 | 9 | 9 | 7 | 14 | 2.78 |
| TEA | 2 | 3 | 3 | 3 | 4 | 3 | 4 | 5 | 5 | 5 | 4 | 5.36 |
| COTTON LINT | 906 | 701 | 1246 | 1172 | 871 | 779 | 1017 | 1347 | 1527 | 1823 | 1269 | 6.83 |
| JUTE AND SIMILAR FIBRES | 1 | 1 | 1 | 1 | 1 | 1 | 2 | 1 | | | | |
| TOBACCO UNMANUFACTURED | 285 | 314 | 313 | 335 | 293 | 293 | 314 | 364 | 299 | 293 | 300 | - .43 |
| NATURAL RUBBER | 44 | 21 | 27 | 26 | 29 | 29 | 25 | 20 | 21 | 28 | 18 | - 2.05 |
| WOOL GREASY | 1 | 1 | 1 | 1 | 1 | | | | | | 1 | |
| BOVINE CATTLE 1/ | 319 | 405 | 699 | 360 | 421 | 684 | 651 | 592 | 436 | 424 | 441 | - .49 |
| SHEEP AND GOATS 1/ | 134 | 174 | 214 | 293 | 344 | 250 | 214 | 153 | 135 | 144 | 225 | - 4.08 |
| PIGS 1/ | 33 | 101 | 107 | 213 | 47 | 56 | 54 | 201 | 145 | 254 | 171 | 8.33 |
| TOTAL MEAT | 254 | 369 | 441 | 403 | 472 | 693 | 700 | 721 | 777 | 973 | 1073 | 12.69 |
| MILK DRY | 6 | 18 | 23 | 21 | 17 | 17 | 16 | 7 | 5 | 36 | 55 | 2.02 |
| TOTAL EGGS IN SHELL | 16 | 11 | 18 | 21 | 22 | 22 | 38 | 39 | 30 | 61 | 87 | 20.49 |
| **FISHERY PRODUCTS** | | | | | | | | | | | | |
| FISH FRESH FROZEN | 213 | 234 | 264 | 200 | 236 | 250 | 352 | 383 | 413 | 418 | 376 | 8.14 |
| FISH CURED | 49 | 52 | 49 | 49 | 47 | 62 | 65 | 65 | 64 | 75 | 71 | 5.11 |
| SHELLFISH | 24 | 36 | 47 | 39 | 42 | 48 | 71 | 119 | 133 | 114 | 85 | 15.33 |
| FISH CANNED AND PREPARED | 43 | 43 | 52 | 39 | 36 | 46 | 51 | 63 | 64 | 78 | 67 | 6.93 |
| SHELLFISH CANNED+PREPAR | 11 | 9 | 10 | 8 | 8 | 9 | 9 | 11 | 10 | 10 | 9 | 1.34 |
| FISH BODY AND LIVER OIL | 47 | 95 | 121 | 101 | 93 | 91 | 60 | 110 | 101 | 137 | 137 | 2.67 |
| FISH MEAL | 49 | 42 | 63 | 85 | 35 | 63 | 61 | 82 | 43 | 108 | 30 | - .04 |
| **FOREST PRODUCTS 2/** | | | | | | | | | | | | |
| SAWLOGS CONIFEROUS | 9247 | 14104 | 14248 | 12118 | 12196 | 14842 | 14362 | 15565 | 17865 | 15135 | 11676 | .83 |
| SAWLOGS NONCONIFEROUS | 522 | 497 | 567 | 622 | 328 | 470 | 481 | 522 | 630 | 784 | 751 | 4.64 |
| PULPWOOD+PARTICLE | 5837 | 6768 | 7837 | 8402 | 6867 | 8337 | 8710 | 8216 | 9463 | 9887 | 10576 | 4.22 |
| FUELWOOD | | 15 | 19 | 18 | 34 | 27 | 33 | 28 | 16 | 11 | 18 | - 2.04 |
| SAWNWOOD CONIFEROUS | 17250 | 25705 | 27339 | 22944 | 18553 | 26379 | 32305 | 34492 | 35407 | 33612 | 31770 | 4.70 |
| SAWNWOOD NONCONIFEROUS | 808 | 1006 | 1072 | 705 | 807 | 814 | 847 | 1341 | 1025 | 1190 | 1209 | 3.59 |
| WOOD-BASED PANELS | 775 | 1225 | 1558 | 1518 | 1507 | 1567 | 1500 | 1781 | 1608 | 1772 | 2021 | 3.80 |
| PULP FOR PAPER | 4564 | 6578 | 7162 | 8011 | 6621 | 7603 | 7657 | 8051 | 8787 | 9704 | 9141 | 3.79 |
| PAPER AND PAPERBOARD | 9065 | 10981 | 11255 | 12255 | 9726 | 10935 | 11232 | 11124 | 12326 | 13675 | 13134 | 2.10 |
| **OCEANIA DEVELOPED** | | | | | | | | | | | | |
| **AGRICULTURAL PRODUCTS** | | | | | | | | | | | | |
| WHEAT+FLOUR,WHEAT EQUIV. | 6840 | 8641 | 5592 | 5270 | 8105 | 7787 | 8130 | 11082 | 6903 | 14933 | 10642 | 6.95 |
| RICE MILLED | 90 | 181 | 158 | 137 | 174 | 218 | 256 | 277 | 241 | 457 | 281 | 10.08 |
| BARLEY | 425 | 1828 | 844 | 808 | 1760 | 2022 | 2157 | 1375 | 1757 | 3047 | 1650 | 7.07 |
| MAIZE | 2 | 38 | 19 | 3 | 1 | 88 | 79 | 32 | 75 | 37 | 52 | 22.29 |
| MILLET | 18 | 40 | 25 | 31 | 21 | 20 | 23 | 15 | 18 | 14 | 11 | -10.88 |
| SORGHUM | 45 | 993 | 736 | 748 | 856 | 815 | 829 | 385 | 516 | 580 | 463 | - 7.45 |
| POTATOES | 20 | 16 | 21 | 16 | 21 | 25 | 29 | 20 | 18 | 23 | 21 | 2.17 |

1/ THOUSAND HEAD
2/ EXCEPT FOR PULP FOR PAPER AND PAPER AND PAPERBOARD, ALL FOREST PRODUCTS ARE EXPRESSED IN THOUSAND CUBIC METRES

ANNEX TABLE 4. VOLUME OF EXPORTS OF MAJOR AGRICULTURAL, FISHERY AND FOREST PRODUCTS

| | 1967 | 1972 | 1973 | 1974 | 1975 | 1976 | 1977 | 1978 | 1979 | 1980 | 1981 | ANNUAL RATE OF CHANGE 1972-81 PERCENT |
|---|---|---|---|---|---|---|---|---|---|---|---|---|
| | | | | | | THOUSAND METRIC TONS | | | | | | |
| SUGAR,TOTAL (RAW EQUIV.) | 1665 | 2009 | 2085 | 1782 | 1996 | 2000 | 2556 | 2478 | 1840 | 2201 | 2561 | 2.22 |
| PULSES | 24 | 37 | 44 | 42 | 36 | 33 | 40 | 36 | 45 | 72 | 64 | 5.53 |
| | | | | | | | | | | | | |
| SOYBEANS | | | 1 | 2 | 4 | 32 | | | | | | |
| GROUNDNUTS SHELLED BASIS | | 1 | 7 | 7 | 2 | 2 | 4 | 2 | 2 | 12 | 6 | 9.18 |
| OILSEED CAKE AND MEAL | 2 | 2 | 1 | | 1 | 3 | 2 | 1 | 1 | 1 | | |
| ORANGES+TANGER+CLEMEN | 26 | 34 | 32 | 24 | 15 | 18 | 11 | 22 | 25 | 38 | 32 | 1.08 |
| LEMONS AND LIMES | 1 | 1 | 1 | 1 | 1 | 1 | 1 | | | 4 | 1 | |
| COCOA BEANS | | 1 | 1 | 1 | | | | | | | | |
| TEA | 1 | 1 | 1 | 1 | 1 | 1 | | 1 | | | | |
| | | | | | | | | | | | | |
| COTTON LINT | | 2 | 22 | 3 | 8 | 16 | 6 | 10 | 24 | 49 | 59 | 30.58 |
| | | | | | | | | | | | | |
| TOBACCO UNMANUFACTURED | | | | | | | | 1 | | 1 | 1 | |
| NATURAL RUBBER | | | | | | | | | | 1 | | |
| | | | | | | | | | | | | |
| WOOL GREASY | 811 | 905 | 859 | 634 | 588 | 750 | 826 | 630 | 705 | 650 | 680 | - 2.22 |
| BOVINE CATTLE 1/ | 6 | 7 | 17 | 34 | 13 | 33 | 45 | 71 | 107 | 74 | 109 | 32.43 |
| SHEEP AND GOATS 1/ | 351 | 891 | 1145 | 1159 | 1456 | 1847 | 3409 | 4143 | 3898 | 6173 | 5763 | 26.21 |
| PIGS 1/ | 1 | 2 | 1 | 1 | 1 | 1 | | | 1 | 1 | | |
| TOTAL MEAT | 897 | 1367 | 1542 | 1208 | 1183 | 1446 | 1643 | 1667 | 1815 | 1494 | 1601 | 2.70 |
| MILK DRY | 19 | 37 | 48 | 51 | 56 | 53 | 100 | 109 | 123 | 161 | 137 | 17.94 |
| TOTAL EGGS IN SHELL | 3 | 4 | 4 | 2 | 2 | 2 | 1 | 1 | 1 | 1 | 1 | -11.43 |
| | | | | | | | | | | | | |
| FISHERY PRODUCTS | | | | | | | | | | | | |
| | | | | | | | | | | | | |
| FISH FRESH FROZEN | 4 | 14 | 14 | 13 | 12 | 19 | 28 | 32 | 54 | 32 | 32 | 15.35 |
| SHELLFISH | 10 | 18 | 17 | 16 | 16 | 14 | 17 | 20 | 32 | 22 | 23 | 5.20 |
| FISH CANNED AND PREPARED | | | 2 | | 1 | 1 | | | 1 | | | |
| SHELLFISH CANNED+PREPAR | 1 | 4 | 3 | 2 | 2 | 2 | 2 | 2 | 2 | 2 | 2 | - 8.43 |
| FISH BODY AND LIVER OIL | 4 | 6 | 8 | 8 | 4 | 8 | 5 | 4 | 5 | 5 | 5 | - 4.10 |
| | | | | | | | | | | | | |
| FOREST PRODUCTS 2/ | | | | | | | | | | | | |
| | | | | | | | | | | | | |
| SAWLOGS CONIFEROUS | 796 | 1844 | 1916 | 1302 | 534 | 958 | 1027 | 936 | 1236 | 971 | 529 | - 8.41 |
| SAWLOGS NONCONIFEROUS | 1 | 14 | 9 | 12 | 3 | 1 | 3 | 2 | 1 | 4 | 4 | -17.23 |
| PULPWOOD+PARTICLE | | 1047 | 2199 | 2931 | 3061 | 3866 | 5326 | 5074 | 5357 | 7064 | 6676 | 19.72 |
| FUELWOOD | | | | | 1 | | | | | | | |
| SAWNWOOD CONIFEROUS | 97 | 266 | 248 | 245 | 160 | 232 | 295 | 367 | 509 | 617 | 546 | 12.39 |
| SAWNWOOD NONCONIFEROUS | 29 | 27 | 54 | 51 | 32 | 23 | 31 | 30 | 41 | 54 | 36 | 1.00 |
| WOOD-BASED PANELS | 39 | 75 | 93 | 52 | 61 | 28 | 32 | 52 | 104 | 142 | 138 | 7.25 |
| PULP FOR PAPER | 74 | 114 | 142 | 232 | 335 | 375 | 452 | 435 | 464 | 475 | 518 | 17.43 |
| PAPER AND PAPERBOARD | 148 | 202 | 189 | 214 | 204 | 269 | 302 | 332 | 359 | 418 | 447 | 10.77 |
| | | | | | | | | | | | | |
| **AFRICA DEVELOPING** | | | | | | | | | | | | |
| | | | | | | | | | | | | |
| AGRICULTURAL PRODUCTS | | | | | | | | | | | | |
| | | | | | | | | | | | | |
| WHEAT+FLOUR,WHEAT EQUIV. | 68 | 74 | 66 | 36 | 22 | 17 | 17 | 35 | 25 | 15 | 4 | -19.77 |
| RICE MILLED | 63 | 53 | 45 | 31 | 18 | 57 | 57 | 13 | 12 | 24 | 12 | -13.31 |
| BARLEY | 6 | | 65 | 2 | 5 | | 1 | | 2 | | | |
| MAIZE | 864 | 726 | 807 | 626 | 1009 | 472 | 434 | 646 | 359 | 63 | 244 | -17.57 |
| MILLET | 65 | 10 | 29 | 59 | 10 | 79 | 13 | 31 | 68 | 36 | 32 | 9.21 |
| SORGHUM | 8 | 5 | 5 | 5 | 10 | 2 | | | 53 | | | |
| | | | | | | | | | | | | |
| POTATOES | 134 | 121 | 104 | 83 | 97 | 91 | 82 | 58 | 50 | 56 | 38 | -10.83 |
| SUGAR,TOTAL (RAW EQUIV.) | 1303 | 1476 | 1590 | 1466 | 1132 | 1355 | 1460 | 1302 | 1619 | 1658 | 1518 | .93 |
| PULSES | 272 | 464 | 465 | 357 | 319 | 410 | 261 | 154 | 172 | 177 | 103 | -14.90 |
| | | | | | | | | | | | | |
| SOYBEANS | 8 | 8 | 9 | 2 | 21 | 3 | 13 | 36 | 1 | | 1 | |
| GROUNDNUTS SHELLED BASIS | 1058 | 375 | 384 | 198 | 169 | 296 | 197 | 71 | 89 | 88 | 44 | -19.90 |
| GROUNDNUT OIL | 272 | 315 | 239 | 155 | 226 | 290 | 258 | 98 | 158 | 90 | 38 | -15.81 |
| COPRA | 74 | 59 | 69 | 62 | 42 | 60 | 55 | 34 | 37 | 24 | 18 | -11.98 |
| COCONUT OIL | 14 | 11 | 17 | 18 | 9 | 11 | 6 | 12 | 15 | 17 | 19 | 2.46 |
| PALM NUTS KERNELS | 298 | 334 | 254 | 319 | 269 | 353 | 239 | 152 | 131 | 145 | 106 | -11.85 |
| PALM OIL | 167 | 151 | 135 | 196 | 209 | 157 | 117 | 93 | 61 | 121 | 88 | - 8.25 |
| OILSEED CAKE AND MEAL | 804 | 909 | 725 | 617 | 677 | 755 | 709 | 464 | 664 | 488 | 369 | - 6.85 |
| | | | | | | | | | | | | |
| BANANAS | 384 | 462 | 438 | 465 | 354 | 320 | 312 | 347 | 295 | 221 | 192 | - 8.70 |
| ORANGES+TANGER+CLEMEN | 703 | 794 | 914 | 729 | 592 | 664 | 744 | 873 | 672 | 841 | 763 | - .03 |
| LEMONS AND LIMES | 9 | 4 | 6 | 3 | 1 | 1 | 1 | 2 | 1 | 1 | 1 | -16.54 |
| | | | | | | | | | | | | |
| COFFEE GREEN+ROASTED | 911 | 1087 | 1187 | 1177 | 1109 | 1151 | 880 | 927 | 1017 | 892 | 912 | - 3.05 |
| COCOA BEANS | 838 | 977 | 889 | 864 | 819 | 866 | 688 | 780 | 688 | 785 | 813 | - 2.42 |
| TEA | 79 | 137 | 141 | 137 | 135 | 149 | 165 | 178 | 185 | 167 | 154 | 2.86 |
| | | | | | | | | | | | | |
| COTTON LINT | 338 | 397 | 410 | 318 | 271 | 351 | 300 | 308 | 329 | 331 | 289 | - 2.37 |
| JUTE AND SIMILAR FIBRES | 2 | 2 | 1 | | | | | | | | | |
| | | | | | | | | | | | | |
| TOBACCO UNMANUFACTURED | 82 | 114 | 131 | 131 | 113 | 141 | 129 | 139 | 131 | 174 | 186 | 4.27 |
| NATURAL RUBBER | 161 | 191 | 197 | 203 | 186 | 159 | 153 | 145 | 142 | 135 | 135 | - 4.96 |
| | | | | | | | | | | | | |
| WOOL GREASY | 6 | 5 | 5 | 6 | 4 | 3 | 4 | 5 | 5 | 4 | 4 | - 3.50 |
| BOVINE CATTLE 1/ | 1116 | 1500 | 1407 | 1265 | 1025 | 1129 | 1026 | 1091 | 1126 | 1276 | 1413 | - 1.04 |
| SHEEP AND GOATS 1/ | 3113 | 3684 | 3368 | 3161 | 3515 | 2548 | 2461 | 3066 | 3080 | 3304 | 3395 | - .87 |
| PIGS 1/ | 1 | 22 | 17 | 13 | 13 | 15 | 4 | 1 | 3 | 2 | 2 | -26.68 |
| TOTAL MEAT | 79 | 110 | 130 | 119 | 104 | 113 | 118 | 100 | 98 | 50 | 51 | - 8.42 |
| MILK DRY | 1 | 2 | 3 | 1 | | 1 | | 2 | 2 | | | |
| TOTAL EGGS IN SHELL | 1 | 1 | 1 | 1 | 1 | 1 | 1 | | | | | |

1/ THOUSAND HEAD
2/ EXCEPT FOR PULP FOR PAPER AND PAPER AND PAPERBOARD, ALL FOREST PRODUCTS ARE EXPRESSED IN THOUSAND CUBIC METRES

ANNEX TABLE 4. VOLUME OF EXPORTS OF MAJOR AGRICULTURAL, FISHERY AND FOREST PRODUCTS

| | 1967 | 1972 | 1973 | 1974 | 1975 | 1976 | 1977 | 1978 | 1979 | 1980 | 1981 | ANNUAL RATE OF CHANGE 1972-81 PERCENT |
|---|---|---|---|---|---|---|---|---|---|---|---|---|
| | | | | | ....THOUSAND METRIC TONS.... | | | | | | | |
| **FISHERY PRODUCTS** | | | | | | | | | | | | |
| FISH FRESH FROZEN | 17 | 63 | 106 | 106 | 76 | 75 | 94 | 105 | 104 | 113 | 77 | 2.00 |
| FISH CURED | 56 | 62 | 49 | 42 | 45 | 35 | 36 | 37 | 36 | 36 | 36 | - 5.02 |
| SHELLFISH | 5 | 19 | 23 | 29 | 39 | 43 | 44 | 49 | 46 | 46 | 18 | 4.36 |
| FISH CANNED AND PREPARED | 52 | 61 | 83 | 80 | 59 | 76 | 68 | 61 | 76 | 76 | 77 | .80 |
| FISH BODY AND LIVER OIL | 13 | 25 | 31 | 18 | 12 | 7 | 7 | 7 | 8 | 8 | 7 | -15.19 |
| FISH MEAL | 63 | 150 | 142 | 95 | 83 | 43 | 19 | 37 | 30 | 28 | 15 | -21.87 |
| **FOREST PRODUCTS 2/** | | | | | | | | | | | | |
| SAWLOGS CONIFEROUS | | 13 | 14 | 14 | 15 | 11 | 2 | 2 | 2 | | | |
| SAWLOGS NONCONIFEROUS | 5603 | 7174 | 8260 | 6580 | 5139 | 6435 | 6547 | 6416 | 6312 | 6144 | 5189 | - 2.70 |
| PULPWOOD+PARTICLE | | 1 | 2 | 69 | 70 | 127 | 100 | 75 | 112 | 84 | 173 | 59.00 |
| FUELWOOD | 71 | 11 | 28 | 27 | 9 | 8 | 9 | 9 | 9 | 1 | | |
| SAWNWOOD CONIFEROUS | 64 | 73 | 103 | 107 | 98 | 113 | 119 | 116 | 126 | 103 | 94 | 2.29 |
| SAWNWOOD NONCONIFEROUS | 693 | 738 | 933 | 813 | 662 | 701 | 749 | 750 | 722 | 679 | 624 | - 2.33 |
| WOOD-BASED PANELS | 212 | 327 | 340 | 300 | 207 | 219 | 237 | 257 | 227 | 241 | 232 | - 3.66 |
| PULP FOR PAPER | 130 | 187 | 201 | 219 | 155 | 255 | 190 | 233 | 259 | 259 | 259 | 3.99 |
| PAPER AND PAPERBOARD | 21 | 17 | 18 | 30 | 21 | 24 | 22 | 18 | 27 | 49 | 48 | 9.86 |
| **LATIN AMERICA** | | | | | | | | | | | | |
| **AGRICULTURAL PRODUCTS** | | | | | | | | | | | | |
| WHEAT+FLOUR,WHEAT EQUIV. | 2370 | 1771 | 3098 | 1836 | 2000 | 3304 | 5991 | 1765 | 4382 | 4587 | 3955 | 9.22 |
| RICE MILLED | 336 | 195 | 330 | 348 | 439 | 536 | 997 | 733 | 578 | 551 | 660 | 12.37 |
| BARLEY | 65 | 111 | 161 | 110 | 28 | 43 | 130 | 18 | 58 | 74 | 33 | -11.40 |
| MAIZE | 6051 | 3645 | 4113 | 6666 | 5088 | 4560 | 6864 | 5927 | 5990 | 3541 | 9135 | 4.68 |
| MILLET | 213 | 81 | 118 | 78 | 94 | 124 | 172 | 196 | 139 | 63 | 133 | 3.38 |
| SORGHUM | 930 | 635 | 2108 | 3169 | 2180 | 3499 | 4313 | 4625 | 3923 | 1544 | 5031 | 12.87 |
| POTATOES | 13 | 36 | 11 | 21 | 50 | 96 | 106 | 67 | 76 | 49 | 41 | 11.90 |
| SUGAR,TOTAL (RAW EQUIV.) | 10175 | 10851 | 11942 | 12048 | 11021 | 10437 | 12928 | 12309 | 12527 | 11884 | 12854 | 1.36 |
| PULSES | 137 | 163 | 166 | 175 | 233 | 312 | 424 | 465 | 390 | 340 | 290 | 10.59 |
| SOYBEANS | 306 | 1079 | 1841 | 2831 | 3435 | 3934 | 3441 | 2841 | 3813 | 4493 | 4280 | 12.50 |
| SOYBEAN OIL | | 60 | 116 | 42 | 285 | 562 | 544 | 570 | 609 | 840 | 1354 | 41.49 |
| GROUNDNUTS SHELLED BASIS | 21 | 62 | 57 | 56 | 68 | 30 | 59 | 60 | 115 | 107 | 97 | 7.80 |
| GROUNDNUT OIL | 70 | 114 | 124 | 101 | 38 | 140 | 181 | 155 | 209 | 207 | 80 | 5.31 |
| COPRA | 12 | 2 | 1 | 2 | 2 | 2 | | | 2 | | | |
| COCONUT OIL | 3 | 11 | 9 | 5 | 5 | 5 | 5 | 9 | 8 | 4 | 4 | - 6.85 |
| PALM NUTS KERNELS | 2 | 5 | 6 | 5 | 4 | 2 | 3 | 9 | 7 | 5 | 2 | - 3.79 |
| PALM OIL | 4 | 3 | 6 | 6 | 3 | 5 | 3 | 4 | 5 | 2 | | |
| OILSEED CAKE AND MEAL | 1555 | 2698 | 2869 | 3130 | 4299 | 5798 | 7352 | 7676 | 7469 | 8985 | 10952 | 17.72 |
| BANANAS | 4194 | 5329 | 5345 | 5055 | 4779 | 4839 | 5232 | 5454 | 5513 | 5474 | 5288 | .61 |
| ORANGES+TANGER+CLEMEN | 172 | 216 | 218 | 210 | 190 | 173 | 224 | 269 | 313 | 311 | 300 | 5.42 |
| LEMONS AND LIMES | 1 | 8 | 11 | 14 | 22 | 25 | 29 | 47 | 74 | 54 | 51 | 26.88 |
| COFFEE GREEN+ROASTED | 1940 | 2165 | 2232 | 1826 | 2055 | 2032 | 1547 | 1962 | 2188 | 2205 | 2235 | .42 |
| COCOA BEANS | 216 | 226 | 174 | 255 | 270 | 210 | 187 | 211 | 225 | 183 | 200 | - 1.34 |
| TEA | 15 | 24 | 25 | 30 | 23 | 32 | 34 | 41 | 39 | 44 | 31 | 5.92 |
| COTTON LINT | 796 | 862 | 829 | 664 | 806 | 607 | 689 | 896 | 734 | 641 | 632 | - 2.18 |
| JUTE AND SIMILAR FIBRES | 4 | 4 | 4 | 3 | 1 | 1 | | 1 | | | | |
| TOBACCO UNMANUFACTURED | 121 | 184 | 186 | 244 | 244 | 255 | 238 | 274 | 276 | 256 | 264 | 3.94 |
| NATURAL RUBBER | 12 | 9 | 8 | 5 | 6 | 6 | 5 | 6 | 4 | 4 | 5 | - 8.01 |
| WOOL GREASY | 148 | 78 | 81 | 64 | 108 | 92 | 108 | 107 | 80 | 105 | 133 | 4.92 |
| BOVINE CATTLE 1/ | 1068 | 1487 | 1026 | 1037 | 960 | 1103 | 1093 | 1662 | 1403 | 796 | 864 | - 2.11 |
| SHEEP AND GOATS 1/ | 92 | 81 | 48 | 65 | 93 | 106 | 110 | 126 | 94 | 64 | 309 | 10.79 |
| PIGS 1/ | 40 | 42 | 31 | 33 | 42 | 65 | 31 | 24 | 17 | 2 | | |
| TOTAL MEAT | 723 | 1039 | 890 | 504 | 449 | 775 | 787 | 834 | 855 | 806 | 1022 | 2.25 |
| MILK DRY | 1 | 12 | 15 | 9 | 14 | 34 | 18 | 10 | 4 | 3 | 9 | -10.98 |
| TOTAL EGGS IN SHELL | 2 | 1 | 1 | 1 | 1 | 3 | 3 | 1 | 3 | 12 | 13 | 30.78 |
| **FISHERY PRODUCTS** | | | | | | | | | | | | |
| FISH FRESH FROZEN | 40 | 64 | 107 | 131 | 146 | 197 | 301 | 361 | 409 | 332 | 122 | 14.66 |
| FISH CURED | 1 | 3 | 7 | 9 | 5 | 3 | 9 | 3 | 12 | 14 | 13 | 12.66 |
| SHELLFISH | 71 | 98 | 94 | 90 | 93 | 100 | 99 | 142 | 178 | 135 | 125 | 5.86 |
| FISH CANNED AND PREPARED | 9 | 21 | 20 | 20 | 16 | 28 | 48 | 73 | 77 | 125 | 108 | 26.89 |
| SHELLFISH CANNED+PREPAR | 3 | 2 | 1 | 1 | 3 | 3 | 5 | 2 | 5 | 3 | 1 | 4.91 |
| FISH BODY AND LIVER OIL | 211 | 318 | 10 | 93 | 148 | 39 | 46 | 69 | 129 | 98 | 5 | -12.35 |
| FISH MEAL | 1728 | 1711 | 402 | 749 | 909 | 842 | 733 | 843 | 1146 | 1005 | 921 | 1.59 |
| **FOREST PRODUCTS 2/** | | | | | | | | | | | | |
| SAWLOGS CONIFEROUS | 14 | 9 | 14 | 9 | 15 | 23 | 167 | 689 | 968 | 1029 | 384 | 84.90 |
| SAWLOGS NONCONIFEROUS | 394 | 217 | 524 | 202 | 55 | 86 | 49 | 60 | 86 | 114 | 60 | -15.00 |
| PULPWOOD+PARTICLE | 331 | 382 | 284 | 183 | 107 | 115 | 53 | 53 | 53 | 53 | 53 | -20.97 |
| FUELWOOD | 3 | 1 | 2 | 2 | 3 | 4 | 18 | 26 | 37 | 29 | 13 | 51.12 |
| SAWNWOOD CONIFEROUS | 1520 | 1718 | 1530 | 1131 | 1134 | 1050 | 1429 | 1477 | 1678 | 1718 | 1268 | .70 |
| SAWNWOOD NONCONIFEROUS | 341 | 622 | 870 | 835 | 590 | 629 | 838 | 727 | 1121 | 1130 | 837 | 4.26 |
| WOOD-BASED PANELS | 110 | 266 | 295 | 265 | 252 | 326 | 374 | 487 | 488 | 606 | 619 | 11.39 |
| PULP FOR PAPER | 89 | 262 | 296 | 314 | 328 | 377 | 433 | 706 | 1014 | 1306 | 1362 | 22.54 |
| PAPER AND PAPERBOARD | 92 | 110 | 186 | 213 | 146 | 199 | 222 | 268 | 331 | 376 | 479 | 14.45 |

1/ THOUSAND HEAD
2/ EXCEPT FOR PULP FOR PAPER AND PAPER AND PAPERBOARD, ALL FOREST PRODUCTS ARE EXPRESSED IN THOUSAND CUBIC METRES

ANNEX TABLE 4. VOLUME OF EXPORTS OF MAJOR AGRICULTURAL, FISHERY AND FOREST PRODUCTS

| | 1967 | 1972 | 1973 | 1974 | 1975 | 1976 | 1977 | 1978 | 1979 | 1980 | 1981 | ANNUAL RATE OF CHANGE 1972-81 PERCENT |
|---|---|---|---|---|---|---|---|---|---|---|---|---|
| | | | | | | THOUSAND METRIC TONS | | | | | | |
| **NEAR EAST DEVELOPING** | | | | | | | | | | | | |
| **AGRICULTURAL PRODUCTS** | | | | | | | | | | | | |
| WHEAT+FLOUR,WHEAT EQUIV. | 113 | 616 | 599 | 23 | 12 | 21 | 627 | 2079 | 825 | 494 | 485 | 22.26 |
| RICE MILLED | 456 | 518 | 341 | 181 | 130 | 256 | 276 | 223 | 211 | 259 | 226 | - 4.11 |
| BARLEY | 65 | 142 | 17 | 7 | 12 | 366 | 302 | 50 | 88 | 229 | 421 | 31.16 |
| MAIZE | 3 | 7 | 3 | 2 | 1 | 14 | 8 | 43 | 111 | 155 | 22 | 50.57 |
| MILLET | 14 | 7 | 9 | 4 | 4 | 6 | 3 | 4 | 2 | 2 | | |
| SORGHUM | 2 | 61 | 104 | 98 | 48 | 75 | 137 | 66 | 196 | 286 | 256 | 16.34 |
| POTATOES | 245 | 284 | 326 | 299 | 208 | 380 | 437 | 289 | 311 | 462 | 345 | 3.40 |
| SUGAR,TOTAL (RAW EQUIV.) | 100 | 147 | 50 | 54 | 54 | 43 | 59 | 51 | 34 | 41 | 47 | - 8.04 |
| PULSES | 160 | 143 | 170 | 105 | 109 | 121 | 176 | 256 | 303 | 298 | 494 | 15.18 |
| GROUNDNUTS SHELLED BASIS | 130 | 149 | 166 | 145 | 223 | 321 | 184 | 120 | 56 | 59 | 120 | - 9.41 |
| COCONUT OIL | | | | | | | 1 | | | | | |
| OILSEED CAKE AND MEAL | 598 | 751 | 545 | 401 | 452 | 368 | 252 | 225 | 214 | 265 | 137 | -14.55 |
| BANANAS | 16 | 16 | 10 | 6 | 10 | 9 | 4 | 2 | 5 | 17 | 6 | - 6.46 |
| ORANGES+TANGER+CLEMEN | 257 | 527 | 766 | 722 | 724 | 720 | 754 | 645 | 608 | 632 | 751 | .40 |
| LEMONS AND LIMES | 78 | 108 | 150 | 138 | 119 | 159 | 131 | 153 | 152 | 201 | 203 | 5.45 |
| COFFEE GREEN+ROASTED | 4 | 10 | 8 | 6 | 4 | 3 | 3 | 4 | 3 | 2 | 2 | -16.01 |
| TEA | 10 | 19 | 26 | 19 | 4 | 8 | 7 | 10 | 16 | 16 | 12 | - 3.10 |
| COTTON LINT | 895 | 1049 | 1097 | 706 | 856 | 1004 | 710 | 765 | 677 | 616 | 533 | - 6.46 |
| TOBACCO UNMANUFACTURED | 100 | 137 | 120 | 123 | 75 | 86 | 71 | 84 | 77 | 94 | 141 | - 2.21 |
| WOOL GREASY | 17 | 21 | 25 | 10 | 8 | 7 | 12 | 9 | 7 | 7 | 3 | -14.86 |
| BOVINE CATTLE 1/ | 120 | 92 | 52 | 77 | 18 | 11 | 16 | 12 | 21 | 9 | 58 | -13.47 |
| SHEEP AND GOATS 1/ | 1231 | 932 | 987 | 980 | 765 | 828 | 724 | 1300 | 1424 | 2028 | 3660 | 13.35 |
| TOTAL MEAT | 1 | 13 | 30 | 22 | 14 | 9 | 11 | 15 | 15 | 21 | 40 | 3.97 |
| TOTAL EGGS IN SHELL | 11 | 21 | 15 | 17 | 12 | 1 | 3 | 7 | 10 | 7 | 7 | -10.60 |
| **FISHERY PRODUCTS** | | | | | | | | | | | | |
| FISH FRESH FROZEN | 10 | 12 | 20 | 16 | 6 | 4 | 3 | 3 | 4 | 4 | 3 | -17.52 |
| FISH CURED | 18 | 21 | .17 | 13 | 12 | 10 | 12 | 2 | 3 | 2 | 2 | -24.33 |
| SHELLFISH | 4 | 13 | 16 | 10 | 7 | 10 | 10 | 8 | 8 | 8 | 3 | -10.33 |
| FISH CANNED AND PREPARED | 1 | 1 | 1 | 1 | 1 | 3 | 2 | 2 | 2 | 2 | 1 | 8.90 |
| SHELLFISH CANNED+PREPAR | 1 | | 1 | 2 | 2 | 2 | 3 | 2 | 2 | | | |
| FISH BODY AND LIVER OIL | | 1 | 1 | | | | 1 | 2 | 2 | 1 | 1 | |
| **FOREST PRODUCTS 2/** | | | | | | | | | | | | |
| SAWLOGS CONIFEROUS | 1 | 14 | 7 | 5 | 4 | 3 | | 1 | 1 | 1 | 2 | |
| SAWLOGS NONCONIFEROUS | 20 | 22 | 24 | 8 | 17 | 10 | 9 | 5 | 3 | 4 | 36 | - 9.65 |
| FUELWOOD | 9 | 9 | 9 | 7 | 8 | 8 | 6 | 5 | 8 | 10 | 8 | - .33 |
| SAWNWOOD CONIFEROUS | 2 | 37 | 37 | 61 | 49 | 60 | 69 | 60 | 103 | 98 | 112 | 13.05 |
| SAWNWOOD NONCONIFEROUS | 19 | 28 | 23 | 21 | 1 | 1 | 1 | | 2 | 3 | 6 | |
| WOOD-BASED PANELS | 13 | 26 | 32 | 31 | 27 | 29 | 26 | 26 | 24 | 25 | 25 | - 2.33 |
| PULP FOR PAPER | | | | 3 | 1 | | | | | | | |
| PAPER AND PAPERBOARD | 1 | 3 | 10 | 22 | 9 | 10 | 11 | 10 | 16 | 14 | 20 | 11.97 |
| **FAR EAST DEVELOPING** | | | | | | | | | | | | |
| **AGRICULTURAL PRODUCTS** | | | | | | | | | | | | |
| WHEAT+FLOUR,WHEAT EQUIV. | 185 | 325 | 520 | 107 | 92 | 64 | 234 | 873 | 670 | 288 | 244 | 6.58 |
| RICE MILLED | 2931 | 3228 | 2293 | 2018 | 1911 | 3720 | 4830 | 3131 | 5085 | 5437 | 6212 | 11.73 |
| BARLEY | | 1 | 19 | 95 | | 32 | 39 | 13 | 73 | 268 | 246 | 64.30 |
| MAIZE | 1327 | 1952 | 1630 | 2554 | 2243 | 2483 | 1768 | 2152 | 2143 | 2340 | 2704 | 2.53 |
| MILLET | 2 | 1 | 4 | 2 | 1 | 1 | 1 | 8 | 7 | 2 | 2 | 10.21 |
| SORGHUM | 99 | 134 | 135 | 189 | 213 | 182 | 138 | 166 | 170 | 208 | 289 | 5.23 |
| POTATOES | 23 | 35 | 40 | 36 | 46 | 95 | 73 | 55 | 99 | 110 | 81 | 12.97 |
| SUGAR,TOTAL (RAW EQUIV.) | 1215 | 1816 | 1989 | 2557 | 2804 | 3556 | 4475 | 2765 | 3118 | 2616 | 2836 | 4.40 |
| PULSES | 191 | 216 | 219 | 167 | 170 | 191 | 181 | 245 | 291 | 313 | 339 | 6.49 |
| SOYBEANS | 25 | 20 | 59 | 18 | 32 | 38 | 47 | 30 | 27 | 26 | 21 | - 2.10 |
| SOYBEAN OIL | | 9 | 8 | 7 | 4 | 2 | 4 | 7 | 6 | 27 | 27 | 13.10 |
| GROUNDNUTS SHELLED BASIS | 30 | 51 | 65 | 111 | 89 | 177 | 45 | 32 | 46 | 55 | 134 | - .76 |
| GROUNDNUT OIL | 7 | 6 | 10 | 7 | 9 | 10 | 5 | 6 | 16 | 5 | 5 | - 2.24 |
| COPRA | 922 | 1109 | 800 | 285 | 834 | 878 | 683 | 445 | 193 | 233 | 173 | -16.34 |
| COCONUT OIL | 363 | 642 | 525 | 508 | 760 | 1004 | 845 | 1112 | 976 | 1060 | 1192 | 9.33 |
| PALM NUTS KERNELS | 66 | 57 | 42 | 29 | 33 | 33 | 30 | 13 | 23 | 45 | 23 | - 6.78 |
| PALM OIL | 384 | 1147 | 1284 | 1411 | 1726 | 1897 | 2067 | 2168 | 2634 | 3295 | 3061 | 12.42 |
| OILSEED CAKE AND MEAL | 1418 | 2166 | 2243 | 2006 | 2060 | 3353 | 2870 | 2597 | 3456 | 3061 | 2974 | 5.15 |
| BANANAS | 27 | 461 | 503 | 705 | 872 | 846 | 738 | 832 | 921 | 972 | 920 | 7.48 |
| ORANGES+TANGER+CLEMEN | 19 | 33 | 41 | 39 | 137 | 86 | 113 | 65 | 81 | 75 | 43 | 5.11 |
| COFFEE GREEN+ROASTED | 265 | 204 | 206 | 203 | 226 | 262 | 267 | 339 | 335 | 375 | 369 | 8.41 |
| COCOA BEANS | 3 | 7 | 10 | 14 | 15 | 18 | 18 | 24 | 32 | 41 | 65 | 24.01 |
| TEA | 485 | 464 | 457 | 455 | 507 | 513 | 499 | 459 | 475 | 525 | 553 | 1.49 |
| COTTON LINT | 213 | 310 | 248 | 96 | 244 | 218 | 56 | 128 | 134 | 375 | 468 | 3.04 |
| JUTE AND SIMILAR FIBRES | 1037 | 716 | 867 | 860 | 566 | 646 | 544 | 473 | 522 | 467 | 529 | - 6.02 |

1/ THOUSAND HEAD
2/ EXCEPT FOR PULP FOR PAPER AND PAPER AND PAPERBOARD, ALL FOREST PRODUCTS ARE EXPRESSED IN THOUSAND CUBIC METRES

ANNEX TABLE 4. VOLUME OF EXPORTS OF MAJOR AGRICULTURAL, FISHERY AND FOREST PRODUCTS

| | 1967 | 1972 | 1973 | 1974 | 1975 | 1976 | 1977 | 1978 | 1979 | 1980 | 1981 | ANNUAL RATE OF CHANGE 1972-81 PERCENT |
|---|---|---|---|---|---|---|---|---|---|---|---|---|
| | | | | | | THOUSAND METRIC TONS | | | | | | |
| TOBACCO UNMANUFACTURED | 135 | 181 | 196 | 211 | 198 | 210 | 232 | 215 | 212 | 200 | 259 | 2.27 |
| NATURAL RUBBER | 2035 | 2565 | 3051 | 2868 | 2737 | 2967 | 3027 | 3080 | 3179 | 3102 | 2922 | 1.33 |
| WOOL GREASY | 7 | 2 | 2 | 3 | 1 | 2 | | 1 | | | | |
| BOVINE CATTLE 1/ | 90 | 148 | 123 | 114 | 74 | 73 | 98 | 78 | 66 | 55 | 37 | -11.63 |
| SHEEP AND GOATS 1/ | 27 | 47 | 20 | 28 | 28 | 80 | 215 | 57 | 54 | 60 | 74 | 11.54 |
| PIGS 1/ | 39 | 7 | 13 | 5 | 10 | 22 | 7 | 10 | 12 | 8 | 4 | - 3.21 |
| TOTAL MEAT | 5 | 15 | 19 | 26 | 33 | 44 | 60 | 68 | 87 | 94 | 106 | 25.31 |
| MILK DRY | 2 | 3 | 2 | 3 | 4 | 4 | 5 | 7 | 10 | 16 | 9 | 21.15 |
| TOTAL EGGS IN SHELL | 3 | 7 | 4 | 3 | 5 | 6 | 10 | 6 | 5 | 3 | 5 | - .38 |
| **FISHERY PRODUCTS** | | | | | | | | | | | | |
| FISH FRESH FROZEN | 111 | 229 | 302 | 285 | 418 | 289 | 541 | 556 | 557 | 473 | 489 | 9.38 |
| FISH CURED | 42 | 42 | 54 | 36 | 32 | 30 | 29 | 33 | 30 | 26 | - 5.34 | |
| SHELLFISH | 68 | 172 | 218 | 212 | 228 | 291 | 295 | 313 | 348 | 246 | 196 | 3.35 |
| FISH CANNED AND PREPARED | 4 | 7 | 11 | 18 | 18 | 25 | 36 | 47 | 43 | 20 | 19 | 13.17 |
| SHELLFISH CANNED+PREPAR | 11 | 20 | 23 | 26 | 27 | 21 | 26 | 37 | 39 | 24 | 11 | - 1.26 |
| FISH BODY AND LIVER OIL | | | | 1 | 1 | 1 | 1 | 3 | 2 | 1 | 1 | |
| FISH MEAL | 26 | 65 | 78 | 63 | 57 | 84 | 113 | 139 | 167 | 161 | 162 | 13.70 |
| **FOREST PRODUCTS 2/** | | | | | | | | | | | | |
| SAWLOGS NONCONIFEROUS | 17072 | 32177 | 39605 | 34240 | 28203 | 35758 | 37017 | 38458 | 35843 | 31534 | 23869 | - 1.85 |
| PULPWOOD+PARTICLE | 7 | 763 | 754 | 986 | 930 | 697 | 1033 | 860 | 736 | 772 | 772 | - .63 |
| FUELWOOD | 217 | 301 | 212 | 215 | 154 | 179 | 190 | 145 | 142 | 210 | 174 | - 4.26 |
| SAWNWOOD CONIFEROUS | 11 | 109 | 188 | 117 | 134 | 251 | 258 | 425 | 481 | 410 | 283 | 16.07 |
| SAWNWOOD NONCONIFEROUS | 1586 | 3120 | 4352 | 3661 | 3298 | 5551 | 5374 | 5463 | 7236 | 6398 | 5544 | 8.04 |
| WOOD-BASED PANELS | 746 | 2573 | 3076 | 2424 | 2512 | 3110 | 3195 | 3358 | 3237 | 2933 | 3343 | 2.68 |
| PULP FOR PAPER | | 1 | 11 | 5 | | 1 | | | | 1 | 2 | |
| PAPER AND PAPERBOARD | 52 | 99 | 173 | 114 | 104 | 175 | 139 | 156 | 171 | 325 | 346 | 11.99 |
| **ASIAN CENT PLANNED ECON** | | | | | | | | | | | | |
| **AGRICULTURAL PRODUCTS** | | | | | | | | | | | | |
| WHEAT+FLOUR,WHEAT EQUIV. | 69 | 4 | 9 | 4 | 3 | 4 | 5 | 6 | 7 | 3 | 8 | 2.74 |
| RICE MILLED | 2155 | 1637 | 2743 | 2832 | 2336 | 1547 | 1498 | 2094 | 1902 | 1644 | 1042 | - 5.88 |
| BARLEY | 1 | | 16 | | 6 | 2 | | 1 | 2 | 1 | | |
| MAIZE | 147 | 110 | 65 | 130 | 315 | 430 | 356 | 230 | 240 | 104 | 123 | 3.85 |
| MILLET | 15 | 24 | 33 | 30 | 56 | 52 | 37 | 30 | 20 | 5 | 1 | -24.35 |
| POTATOES | 50 | 52 | 54 | 49 | 50 | 55 | 53 | 62 | 81 | 77 | 80 | 5.91 |
| SUGAR,TOTAL (RAW EQUIV.) | 925 | 641 | 632 | 705 | 619 | 660 | 757 | 481 | 501 | 634 | 374 | - 4.24 |
| PULSES | 135 | 128 | 115 | 86 | 83 | 97 | 89 | 76 | 90 | 70 | 106 | - 3.14 |
| SOYBEANS | 565 | 373 | 321 | 375 | 355 | 199 | 130 | 113 | 306 | 140 | 124 | -11.75 |
| SOYBEAN OIL | 3 | | | | | 1 | 2 | 6 | 4 | 4 | | |
| GROUNDNUTS SHELLED BASIS | 96 | 53 | 47 | 38 | 48 | 54 | 32 | 37 | 51 | 80 | 244 | 11.24 |
| GROUNDNUT OIL | 24 | 15 | 13 | 16 | 15 | 16 | 5 | 13 | 18 | 19 | 64 | 9.70 |
| COPRA | | | 1 | | | | | | | | | |
| COCONUT OIL | 2 | | | | | | | | | | | |
| PALM OIL | | | | 1 | | | | | | | | |
| OILSEED CAKE AND MEAL | 38 | 27 | 43 | 31 | 29 | 36 | 30 | 30 | 49 | 88 | 184 | 15.89 |
| BANANAS | 410 | 245 | 270 | 165 | 127 | 96 | 140 | 101 | 117 | 109 | 103 | - 9.33 |
| ORANGES+TANGER+CLEMEN | 67 | 90 | 83 | 74 | 79 | 56 | 80 | 70 | 76 | 68 | 56 | - 3.31 |
| COFFEE GREEN+ROASTED | 5 | 4 | 6 | 6 | 4 | 12 | 4 | 5 | 5 | 6 | 5 | .54 |
| TEA | 52 | 72 | 74 | 84 | 87 | 90 | 112 | 115 | 133 | 137 | 131 | 8.28 |
| COTTON LINT | 4 | 22 | 22 | 22 | 43 | 65 | 71 | 33 | 22 | 2 | 1 | -23.32 |
| JUTE AND SIMILAR FIBRES | 5 | 2 | 2 | 1 | 1 | 4 | 7 | 20 | 32 | 40 | 46 | 56.74 |
| TOBACCO UNMANUFACTURED | 19 | 32 | 43 | 41 | 43 | 43 | 45 | 45 | 35 | 30 | 34 | - 1.40 |
| NATURAL RUBBER | 88 | 32 | 40 | 49 | 17 | 49 | 50 | 41 | 50 | 39 | 29 | .79 |
| WOOL GREASY | 23 | 22 | 23 | 22 | 24 | 25 | 21 | 22 | 24 | 23 | 20 | - .45 |
| BOVINE CATTLE 1/ | 242 | 171 | 162 | 166 | 204 | 195 | 196 | 172 | 221 | 270 | 251 | 4.91 |
| SHEEP AND GOATS 1/ | 1626 | 1186 | 1220 | 1225 | 1030 | 873 | 482 | 443 | 463 | 448 | 330 | -14.84 |
| PIGS 1/ | 1833 | 2689 | 2794 | 2601 | 2775 | 2953 | 3016 | 3129 | 3079 | 4548 | 3170 | 3.78 |
| TOTAL MEAT | 130 | 185 | 192 | 141 | 158 | 196 | 139 | 183 | 220 | 221 | 202 | 2.53 |
| TOTAL EGGS IN SHELL | 42 | 41 | 47 | 46 | 46 | 38 | 35 | 42 | 51 | 71 | 66 | 4.57 |
| **FISHERY PRODUCTS** | | | | | | | | | | | | |
| FISH FRESH FROZEN | 47 | 176 | 193 | 153 | 182 | 174 | 207 | 129 | 134 | 49 | 35 | -14.35 |
| FISH CURED | 7 | 4 | 5 | 4 | 5 | 4 | 3 | 6 | 9 | 2 | 1 | - 8.19 |
| SHELLFISH | 10 | 41 | 45 | 45 | 44 | 54 | 51 | 56 | 68 | 62 | 49 | 4.12 |
| FISH CANNED AND PREPARED | | 3 | 6 | 6 | 6 | 14 | 13 | 21 | 31 | 31 | 22 | 27.78 |
| SHELLFISH CANNED+PREPAR | 2 | 8 | 8 | 7 | 7 | 11 | 11 | 14 | 10 | 8 | 8 | 1.82 |
| FISH MEAL | 2 | 3 | 3 | 3 | 1 | | | 1 | | | | |
| **FOREST PRODUCTS 2/** | | | | | | | | | | | | |
| SAWLOGS CONIFEROUS | 88 | 119 | 129 | 157 | 177 | 128 | 128 | 128 | 123 | 117 | 117 | - 1.83 |
| SAWLOGS NONCONIFEROUS | 56 | 28 | 5 | 3 | 17 | 12 | 12 | 12 | 15 | 8 | 8 | .02 |
| SAWNWOOD CONIFEROUS | 58 | 139 | 53 | 66 | 95 | 103 | 102 | 111 | 102 | 93 | 93 | 1.82 |
| SAWNWOOD NONCONIFEROUS | 46 | 177 | 160 | 118 | 133 | 136 | 91 | 115 | 63 | 52 | 52 | -12.86 |
| WOOD-BASED PANELS | 320 | 953 | 959 | 687 | 770 | 872 | 949 | 1244 | 1096 | 885 | 885 | 1.60 |
| PULP FOR PAPER | 4 | 54 | 18 | 23 | 30 | 22 | 22 | 33 | 35 | 33 | 33 | 1.39 |

1/ THOUSAND HEAD
2/ EXCEPT FOR PULP FOR PAPER AND PAPER AND PAPERBOARD, ALL FOREST PRODUCTS ARE EXPRESSED IN THOUSAND CUBIC METRES

ANNEX TABLE 4.  VOLUME OF EXPORTS OF MAJOR AGRICULTURAL, FISHERY AND FOREST PRODUCTS

| | 1967 | 1972 | 1973 | 1974 | 1975 | 1976 | 1977 | 1978 | 1979 | 1980 | 1981 | ANNUAL RATE OF CHANGE 1972-81 PERCENT |
|---|---|---|---|---|---|---|---|---|---|---|---|---|
| | ............................................THOUSAND METRIC TONS........................................... | | | | | | | | | | | |
| PAPER AND PAPERBOARD | 89 | 115 | 116 | 107 | 132 | 122 | 122 | 121 | 95 | 158 | 158 | 2.54 |

1/ THOUSAND HEAD
2/ EXCEPT FOR PULP FOR PAPER AND PAPER AND PAPERBOARD, ALL FOREST PRODUCTS ARE EXPRESSED IN THOUSAND CUBIC METRES

ANNEX TABLE 5. WORLD AVERAGE EXPORT UNIT VALUES OF SELECTED AGRICULTURAL, FISHERY AND FOREST PRODUCTS

| | 1967 | 1972 | 1973 | 1974 | 1975 | 1976 | 1977 | 1978 | 1979 | 1980 | 1981 | ANNUAL RATE OF CHANGE 1972-81 PERCENT |
|---|---|---|---|---|---|---|---|---|---|---|---|---|
| | | | | | | US $ PER METRIC TON | | | | | | |

AGRICULTURAL PRODUCTS

| | 1967 | 1972 | 1973 | 1974 | 1975 | 1976 | 1977 | 1978 | 1979 | 1980 | 1981 | RATE |
|---|---|---|---|---|---|---|---|---|---|---|---|---|
| WHEAT | 68 | 69 | 106 | 171 | 169 | 153 | 125 | 131 | 163 | 184 | 187 | 7.30 |
| WHEAT FLOUR | 86 | 93 | 135 | 210 | 237 | 215 | 191 | 199 | 224 | 283 | 293 | 9.64 |
| RICE MILLED | 157 | 137 | 226 | 401 | 377 | 280 | 268 | 353 | 330 | 392 | 445 | 8.36 |
| BARLEY | 68 | 59 | 94 | 135 | 140 | 138 | 132 | 137 | 145 | 175 | 175 | 9.11 |
| MAIZE | 56 | 63 | 92 | 128 | 135 | 123 | 111 | 117 | 128 | 150 | 152 | 6.78 |
| POTATOES | 64 | 71 | 114 | 111 | 149 | 246 | 197 | 157 | 188 | 185 | 177 | 8.97 |
| SUGAR CENTRIFUGAL RAW | 100 | 150 | 189 | 399 | 556 | 376 | 295 | 340 | 356 | 542 | 510 | 10.25 |
| SOYBEANS | 109 | 126 | 216 | 246 | 225 | 216 | 272 | 250 | 271 | 264 | 279 | 5.98 |
| SOYBEAN OIL | 272 | 288 | 358 | 701 | 695 | 456 | 586 | 617 | 675 | 625 | 541 | 5.79 |
| GROUNDNUTS SHELLED | 173 | 245 | 339 | 511 | 513 | 467 | 592 | 660 | 668 | 684 | 978 | 12.68 |
| GROUNDNUT OIL | 320 | 373 | 444 | 937 | 804 | 723 | 814 | 942 | 964 | 762 | 993 | 8.41 |
| COPRA | 163 | 118 | 210 | 507 | 237 | 183 | 312 | 372 | 572 | 398 | 303 | 9.82 |
| COCONUT OIL | 262 | 207 | 358 | 929 | 418 | 361 | 550 | 627 | 939 | 652 | 537 | 9.16 |
| PALM NUTS KERNELS | 126 | 107 | 179 | 363 | 178 | 160 | 266 | 262 | 331 | 269 | 242 | 7.16 |
| PALM OIL | 197 | 188 | 255 | 529 | 462 | 362 | 514 | 554 | 617 | 563 | 530 | 10.54 |
| PALM KERNEL OIL | 253 | 238 | 342 | 826 | 455 | 402 | 538 | 617 | 853 | 660 | 551 | 8.54 |
| OLIVE OIL | 680 | 806 | 1168 | 1793 | 1860 | 1307 | 1259 | 1341 | 1632 | 1919 | 1710 | 5.45 |
| CASTOR BEANS | 117 | 158 | 384 | 329 | 207 | 251 | 334 | 333 | 367 | 367 | 347 | 5.62 |
| CASTOR BEAN OIL | 321 | 453 | 967 | 838 | 575 | 557 | 883 | 801 | 802 | 970 | 848 | 4.27 |
| COTTONSEED | 78 | 75 | 100 | 136 | 139 | 147 | 167 | 177 | 169 | 183 | 187 | 9.11 |
| COTTONSEED OIL | 292 | 317 | 355 | 602 | 675 | 555 | 599 | 607 | 682 | 627 | 626 | 6.56 |
| LINSEED | 121 | 121 | 258 | 426 | 336 | 291 | 273 | 216 | 281 | 311 | 324 | 4.15 |
| LINSEED OIL | 174 | 196 | 316 | 900 | 762 | 520 | 500 | 373 | 542 | 611 | 626 | 6.47 |
| BANANAS | 93 | 89 | 94 | 99 | 128 | 138 | 144 | 151 | 168 | 183 | 201 | 9.64 |
| ORANGES | 124 | 137 | 153 | 164 | 202 | 201 | 220 | 267 | 347 | 361 | 332 | 11.97 |
| APPLES | 153 | 186 | 249 | 241 | 317 | 274 | 352 | 412 | 399 | 445 | 412 | 9.37 |
| RAISINS | 326 | 362 | 726 | 907 | 716 | 677 | 965 | 1080 | 1539 | 1673 | 1488 | 14.82 |
| DATES | 110 | 154 | 166 | 213 | 245 | 242 | 323 | 417 | 431 | 479 | 613 | 16.54 |
| COFFEE GREEN | 711 | 902 | 1137 | 1259 | 1180 | 2285 | 4245 | 3176 | 3153 | 3321 | 2231 | 15.54 |
| COCOA BEANS | 542 | 567 | 841 | 1327 | 1400 | 1507 | 2811 | 3136 | 3271 | 2811 | 1803 | 17.36 |
| TEA | 1048 | 974 | 933 | 1098 | 1268 | 1236 | 2204 | 2072 | 1996 | 2056 | 1964 | 10.77 |
| COTTON LINT | 599 | 774 | 879 | 1295 | 1120 | 1295 | 1537 | 1361 | 1530 | 1629 | 1716 | 8.25 |
| JUTE | 286 | 228 | 250 | 243 | 238 | 266 | 277 | 356 | 380 | 378 | 305 | 5.60 |
| JUTE-LIKE FIBRES | 141 | 205 | 193 | 170 | 203 | 210 | 250 | 245 | 248 | 260 | 184 | 2.29 |
| SISAL | 136 | 151 | 320 | 716 | 469 | 342 | 380 | 379 | 482 | 587 | 521 | 8.12 |
| TOBACCO UNMANUFACTURED | 1276 | 1371 | 1501 | 1756 | 2079 | 2176 | 2357 | 2639 | 2741 | 2823 | 2952 | 9.08 |
| NATURAL RUBBER | 426 | 336 | 552 | 825 | 556 | 749 | 806 | 919 | 1208 | 1310 | 1126 | 13.17 |
| RUBBER NATURAL DRY | 357 | 309 | 573 | 714 | 545 | 720 | 794 | 915 | 1180 | 1313 | 1067 | 13.66 |
| WOOL GREASY | 1170 | 932 | 2057 | 2803 | 1765 | 1797 | 2160 | 2220 | 2460 | 2822 | 2949 | 8.07 |
| CATTLE 1/ | 138 | 231 | 284 | 265 | 305 | 287 | 310 | 352 | 417 | 443 | 426 | 7.15 |
| BEEF AND VEAL | 722 | 1256 | 1661 | 1521 | 1725 | 1651 | 1851 | 2171 | 2431 | 2527 | 2378 | 7.43 |
| MUTTON AND LAMB | 492 | 586 | 872 | 1223 | 1071 | 1009 | 1143 | 1388 | 1590 | 1731 | 1847 | 11.09 |
| PIGS 1/ | 36 | 57 | 78 | 81 | 90 | 90 | 100 | 104 | 111 | 106 | 109 | 6.31 |
| BACON HAM OF SWINE | 829 | 1027 | 1507 | 1620 | 2069 | 1979 | 1849 | 2223 | 2608 | 2849 | 2714 | 10.00 |
| MEAT CHIKENS | 632 | 745 | 1045 | 1033 | 1138 | 1183 | 1233 | 1316 | 1397 | 1470 | 1370 | 6.16 |
| MEAT PREPARATIONS | 871 | 1272 | 1537 | 1734 | 1499 | 1540 | 1521 | 1615 | 2148 | 2619 | 2565 | 7.10 |
| EVAP CCND WHOLE COW MILK | 321 | 432 | 482 | 560 | 682 | 638 | 658 | 757 | 854 | 930 | 919 | 8.76 |
| MILK OF COWS SKIMMED DRY | 360 | 579 | 660 | 842 | 992 | 812 | 638 | 744 | 842 | 1073 | 1116 | 5.10 |
| BUTTER OF COWMILK | 791 | 1223 | 991 | 1315 | 1724 | 1670 | 1726 | 2236 | 2271 | 2467 | 2639 | 10.75 |
| CHEESE OF WHOLE COWMILK | 857 | 1255 | 1461 | 1713 | 2021 | 1969 | 2146 | 2509 | 2750 | 2905 | 2652 | 9.28 |

FISHERY PRODUCTS

| | 1967 | 1972 | 1973 | 1974 | 1975 | 1976 | 1977 | 1978 | 1979 | 1980 | 1981 | RATE |
|---|---|---|---|---|---|---|---|---|---|---|---|---|
| FISH FRESH FROZEN | 338 | 539 | 664 | 668 | 745 | 896 | 1050 | 1129 | 1231 | 1218 | 1284 | 10.53 |
| FISH CURED | 443 | 652 | 874 | 1190 | 1256 | 1438 | 1582 | 1740 | 1953 | 2212 | 2214 | 13.61 |
| SHELLFISH | 983 | 1386 | 1787 | 1838 | 2078 | 2555 | 2796 | 3191 | 3617 | 3999 | 4265 | 13.24 |
| FISH CANNED AND PREPARED | 743 | 958 | 1186 | 1342 | 1330 | 1447 | 1709 | 2037 | 2282 | 2200 | 2199 | 10.12 |
| SHELLFISH CANNED+PREPAR | 1423 | 1718 | 2240 | 2620 | 2861 | 3133 | 3616 | 3722 | 4296 | 4706 | 4982 | 11.65 |
| FISH BODY AND LIVER OIL | 128 | 158 | 272 | 467 | 338 | 362 | 429 | 433 | 416 | 430 | 419 | 7.75 |
| FISH MEAL | 119 | 166 | 401 | 377 | 243 | 324 | 428 | 419 | 390 | 427 | 438 | 7.06 |

FOREST PRODUCTS

| | 1967 | 1972 | 1973 | 1974 | 1975 | 1976 | 1977 | 1978 | 1979 | 1980 | 1981 | RATE |
|---|---|---|---|---|---|---|---|---|---|---|---|---|
| SAWLOGS CONIFEROUS 2/ | 19 | 27 | 46 | 53 | 52 | 52 | 59 | 63 | 84 | 90 | 85 | 11.54 |
| SAWLOGS NONCONIFEROUS 2/ | 24 | 26 | 40 | 48 | 39 | 50 | 54 | 57 | 93 | 102 | 90 | 14.44 |
| PULPWOOD+PARTICLE 2/ | 10 | 14 | 17 | 22 | 25 | 23 | 24 | 25 | 26 | 36 | 38 | 9.59 |
| FUELWOOD 2/ | 14 | 18 | 21 | 37 | 43 | 59 | 48 | 64 | 84 | 106 | 114 | 22.16 |
| SAWNWOOD CONIFEROUS 2/ | 38 | 53 | 74 | 96 | 89 | 93 | 101 | 108 | 131 | 138 | 126 | 9.10 |
| SAWNWOOD NONCONIF. 2/ | 62 | 80 | 105 | 133 | 128 | 134 | 151 | 163 | 215 | 242 | 219 | 11.63 |
| WOOD-BASED PANELS 2/ | 110 | 132 | 167 | 187 | 183 | 197 | 214 | 230 | 286 | 321 | 302 | 9.46 |
| PULP FOR PAPER | 117 | 147 | 174 | 279 | 351 | 336 | 313 | 280 | 360 | 440 | 444 | 10.83 |
| PAPER AND PAPERBOARD | 170 | 207 | 245 | 348 | 415 | 406 | 421 | 451 | 504 | 570 | 567 | 10.93 |

1/ U.S. DOLLARS PER HEAD
2/ U.S. DOLLARS PER CUBIC METRE

ANNEX TABLE 6. VOLUME OF IMPORTS OF MAJOR AGRICULTURAL, FISHERY AND FOREST PRODUCTS

| | 1967 | 1972 | 1973 | 1974 | 1975 | 1976 | 1977 | 1978 | 1979 | 1980 | 1981 | ANNUAL RATE OF CHANGE 1972-81 PERCENT |
|---|---|---|---|---|---|---|---|---|---|---|---|---|
| | | | | | | ........THOUSAND METRIC TONS........ | | | | | | |
| **WORLD** | | | | | | | | | | | | |
| **AGRICULTURAL PRODUCTS** | | | | | | | | | | | | |
| WHEAT+FLOUR,WHEAT EQUIV. | 50745 | 59423 | 74392 | 65832 | 72165 | 70314 | 69411 | 77527 | 84071 | 95735 | 101164 | 4.95 |
| RICE MILLED | 8253 | 8803 | 9154 | 8448 | 7620 | 9248 | 10121 | 10262 | 12292 | 12966 | 13636 | 5.76 |
| BARLEY | 7037 | 13989 | 12096 | 12422 | 12512 | 13703 | 12355 | 14790 | 14824 | 15198 | 18723 | 3.39 |
| MAIZE | 27364 | 37861 | 46849 | 48902 | 51657 | 61681 | 54931 | 67768 | 74532 | 79676 | 79370 | 8.32 |
| MILLET | 338 | 292 | 468 | 464 | 322 | 353 | 405 | 395 | 300 | 239 | 244 | - 4.57 |
| SORGHUM | 7236 | 5294 | 7286 | 10184 | 9224 | 10441 | 10681 | 10369 | 10121 | 10896 | 13102 | 7.10 |
| POTATOES | 3228 | 4878 | 3836 | 3829 | 3765 | 4327 | 4728 | 3913 | 4581 | 4695 | 4779 | 1.42 |
| SUGAR,TOTAL (RAW EQUIV.) | 19614 | 21365 | 22777 | 22292 | 21568 | 22175 | 26915 | 23927 | 25259 | 26449 | 28071 | 2.85 |
| PULSES | 1734 | 2061 | 2021 | 1684 | 1866 | 1883 | 2053 | 2030 | 2264 | 2811 | 2976 | 4.61 |
| SOYBEANS | 8273 | 13846 | 14675 | 17503 | 16313 | 19983 | 19623 | 23401 | 26123 | 26997 | 26364 | 8.28 |
| SOYBEAN OIL | 559 | 1116 | 1051 | 1503 | 1369 | 1615 | 2078 | 2379 | 2530 | 3143 | 3327 | 14.27 |
| GROUNDNUTS SHELLED BASIS | 1442 | 879 | 988 | 889 | 927 | 1062 | 840 | 823 | 802 | 728 | 884 | - 1.92 |
| GROUNDNUT OIL | 464 | 518 | 537 | 387 | 428 | 513 | 596 | 476 | 477 | 512 | 342 | - 1.53 |
| COPRA | 1246 | 1309 | 1061 | 545 | 1033 | 1215 | 919 | 804 | 465 | 481 | 406 | -10.27 |
| COCONUT OIL | 464 | 848 | 764 | 625 | 953 | 1415 | 1081 | 1263 | 1204 | 1134 | 1400 | 6.98 |
| PALM NUTS KERNELS | 373 | 398 | 295 | 343 | 278 | 349 | 292 | 169 | 161 | 182 | 147 | -10.24 |
| PALM OIL | 626 | 1372 | 1549 | 1559 | 1884 | 2018 | 2471 | 2306 | 2707 | 3269 | 2886 | 9.84 |
| OILSEED CAKE AND MEAL | 9320 | 14337 | 15395 | 14830 | 14910 | 18562 | 19255 | 22081 | 23928 | 25467 | 27652 | 8.22 |
| BANANAS | 5083 | 6415 | 6384 | 6345 | 6307 | 6357 | 6576 | 6858 | 7014 | 6799 | 6752 | 1.03 |
| ORANGES+TANGER+CLEMEN | 3697 | 4716 | 4951 | 4870 | 4991 | 5117 | 5276 | 4964 | 5110 | 5261 | 4987 | .72 |
| LEMONS AND LIMES | 651 | 733 | 778 | 836 | 829 | 934 | 910 | 959 | 965 | 1003 | 962 | 3.29 |
| COFFEE GREEN+ROASTED | 3015 | 3474 | 3654 | 3463 | 3676 | 3776 | 3126 | 3435 | 3916 | 3799 | 3780 | .76 |
| COCOA BEANS | 1104 | 1250 | 1171 | 1155 | 1192 | 1159 | 1006 | 1094 | 1040 | 1092 | 1265 | - .79 |
| TEA | 691 | 752 | 758 | 822 | 806 | 846 | 899 | 828 | 886 | 913 | 929 | 2.28 |
| COTTON LINT | 3894 | 3959 | 4731 | 4125 | 4058 | 4103 | 4018 | 4504 | 4518 | 5030 | 4339 | 1.22 |
| JUTE AND SIMILAR FIBRES | 1019 | 796 | 884 | 804 | 569 | 658 | 557 | 488 | 580 | 578 | 599 | - 4.62 |
| TOBACCO UNMANUFACTURED | 1016 | 1204 | 1239 | 1286 | 1303 | 1301 | 1260 | 1429 | 1396 | 1415 | 1448 | 1.98 |
| NATURAL RUBBER | 2409 | 2950 | 3259 | 3310 | 3107 | 3272 | 3378 | 3344 | 3473 | 3350 | 3283 | 1.00 |
| WOOL GREASY | 1102 | 1200 | 950 | 749 | 847 | 1033 | 869 | 868 | 914 | 844 | 857 | - 1.78 |
| BOVINE CATTLE 1/ | 5646 | 7941 | 7090 | 5967 | 6423 | 6695 | 6778 | 7324 | 7254 | 6848 | 7123 | .10 |
| SHEEP AND GOATS 1/ | 8545 | 11900 | 11151 | 10298 | 11213 | 10704 | 13143 | 14338 | 16630 | 18192 | 19498 | 6.99 |
| PIGS 1/ | 3178 | 5973 | 5779 | 5985 | 6377 | 6802 | 6704 | 7761 | 8149 | 10620 | 9753 | 6.76 |
| TOTAL MEAT | 3707 | 5278 | 5489 | 5044 | 5536 | 6016c | 6616 | 6927 | 7552 | 7857 | 8372 | 5.89 |
| MILK DRY | 182 | 245 | 247 | 260 | 259 | 326 | 438 | 428 | 466 | 549 | 500 | 10.68 |
| TOTAL EGGS IN SHELL | 313 | 433 | 444 | 505 | 528 | 516 | 574 | 637 | 675 | 740 | 772 | 6.83 |
| **FISHERY PRODUCTS** | | | | | | | | | | | | |
| FISH FRESH FROZEN | 1664 | 2439 | 2770 | 2864 | 2797 | 2916 | 3127 | 3467 | 3829 | 3815 | 3434 | 4.64 |
| FISH CURED | 514 | 480 | 413 | 377 | 377 | 363 | 333 | 338 | 365 | 350 | 328 | - 3.08 |
| SHELLFISH | 406 | 686 | 716 | 769 | 820 | 938 | 893 | 1050 | 1203 | 1114 | 1001 | 5.88 |
| FISH CANNED AND PREPARED | 542 | 684 | 735 | 767 | 713 | 831 | 765 | 843 | 877 | 883 | 874 | 2.82 |
| SHELLFISH CANNED+PREPAR | 90 | 115 | 134 | 130 | 129 | 144 | 153 | 156 | 160 | 156 | 152 | 3.28 |
| FISH BODY AND LIVER OIL | 847 | 739 | 631 | 624 | 631 | 613 | 569 | 653 | 734 | 783 | 729 | 1.36 |
| FISH MEAL | 2913 | 3114 | 1720 | 1908 | 2288 | 2193 | 2211 | 2027 | 2345 | 2277 | 2121 | - .49 |
| **FOREST PRODUCTS 2/** | | | | | | | | | | | | |
| SAWLOGS CONIFEROUS | 16414 | 26420 | 29838 | 26831 | 24329 | 27655 | 29218 | 29809 | 31486 | 27930 | 23057 | - .14 |
| SAWLOGS NONCONIFEROUS | 25717 | 41834 | 49430 | 45228 | 35757 | 44222 | 46205 | 47605 | 48213 | 42178 | 33999 | - 1.06 |
| PULPWOOD+PARTICLE | 18635 | 22879 | 28801 | 33914 | 31445 | 31875 | 36146 | 33903 | 38638 | 42197 | 39147 | 5.29 |
| FUELWOOD | 1538 | 1105 | 1679 | 1816 | 1684 | 1550 | 1627 | 1337 | 1383 | 1399 | 976 | - 2.63 |
| SAWNWOOD CONIFEROUS | 42255 | 56773 | 60799 | 52077 | 42284 | 54359 | 60623 | 65094 | 67158 | 62801 | 57893 | 1.88 |
| SAWNWOOD NONCONIFEROUS | 5566 | 7804 | 10562 | 9563 | 8069 | 10438 | 11411 | 11867 | 13553 | 12702 | 11594 | 4.87 |
| WOOD-BASED PANELS | 6879 | 13116 | 16063 | 13710 | 12377 | 14543 | 14538 | 15856 | 16758 | 15398 | 15783 | 1.91 |
| PULP FOR PAPER | 11903 | 14881 | 16568 | 17387 | 13504 | 15258 | 15337 | 17380 | 18562 | 18852 | 18028 | 2.28 |
| PAPER AND PAPERBOARD | 17955 | 25176 | 27010 | 28939 | 23003 | 26556 | 27734 | 30354 | 32332 | 33699 | 33353 | 3.40 |
| **WESTERN EUROPE** | | | | | | | | | | | | |
| **AGRICULTURAL PRODUCTS** | | | | | | | | | | | | |
| WHEAT+FLOUR,WHEAT EQUIV. | 10378 | 13410 | 13527 | 12488 | 12394 | 13109 | 12521 | 13300 | 12885 | 14024 | 13171 | .25 |
| RICE MILLED | 586 | 770 | 804 | 806 | 809 | 1225 | 1352 | 1567 | 1392 | 1335 | 1496 | 9.08 |
| BARLEY | 4955 | 5694 | 5364 | 6345 | 5477 | 6329 | 6136 | 6567 | 5105 | 5255 | 6065 | - .09 |
| MAIZE | 19374 | 20166 | 22641 | 24324 | 25301 | 26440 | 26733 | 24757 | 24817 | 23438 | 21787 | .60 |
| MILLET | 222 | 114 | 138 | 108 | 112 | 90 | 182 | 195 | 150 | 98 | 109 | .71 |
| SORGHUM | 2034 | 578 | 1139 | 2800 | 2669 | 2893 | 2146 | 1425 | 1166 | 1251 | 1090 | - .11 |
| POTATOES | 1945 | 2549 | 2390 | 2235 | 2372 | 3149 | 2999 | 2565 | 2811 | 3051 | 2979 | 2.73 |
| SUGAR,TOTAL (RAW EQUIV.) | 4709 | 4823 | 4804 | 5165 | 5096 | 4467 | 4112 | 3431 | 3346 | 3096 | 3069 | - 6.21 |
| PULSES | 831 | 1098 | 1103 | 786 | 794 | 828 | 888 | 907 | 1054 | 1013 | 910 | - .21 |
| SOYBEANS | 4762 | 8323 | 8327 | 11275 | 10524 | 11719 | 11612 | 14201 | 15311 | 16217 | 14340 | 7.53 |
| SOYBEAN OIL | 155 | 368 | 316 | 545 | 575 | 532 | 502 | 559 | 580 | 675 | 663 | 6.75 |
| GROUNDNUTS SHELLED BASIS | 1188 | 610 | 712 | 628 | 621 | 749 | 577 | 556 | 545 | 428 | 383 | - 5.34 |
| GROUNDNUT OIL | 390 | 435 | 422 | 327 | 338 | 351 | 355 | 325 | 407 | 446 | 289 | - 1.38 |
| COPRA | 711 | 822 | 630 | 354 | 816 | 961 | 670 | 515 | 294 | 252 | 183 | -12.81 |

1/ THOUSAND HEAD
2/ EXCEPT FOR PULP FOR PAPER AND PAPER AND PAPERBOARD, ALL FOREST PRODUCTS ARE EXPRESSED IN THOUSAND CUBIC METRES

ANNEX TABLE 6.   VOLUME OF IMPORTS OF MAJOR AGRICULTURAL, FISHERY AND FOREST PRODUCTS

| | 1967 | 1972 | 1973 | 1974 | 1975 | 1976 | 1977 | 1978 | 1979 | 1980 | 1981 | ANNUAL RATE OF CHANGE 1972-81 PERCENT |
|---|---|---|---|---|---|---|---|---|---|---|---|---|
| | | | | | | THOUSAND METRIC TONS | | | | | | |
| COCONUT OIL | 153 | 287 | 277 | 177 | 281 | 427 | 331 | 395 | 390 | 414 | 540 | 8.35 |
| PALM NUTS KERNELS | 318 | 350 | 251 | 329 | 260 | 327 | 271 | 153 | 137 | 147 | 128 | -10.86 |
| PALM OIL | 394 | 693 | 752 | 698 | 797 | 860 | 829 | 781 | 856 | 833 | 722 | 1.23 |
| OILSEED CAKE AND MEAL | 7484 | 10383 | 11039 | 9927 | 10101 | 12778 | 12860 | 15320 | 16705 | 17392 | 18046 | 7.55 |
| BANANAS | 2279 | 2554 | 2556 | 2427 | 2329 | 2256 | 2430 | 2525 | 2460 | 2239 | 2196 | - 1.15 |
| ORANGES+TANGER+CLEMEN | 2806 | 3309 | 3459 | 3200 | 3198 | 3176 | 3322 | 3143 | 3227 | 3222 | 2978 | - .85 |
| LEMONS AND LIMES | 380 | 368 | 378 | 386 | 398 | 432 | 408 | 428 | 432 | 429 | 408 | 1.55 |
| COFFEE GREEN+ROASTED | 1284 | 1606 | 1674 | 1642 | 1747 | 1810 | 1543 | 1703 | 1955 | 1929 | 1991 | 2.18 |
| COCOA BEANS | 546 | 602 | 584 | 574 | 564 | 565 | 561 | 590 | 569 | 616 | 658 | .77 |
| TEA | 319 | 289 | 298 | 313 | 289 | 297 | 336 | 250 | 278 | 297 | 273 | - .88 |
| COTTON LINT | 1449 | 1281 | 1543 | 1145 | 1188 | 1318 | 1135 | 1216 | 1150 | 1258 | 1015 | - 2.15 |
| JUTE AND SIMILAR FIBRES | 561 | 398 | 353 | 356 | 177 | 232 | 216 | 157 | 182 | 132 | 124 | -12.02 |
| TOBACCO UNMANUFACTURED | 561 | 646 | 681 | 661 | 677 | 695 | 677 | 785 | 743 | 701 | 669 | .92 |
| NATURAL RUBBER | 724 | 910 | 947 | 958 | 875 | 941 | 950 | 861 | 925 | 892 | 841 | - .81 |
| WOOL GREASY | 596 | 597 | 423 | 370 | 391 | 528 | 418 | 425 | 437 | 389 | 382 | - 2.25 |
| BOVINE CATTLE 1/ | 2557 | 3933 | 3305 | 2691 | 3444 | 3306 | 3175 | 3472 | 3529 | 3416 | 3222 | - .14 |
| SHEEP AND GOATS 1/ | 1745 | 3017 | 2529 | 1968 | 2570 | 2370 | 2354 | 2724 | 2913 | 2920 | 2161 | .08 |
| PIGS 1/ | 1144 | 3000 | 2819 | 3009 | 3314 | 3629 | 3284 | 3870 | 4382 | 5202 | 5454 | 7.49 |
| TOTAL MEAT | 2437 | 3350 | 3446 | 2876 | 3104 | 3311 | 3461 | 3765 | 3787 | 3760 | 3504 | 1.84 |
| MILK DRY | 88 | 118 | 102 | 85 | 92 | 117 | 98 | 115 | 127 | 146 | 124 | 3.37 |
| TOTAL EGGS IN SHELL | 176 | 247 | 270 | 318 | 311 | 307 | 327 | 366 | 400 | 430 | 433 | 6.27 |
| **FISHERY PRODUCTS** | | | | | | | | | | | | |
| FISH FRESH FROZEN | 821 | 1026 | 1143 | 1231 | 1147 | 1132 | 1229 | 1332 | 1470 | 1567 | 1339 | 3.72 |
| FISH CURED | 214 | 233 | 186 | 181 | 158 | 158 | 161 | 168 | 194 | 188 | 184 | - .93 |
| SHELLFISH | 142 | 249 | 245 | 261 | 295 | 328 | 275 | 347 | 368 | 386 | 284 | 3.93 |
| FISH CANNED AND PREPARED | 259 | 283 | 310 | 288 | 274 | 307 | 294 | 287 | 313 | 326 | 322 | 1.22 |
| SHELLFISH CANNED+PREPAR | 33 | 46 | 57 | 56 | 60 | 63 | 68 | 73 | 80 | 82 | 78 | 6.09 |
| FISH BODY AND LIVER OIL | 739 | 665 | 569 | 551 | 558 | 537 | 510 | 584 | 666 | 675 | 675 | 1.44 |
| FISH MEAL | 1722 | 1855 | 1106 | 1086 | 1204 | 1187 | 1084 | 1074 | 1221 | 1192 | 1195 | - 1.97 |
| **FOREST PRODUCTS 2/** | | | | | | | | | | | | |
| SAWLOGS CONIFEROUS | 2511 | 2767 | 4316 | 4756 | 3221 | 4417 | 4890 | 4094 | 4547 | 5103 | 4497 | 3.79 |
| SAWLOGS NONCONIFEROUS | 6295 | 9070 | 10952 | 8928 | 6985 | 8858 | 8746 | 7671 | 8011 | 8396 | 6878 | - 2.76 |
| PULPWOOD+PARTICLE | 11258 | 11882 | 14941 | 18155 | 17920 | 17241 | 16706 | 15282 | 17866 | 20831 | 21810 | 4.46 |
| FUELWOOD | 1014 | 837 | 1413 | 1597 | 1470 | 1343 | 1379 | 1106 | 1129 | 1167 | 728 | - 3.07 |
| SAWNWOOD CONIFEROUS | 22088 | 25396 | 28214 | 23709 | 17177 | 23111 | 22096 | 23684 | 27274 | 25507 | 21703 | - .30 |
| SAWNWOOD NONCONIFEROUS | 2647 | 3995 | 5677 | 4033 | 3620 | 5435 | 5521 | 5620 | 6831 | 6088 | 5091 | 4.11 |
| WOOD-BASED PANELS | 3991 | 6274 | 8157 | 6952 | 6076 | 7564 | 7524 | 8440 | 9652 | 8940 | 8763 | 3.87 |
| PULP FOR PAPER | 6948 | 8380 | 9305 | 9594 | 7234 | 8370 | 8217 | 9369 | 9949 | 9943 | 9524 | 1.56 |
| PAPER AND PAPERBOARD | 6978 | 11433 | 12502 | 13523 | 9907 | 12368 | 12631 | 13596 | 15064 | 15099 | 15231 | 3.33 |
| **USSR AND EASTERN EUROPE** | | | | | | | | | | | | |
| **AGRICULTURAL PRODUCTS** | | | | | | | | | | | | |
| WHEAT+FLOUR,WHEAT EQUIV. | 6090 | 12986 | 19997 | 7294 | 13297 | 12920 | 11783 | 12915 | 15817 | 20886 | 23824 | 5.90 |
| RICE MILLED | 645 | 503 | 419 | 441 | 544 | 647 | 726 | 710 | 940 | 995 | 1579 | 13.59 |
| BARLEY | 776 | 5487 | 3416 | 2368 | 3283 | 4118 | 2225 | 4137 | 4559 | 4311 | 6025 | 3.59 |
| MAIZE | 1101 | 6090 | 7816 | 6927 | 9131 | 17664 | 7493 | 17809 | 20175 | 18863 | 21512 | 15.67 |
| POTATOES | 503 | 1365 | 584 | 642 | 514 | 368 | 664 | 301 | 512 | 297 | 337 | -11.13 |
| SUGAR,TOTAL (RAW EQUIV.) | 3178 | 2757 | 3504 | 2863 | 3915 | 4531 | 5566 | 4637 | 4878 | 5708 | 6275 | 8.98 |
| PULSES | 28 | 34 | 32 | 49 | 59 | 39 | 33 | 39 | 41 | 54 | 70 | 4.96 |
| SOYBEANS | 145 | 478 | 914 | 265 | 520 | 2089 | 1544 | 1409 | 2360 | 1768 | 1656 | 19.52 |
| SOYBEAN OIL | 38 | 87 | 34 | 38 | 31 | 72 | 94 | 103 | 122 | 137 | 173 | 16.88 |
| GROUNDNUTS SHELLED BASIS | 65 | 69 | 52 | 66 | 59 | 54 | 59 | 57 | 46 | 54 | 62 | - 1.49 |
| GROUNDNUT OIL | 2 | 1 | 1 | 4 | 4 | 2 | 2 | 1 | 2 | 1 | | |
| COPRA | 3 | 35 | 28 | 29 | 29 | 25 | 38 | 26 | 25 | 30 | 20 | - 3.02 |
| COCONUT OIL | 23 | 38 | 24 | 27 | 42 | 93 | 48 | 66 | 58 | 89 | 77 | 12.98 |
| PALM NUTS KERNELS | 20 | 6 | 13 | 3 | 4 | 4 | 4 | 4 | 3 | 4 | | |
| PALM OIL | 5 | 13 | 10 | 22 | 17 | 28 | 67 | 58 | 113 | 112 | 134 | 36.10 |
| OILSEED CAKE AND MEAL | 1212 | 2764 | 3009 | 3404 | 3541 | 3678 | 3733 | 3786 | 4098 | 4681 | 5874 | 6.91 |
| BANANAS | 75 | 174 | 189 | 198 | 267 | 224 | 281 | 299 | 282 | 260 | 236 | 4.54 |
| ORANGES+TANGER+CLEMEN | 395 | 686 | 680 | 762 | 715 | 693 | 727 | 719 | 690 | 750 | 695 | .22 |
| LEMONS AND LIMES | 199 | 253 | 273 | 308 | 310 | 330 | 314 | 327 | 309 | 344 | 308 | 2.15 |
| COFFEE GREEN+ROASTED | 118 | 185 | 171 | 183 | 205 | 199 | 201 | 178 | 201 | 228 | 202 | 1.74 |
| COCOA BEANS | 156 | 239 | 215 | 250 | 280 | 256 | 175 | 202 | 212 | 225 | 227 | - 1.39 |
| TEA | 34 | 64 | 54 | 69 | 88 | 82 | 80 | 71 | 79 | 102 | 116 | 6.14 |
| COTTON LINT | 678 | 744 | 710 | 748 | 769 | 679 | 720 | 681 | 718 | 743 | 645 | - .89 |
| JUTE AND SIMILAR FIBRES | 90 | 88 | 85 | 67 | 83 | 80 | 68 | 70 | 78 | 92 | 111 | 1.67 |
| TOBACCO UNMANUFACTURED | 134 | 160 | 151 | 142 | 147 | 126 | 133 | 135 | 133 | 178 | 205 | 1.72 |
| NATURAL RUBBER | 439 | 450 | 495 | 548 | 473 | 485 | 409 | 433 | 437 | 441 | 418 | - 1.82 |
| WOOL GREASY | 106 | 143 | 148 | 151 | 162 | 162 | 161 | 182 | 188 | 182 | 184 | 3.17 |
| BOVINE CATTLE 1/ | 114 | 61 | 90 | 232 | 506 | 195 | 224 | 84 | 176 | 180 | 167 | 4.54 |
| SHEEP AND GOATS 1/ | 2071 | 1601 | 1907 | 1918 | 1520 | 1401 | 1103 | 1243 | 1251 | 1276 | 1167 | - 5.10 |
| PIGS 1/ | 74 | 145 | 126 | 103 | 185 | 59 | 306 | 523 | 502 | 604 | 973 | 28.02 |
| TOTAL MEAT | 315 | 277 | 265 | 597 | 545 | 416 | 754 | 265 | 644 | 956 | 1221 | 13.68 |

1/ THOUSAND HEAD
2/ EXCEPT FOR PULP FOR PAPER AND PAPER AND PAPERBOARD, ALL FOREST PRODUCTS ARE EXPRESSED IN THOUSAND CUBIC METRES

ANNEX TABLE 6. VOLUME OF IMPORTS OF MAJOR AGRICULTURAL, FISHERY AND FOREST PRODUCTS

| | 1967 | 1972 | 1973 | 1974 | 1975 | 1976 | 1977 | 1978 | 1979 | 1980 | 1981 | ANNUAL RATE OF CHANGE 1972-81 PERCENT |
|---|---|---|---|---|---|---|---|---|---|---|---|---|
| | | | | | ...THOUSAND METRIC TONS... | | | | | | | |
| MILK DRY | 12 | 30 | 22 | 28 | 23 | 28 | 43 | 29 | 42 | 71 | 78 | 12.95 |
| TOTAL EGGS IN SHELL | 52 | 63 | 51 | 51 | 50 | 37 | 43 | 43 | 47 | 43 | 32 | - 4.67 |
| **FISHERY PRODUCTS** | | | | | | | | | | | | |
| FISH FRESH FROZEN | 142 | 128 | 120 | 132 | 141 | 159 | 147 | 222 | 239 | 306 | 257 | 10.94 |
| FISH CURED | 23 | 20 | 18 | 18 | 24 | 28 | 18 | 16 | 17 | 18 | 10 | - 4.76 |
| FISH CANNED AND PREPARED | 27 | 27 | 27 | 26 | 41 | 52 | 41 | 38 | 39 | 41 | 39 | 4.93 |
| FISH BODY AND LIVER OIL | 28 | 21 | 15 | 28 | 34 | 4 | 7 | 6 | 5 | 9 | 3 | -18.83 |
| FISH MEAL | 294 | 453 | 287 | 458 | 498 | 445 | 407 | 390 | 430 | 435 | 370 | - .02 |
| **FOREST PRODUCTS 2/** | | | | | | | | | | | | |
| SAWLOGS CONIFEROUS | 744 | 780 | 1188 | 1248 | 830 | 787 | 885 | 960 | 720 | 1050 | 960 | - .71 |
| SAWLOGS NONCONIFEROUS | 441 | 480 | 577 | 541 | 588 | 556 | 556 | 442 | 416 | 454 | 487 | - 2.22 |
| PULPWOOD+PARTICLE | 1419 | 1397 | 1208 | 1533 | 1722 | 1548 | 1440 | 1345 | 1446 | 1529 | 1204 | - .48 |
| FUELWOOD | 199 | 6 | 5 | 5 | 5 | 5 | 5 | 5 | 4 | 4 | 4 | - 3.64 |
| SAWNWOOD CONIFEROUS | 2650 | 2999 | 2841 | 3438 | 3599 | 2702 | 3157 | 3228 | 2643 | 2663 | 2620 | - 1.89 |
| SAWNWOOD NONCONIFEROUS | 484 | 371 | 354 | 441 | 442 | 366 | 363 | 326 | 270 | 277 | 386 | - 2.84 |
| WOOD-BASED PANELS | 398 | 819 | 923 | 1117 | 1245 | 1386 | 1314 | 1132 | 1045 | 1109 | 1064 | 1.82 |
| PULP FOR PAPER | 598 | 857 | 913 | 859 | 1106 | 1041 | 1029 | 1036 | 1005 | 1155 | 1129 | 2.89 |
| PAPER AND PAPERBOARD | 814 | 1440 | 1417 | 1507 | 1713 | 1706 | 1712 | 1709 | 1784 | 2046 | 1920 | 3.70 |
| **NORTH AMERICA DEVELOPED** | | | | | | | | | | | | |
| **AGRICULTURAL PRODUCTS** | | | | | | | | | | | | |
| WHEAT+FLOUR,WHEAT EQUIV. | 11 | 3 | 4 | 83 | 17 | 23 | 35 | 1 | 5 | 6 | 1 | -17.32 |
| RICE MILLED | 56 | 94 | 92 | 71 | 74 | 80 | 80 | 82 | 91 | 94 | 106 | 1.67 |
| BARLEY | 156 | 360 | 181 | 328 | 307 | 195 | 180 | 108 | 157 | 140 | 127 | -10.40 |
| MAIZE | 760 | 448 | 825 | 1320 | 818 | 838 | 623 | 476 | 849 | 1228 | 1276 | 5.02 |
| POTATOES | 178 | 141 | 175 | 239 | 208 | 213 | 301 | 235 | 242 | 213 | 340 | 6.30 |
| SUGAR,TOTAL (RAW EQUIV.) | 5175 | 5650 | 5706 | 6137 | 4475 | 5034 | 6330 | 4821 | 5399 | 4594 | 5447 | - 1.23 |
| PULSES | 18 | 29 | 32 | 66 | 44 | 34 | 53 | 43 | 39 | 43 | 61 | 3.98 |
| SOYBEANS | 438 | 309 | 232 | 391 | 385 | 422 | 318 | 325 | 351 | 483 | 382 | 3.54 |
| SOYBEAN OIL | 10 | 17 | 19 | 34 | 23 | 31 | 28 | 35 | 22 | 12 | 9 | - 5.57 |
| GROUNDNUTS SHELLED BASIS | 54 | 55 | 62 | 61 | 62 | 64 | 56 | 68 | 64 | 56 | 231 | 7.91 |
| GROUNDNUT OIL | 12 | 7 | 7 | 6 | 7 | 8 | 7 | 6 | 5 | 5 | 4 | - 5.21 |
| COPRA | 277 | 209 | 159 | 27 | | | | | | | | |
| COCONUT OIL | 215 | 374 | 280 | 271 | 435 | 603 | 495 | 503 | 527 | 422 | 476 | 5.35 |
| PALM OIL | 39 | 226 | 196 | 217 | 483 | 416 | 282 | 173 | 163 | 137 | 138 | - 6.95 |
| OILSEED CAKE AND MEAL | 262 | 238 | 216 | 300 | 301 | 386 | 374 | 426 | 491 | 431 | 443 | 8.80 |
| BANANAS | 1817 | 2146 | 2169 | 2268 | 2179 | 2411 | 2410 | 2543 | 2659 | 2669 | 2794 | 3.13 |
| ORANGES+TANGER+CLEMEN | 225 | 259 | 265 | 259 | 264 | 339 | 380 | 303 | 294 | 320 | 333 | 2.94 |
| LEMONS AND LIMES | 17 | 18 | 19 | 20 | 23 | 24 | 27 | 34 | 36 | 38 | 43 | 10.57 |
| COFFEE GREEN+ROASTED | 1363 | 1343 | 1405 | 1246 | 1324 | 1290 | 986 | 1195 | 1277 | 1190 | 1104 | - 2.02 |
| COCOA BEANS | 305 | 308 | 268 | 238 | 248 | 252 | 186 | 226 | 179 | 162 | 264 | - 4.10 |
| TEA | 86 | 93 | 102 | 105 | 96 | 106 | 117 | 91 | 101 | 107 | 107 | .84 |
| COTTON LINT | 140 | 93 | 86 | 72 | 61 | 73 | 53 | 59 | 61 | 65 | 63 | - 3.97 |
| JUTE AND SIMILAR FIBRES | 48 | 16 | 33 | 31 | 23 | 25 | 14 | 17 | 23 | 10 | 16 | - 6.30 |
| TOBACCO UNMANUFACTURED | 123 | 153 | 158 | 163 | 177 | 161 | 142 | 173 | 188 | 191 | 176 | 1.89 |
| NATURAL RUBBER | 516 | 685 | 727 | 759 | 747 | 818 | 903 | 846 | 862 | 695 | 759 | 1.04 |
| WOOL GREASY | 59 | 30 | 18 | 8 | 13 | 17 | 12 | 15 | 11 | 14 | 20 | - 2.04 |
| BOVINE CATTLE 1/ | 783 | 1260 | 1264 | 716 | 516 | 1183 | 1184 | 1308 | 760 | 758 | 849 | - 2.42 |
| SHEEP AND GOATS 1/ | 38 | 58 | 71 | 33 | 61 | 71 | 52 | 40 | 27 | 42 | 41 | - 5.41 |
| PIGS 1/ | 21 | 90 | 88 | 197 | 30 | 46 | 44 | 204 | 138 | 247 | 146 | 9.81 |
| TOTAL MEAT | 491 | 797 | 785 | 637 | 719 | 862 | 755 | 875 | 913 | 854 | 766 | 1.52 |
| TOTAL EGGS IN SHELL | 9 | 6 | 12 | 15 | 12 | 13 | 19 | 18 | 21 | 12 | 12 | 6.26 |
| **FISHERY PRODUCTS** | | | | | | | | | | | | |
| FISH FRESH FROZEN | 386 | 728 | 792 | 689 | 611 | 709 | 727 | 800 | 776 | 699 | 734 | .38 |
| FISH CURED | 33 | 32 | 33 | 31 | 30 | 37 | 30 | 34 | 31 | 26 | 26 | - 2.09 |
| SHELLFISH | 116 | 149 | 140 | 148 | 139 | 157 | 158 | 146 | 155 | 146 | 144 | .24 |
| FISH CANNED AND PREPARED | 82 | 108 | 104 | 131 | 82 | 103 | 78 | 89 | 95 | 99 | 90 | - 2.19 |
| SHELLFISH CANNED+PREPAR | 25 | 31 | 32 | 33 | 27 | 35 | 41 | 38 | 41 | 39 | 42 | 4.08 |
| FISH BODY AND LIVER OIL | 46 | 10 | 11 | 8 | 7 | 11 | 8 | 9 | 9 | 12 | 12 | 2.21 |
| FISH MEAL | 595 | 357 | 63 | 62 | 108 | 128 | 74 | 40 | 82 | 45 | 45 | -13.05 |
| **FOREST PRODUCTS 2/** | | | | | | | | | | | | |
| SAWLOGS CONIFEROUS | 1298 | 2387 | 1954 | 1737 | 1728 | 2025 | 2174 | 2043 | 2458 | 2146 | 1674 | - .14 |
| SAWLOGS NONCONIFEROUS | 587 | 459 | 459 | 492 | 318 | 291 | 294 | 409 | 502 | 471 | 417 | .12 |
| PULPWOOD+PARTICLE | 3536 | 2081 | 1863 | 2187 | 1859 | 2039 | 2273 | 2516 | 2504 | 2249 | 2348 | 2.52 |
| FUELWOOD | 17 | 31 | 26 | 32 | 35 | 30 | 51 | 59 | 63 | 45 | 23 | 3.98 |
| SAWNWOOD CONIFEROUS | 11693 | 21522 | 21750 | 16639 | 14175 | 19583 | 25061 | 28675 | 26582 | 22839 | 22542 | 3.37 |
| SAWNWOOD NONCONIFEROUS | 1198 | 1429 | 1732 | 1412 | 963 | 1287 | 1351 | 1431 | 1571 | 1422 | 1557 | .71 |
| WOOD-BASED PANELS | 1879 | 4666 | 4147 | 3245 | 3147 | 3645 | 3546 | 3956 | 3336 | 2378 | 2851 | - 4.46 |
| PULP FOR PAPER | 2622 | 3239 | 3497 | 3533 | 2687 | 3243 | 3344 | 3477 | 3818 | 3502 | 3538 | 1.22 |
| PAPER AND PAPERBOARD | 6401 | 7143 | 7546 | 7602 | 6165 | 6982 | 7017 | 8387 | 8322 | 8118 | 7595 | 1.49 |

1/ THOUSAND HEAD
2/ EXCEPT FOR PULP FOR PAPER AND PAPER AND PAPERBOARD, ALL FOREST PRODUCTS ARE EXPRESSED IN THOUSAND CUBIC METRES

ANNEX TABLE 6.  VOLUME OF IMPORTS OF MAJOR AGRICULTURAL, FISHERY AND FOREST PRODUCTS

| | 1967 | 1972 | 1973 | 1974 | 1975 | 1976 | 1977 | 1978 | 1979 | 1980 | 1981 | ANNUAL RATE OF CHANGE 1972-81 PERCENT |
|---|---|---|---|---|---|---|---|---|---|---|---|---|
| | | | | | ....THOUSAND METRIC TONS.... | | | | | | | |
| **OCEANIA DEVELOPED** | | | | | | | | | | | | |
| **AGRICULTURAL PRODUCTS** | | | | | | | | | | | | |
| WHEAT+FLOUR,WHEAT EQUIV. | 100 | 47 | | 50 | 134 | 112 | | | 32 | 54 | 53 | |
| RICE MILLED | 5 | 5 | 6 | 7 | 7 | 6 | 9 | 8 | 8 | 8 | 9 | 5.00 |
| MAIZE | 2 | 1 | 1 | 1 | 1 | 1 | 2 | 3 | 3 | 4 | 5 | 27.74 |
| POTATOES | | | | 1 | | | | | | | | |
| SUGAR,TOTAL (RAW EQUIV.) | 130 | 186 | 171 | 153 | 192 | 174 | 185 | 166 | 172 | 151 | 120 | - 2.73 |
| PULSES | 18 | 16 | 12 | 16 | 20 | 13 | 12 | 13 | 12 | 14 | 13 | - 2.48 |
| SOYBEANS | | | | 33 | 16 | 10 | 21 | 15 | | 13 | 41 | |
| SOYBEAN OIL | 6 | 4 | 6 | 10 | 18 | 38 | 33 | 29 | 26 | 32 | 29 | 24.14 |
| GROUNDNUTS SHELLED BASIS | 4 | 6 | 5 | 6 | 5 | 8 | 5 | 12 | 4 | 5 | 9 | 1.86 |
| GROUNDNUT OIL | 9 | 5 | 3 | 4 | 4 | 2 | 4 | 2 | 3 | | 1 | |
| COPRA | 38 | 26 | 24 | 20 | 12 | 10 | 11 | 5 | 7 | 4 | 6 | -18.69 |
| COCONUT OIL | 1 | 8 | 9 | 13 | 11 | 18 | 20 | 18 | 19 | 17 | 16 | 9.31 |
| PALM OIL | 3 | 8 | 7 | 14 | 16 | 17 | 23 | 23 | 28 | 26 | 24 | 15.73 |
| OILSEED CAKE AND MEAL | 20 | 24 | 12 | 21 | 15 | 3 | 6 | 30 | 9 | 13 | 23 | - .54 |
| BANANAS | 30 | 24 | 33 | 37 | 43 | 29 | 35 | 38 | 35 | 37 | 36 | 2.34 |
| ORANGES+TANGER+CLEMEN | 16 | 16 | 18 | 18 | 18 | 15 | 17 | 18 | 14 | 16 | 16 | - 1.13 |
| LEMONS AND LIMES | | | | | | | | | 1 | 1 | 1 | |
| COFFEE GREEN+ROASTED | 21 | 29 | 29 | 32 | 35 | 32 | 34 | 26 | 35 | 41 | 38 | 2.76 |
| COCOA BEANS | 21 | 18 | 21 | 21 | 25 | 16 | 20 | 17 | 15 | 14 | 15 | - 4.50 |
| TEA | 37 | 37 | 36 | 34 | 35 | 33 | 35 | 30 | 30 | 32 | 28 | - 2.57 |
| COTTON LINT | 9 | 9 | 4 | 9 | 4 | 4 | 5 | 4 | 2 | 2 | 2 | -13.98 |
| JUTE AND SIMILAR FIBRES | 10 | 19 | 16 | 26 | 17 | 14 | 12 | 11 | 12 | 9 | 11 | - 8.66 |
| TOBACCO UNMANUFACTURED | 15 | 15 | 14 | 17 | 17 | 17 | 13 | 16 | 13 | 15 | 15 | - .62 |
| NATURAL RUBBER | 46 | 52 | 55 | 74 | 53 | 61 | 55 | 52 | 53 | 54 | 50 | - 1.40 |
| WOOL GREASY | 2 | 4 | 5 | 6 | 1 | 1 | 1 | 1 | 1 | | 1 | |
| BOVINE CATTLE 1/ | | 3 | 3 | 3 | 1 | 1 | 2 | 1 | 1 | 1 | | |
| SHEEP AND GOATS 1/ | | 1 | 1 | | | | | 1 | 1 | 8 | 1 | |
| TOTAL MEAT | 1 | 1 | 2 | 4 | 2 | 2 | 2 | 1 | 2 | 4 | 4 | 11.49 |
| MILK DRY | | | 1 | 1 | 1 | 1 | 1 | 1 | 1 | | 1 | |
| **FISHERY PRODUCTS** | | | | | | | | | | | | |
| FISH FRESH FROZEN | 20 | 22 | 18 | 22 | 19 | 19 | 20 | 21 | 22 | 20 | 19 | - .16 |
| FISH CURED | 3 | 4 | 3 | 5 | 4 | 4 | 5 | 3 | 5 | 5 | 5 | 1.70 |
| SHELLFISH | 1 | 1 | 2 | 1 | 1 | 3 | 3 | 2 | 4 | 3 | 4 | 14.04 |
| FISH CANNED AND PREPARED | 14 | 15 | 25 | 27 | 23 | 19 | 25 | 26 | 22 | 24 | 25 | 2.43 |
| SHELLFISH CANNED+PREPAR | 2 | 3 | 4 | 6 | 5 | 6 | 7 | 7 | 6 | 6 | 6 | 6.45 |
| FISH BODY AND LIVER OIL | 4 | 1 | 1 | 1 | 1 | 1 | 1 | 1 | 1 | | | |
| FISH MEAL | 14 | 27 | 14 | 14 | 24 | 13 | 8 | 3 | 4 | 4 | 4 | -20.50 |
| **FOREST PRODUCTS 2/** | | | | | | | | | | | | |
| SAWLOGS CONIFEROUS | 18 | 5 | 1 | 3 | | 5 | 2 | 2 | | | | |
| SAWLOGS NONCONIFEROUS | 70 | 95 | 101 | 106 | 41 | 46 | 26 | 17 | 11 | 2 | 1 | -39.34 |
| FUELWOOD | | | | | 2 | 1 | | | | | | |
| SAWNWOOD CONIFEROUS | 647 | 672 | 793 | 886 | 637 | 693 | 754 | 638 | 682 | 697 | 773 | - .52 |
| SAWNWOOD NONCONIFEROUS | 169 | 254 | 338 | 449 | 282 | 346 | 445 | 311 | 304 | 317 | 304 | - .15 |
| WOOD-BASED PANELS | 45 | 73 | 92 | 131 | 123 | 137 | 121 | 89 | 99 | 88 | 104 | .15 |
| PULP FOR PAPER | 265 | 242 | 315 | 352 | 301 | 232 | 276 | 239 | 279 | 279 | 284 | - .66 |
| PAPER AND PAPERBOARD | 462 | 492 | 563 | 678 | 683 | 470 | 652 | 584 | 671 | 739 | 745 | 3.35 |
| **AFRICA DEVELOPING** | | | | | | | | | | | | |
| **AGRICULTURAL PRODUCTS** | | | | | | | | | | | | |
| WHEAT+FLOUR,WHEAT EQUIV. | 2900 | 3518 | 3818 | 4566 | 5138 | 5054 | 6086 | 7314 | 7607 | 8506 | 9305 | 11.64 |
| RICE MILLED | 590 | 791 | 976 | 976 | 602 | 878 | 1547 | 1829 | 2122 | 2201 | 2394 | 15.26 |
| BARLEY | 115 | 76 | 106 | 114 | 173 | 68 | 219 | 647 | 418 | 300 | 539 | 24.76 |
| MAIZE | 199 | 480 | 480 | 830 | 859 | 678 | 878 | 1035 | 1210 | 2391 | 2809 | 19.82 |
| MILLET | 95 | 133 | 240 | 234 | 140 | 162 | 158 | 132 | 72 | 83 | 80 | -10.39 |
| SORGHUM | 20 | 40 | 84 | 179 | 39 | 77 | 45 | 97 | 81 | 69 | 129 | 4.56 |
| POTATOES | 132 | 131 | 192 | 208 | 188 | 148 | 210 | 239 | 300 | 241 | 309 | 7.70 |
| SUGAR,TOTAL (RAW EQUIV.) | 1260 | 1338 | 1363 | 1289 | 1274 | 1419 | 1779 | 1950 | 2005 | 2110 | 2378 | 7.51 |
| PULSES | 68 | 77 | 78 | 53 | 89 | 77 | 91 | 88 | 155 | 135 | 156 | 9.96 |
| SOYBEANS | 1 | 1 | 13 | 10 | 9 | 16 | 50 | 23 | 32 | 25 | 17 | 26.63 |
| SOYBEAN OIL | 51 | 100 | 93 | 147 | 155 | 121 | 255 | 294 | 334 | 329 | 331 | 17.41 |
| GROUNDNUTS SHELLED BASIS | 21 | 21 | 24 | 19 | 44 | 18 | 27 | 20 | 14 | 17 | 15 | - 5.48 |
| GROUNDNUT OIL | 12 | 24 | 39 | 6 | 8 | 30 | 23 | 13 | 12 | 15 | 8 | - 6.84 |
| COPRA | 4 | 5 | 6 | 2 | 3 | 3 | 3 | 4 | 4 | 3 | 4 | - 1.36 |
| COCONUT OIL | 8 | 15 | 14 | 13 | 9 | 18 | 20 | 10 | 9 | 10 | 16 | - 1.64 |
| PALM NUTS KERNELS | 2 | | | | 1 | | | | | | | |
| PALM OIL | 9 | 27 | 41 | 38 | 29 | 68 | 81 | 94 | 95 | 132 | 186 | 22.81 |
| OILSEED CAKE AND MEAL | 18 | 41 | 36 | 50 | 58 | 54 | 102 | 122 | 154 | 183 | 245 | 24.36 |
| BANANAS | 35 | 52 | 55 | 43 | 37 | 52 | 46 | 29 | 12 | 15 | 17 | -14.97 |
| ORANGES+TANGER+CLEMEN | 9 | 10 | 10 | 10 | 12 | 10 | 12 | 12 | 11 | 10 | 10 | .28 |

1/ THOUSAND HEAD
2/ EXCEPT FOR PULP FOR PAPER AND PAPER AND PAPERBOARD, ALL FOREST PRODUCTS ARE EXPRESSED IN THOUSAND CUBIC METRES

ANNEX TABLE 6.  VOLUME OF IMPORTS OF MAJOR AGRICULTURAL, FISHERY AND FOREST PRODUCTS

| | 1967 | 1972 | 1973 | 1974 | 1975 | 1976 | 1977 | 1978 | 1979 | 1980 | 1981 | ANNUAL RATE OF CHANGE 1972-81 PERCENT |
|---|---|---|---|---|---|---|---|---|---|---|---|---|
| | ...........................................THOUSAND METRIC TONS............................................ | | | | | | | | | | | |
| LEMONS AND LIMES | | | 1 | 1 | | 1 | 1 | 1 | 1 | 1 | 1 | |
| COFFEE GREEN+ROASTED | 41 | 34 | 42 | 61 | 65 | 77 | 59 | 83 | 70 | 81 | 81 | 8.47 |
| COCOA BEANS | 2 | 2 | 2 | 2 | 2 | 1 | 3 | 1 | 1 | 1 | | |
| TEA | 37 | 41 | 35 | 42 | 45 | 42 | 46 | 55 | 70 | 58 | 69 | 7.23 |
| COTTON LINT | 30 | 33 | 41 | 50 | 54 | 46 | 51 | 42 | 48 | 43 | 54 | 2.35 |
| JUTE AND SIMILAR FIBRES | 34 | 58 | 74 | 94 | 80 | 61 | 73 | 56 | 64 | 65 | 57 | - 2.34 |
| TOBACCO UNMANUFACTURED | 35 | 41 | 45 | 57 | 53 | 46 | 48 | 62 | 63 | 54 | 47 | 2.03 |
| NATURAL RUBBER | 9 | 16 | 18 | 21 | 17 | 18 | 22 | 21 | 20 | 20 | 26 | 3.67 |
| WOOL GREASY | | 1 | 1 | 1 | 1 | 3 | 3 | 4 | 3 | 1 | 1 | 9.15 |
| BOVINE CATTLE 1/ | 825 | 983 | 899 | 756 | 626 | 632 | 688 | 787 | 811 | 832 | 929 | .04 |
| SHEEP AND GOATS 1/ | 1623 | 1384 | 1263 | 1246 | 1229 | 1113 | 1167 | 1144 | 1249 | 1330 | 1420 | .27 |
| PIGS 1/ | 1 | 7 | 2 | | 1 | 1 | 1 | 1 | 1 | | | |
| TOTAL MEAT | 39 | 51 | 40 | 43 | 57 | 84 | 110 | 132 | 129 | 142 | 189 | 19.11 |
| MILK DRY | 6 | 9 | 15 | 25 | 20 | 22 | 22 | 24 | 25 | 36 | 43 | 13.54 |
| TOTAL EGGS IN SHELL | 1 | 2 | 3 | 4 | 8 | 13 | 21 | 44 | 36 | 51 | 56 | 50.05 |
| **FISHERY PRODUCTS** | | | | | | | | | | | | |
| FISH FRESH FROZEN | 77 | 196 | 234 | 315 | 305 | 294 | 298 | 354 | 448 | 450 | 305 | 6.78 |
| FISH CURED | 86 | 53 | 50 | 40 | 46 | 52 | 41 | 39 | 43 | 43 | 41 | - 2.21 |
| SHELLFISH | 1 | 3 | 4 | 3 | 11 | 14 | 18 | 17 | 17 | 16 | | |
| FISH CANNED AND PREPARED | 25 | 56 | 66 | 64 | 62 | 89 | 85 | 127 | 121 | 121 | 125 | 10.71 |
| FISH BODY AND LIVER OIL | | 2 | 3 | 4 | 1 | 3 | 2 | 2 | 3 | 3 | 1 | - 2.57 |
| FISH MEAL | 11 | 18 | 13 | 18 | 12 | 13 | 20 | 23 | 32 | 31 | 5 | - .26 |
| **FOREST PRODUCTS 2/** | | | | | | | | | | | | |
| SAWLOGS CONIFEROUS | 1 | 20 | 8 | 17 | 38 | 43 | 31 | 32 | 53 | 21 | 21 | 7.92 |
| SAWLOGS NONCONIFEROUS | 128 | 191 | 215 | 311 | 153 | 172 | 286 | 197 | 244 | 341 | 342 | 5.31 |
| PULPWOOD+PARTICLE | 5 | 5 | | | | | | | | | | |
| FUELWOOD | 21 | 12 | 5 | 1 | 5 | | | | | | | |
| SAWNWOOD CONIFEROUS | 539 | 621 | 603 | 954 | 764 | 829 | 1251 | 764 | 1019 | 904 | 901 | 4.28 |
| SAWNWOOD NONCONIFEROUS | 124 | 132 | 115 | 218 | 153 | 168 | 158 | 205 | 208 | 225 | 233 | 6.50 |
| WOOD-BASED PANELS | 100 | 129 | 138 | 198 | 185 | 195 | 314 | 276 | 331 | 324 | 323 | 11.85 |
| PULP FOR PAPER | 9 | 31 | 46 | 65 | 56 | 76 | 80 | 80 | 77 | 79 | 79 | 8.98 |
| PAPER AND PAPERBOARD | 276 | 406 | 502 | 584 | 477 | 478 | 521 | 551 | 600 | 610 | 609 | 3.50 |
| **LATIN AMERICA** | | | | | | | | | | | | |
| **AGRICULTURAL PRODUCTS** | | | | | | | | | | | | |
| WHEAT+FLOUR,WHEAT EQUIV. | 6072 | 6661 | 8102 | 8336 | 6893 | 8707 | 7939 | 10529 | 10306 | 11886 | 11672 | 6.23 |
| RICE MILLED | 365 | 417 | 391 | 621 | 565 | 489 | 433 | 436 | 1325 | 1092 | 827 | 10.34 |
| BARLEY | 93 | 116 | 186 | 319 | 262 | 207 | 203 | 358 | 302 | 468 | 450 | 12.40 |
| MAIZE | 374 | 797 | 2334 | 2583 | 3897 | 2438 | 3590 | 4714 | 3975 | 8925 | 6658 | 21.11 |
| MILLET | | 3 | 2 | 4 | 4 | 6 | 2 | 4 | 6 | 3 | | |
| SORGHUM | 30 | 615 | 450 | 1048 | 1348 | 554 | 1316 | 1459 | 1902 | 2783 | 3302 | 21.38 |
| POTATOES | 201 | 448 | 241 | 192 | 198 | 173 | 198 | 202 | 249 | 336 | 245 | - .96 |
| SUGAR,TOTAL (RAW EQUIV.) | 255 | 354 | 427 | 254 | 110 | 275 | 625 | 844 | 678 | 1290 | 1751 | 22.86 |
| PULSES | 202 | 220 | 252 | 274 | 307 | 299 | 401 | 291 | 283 | 823 | 831 | 13.25 |
| SOYBEANS | 64 | 134 | 184 | 590 | 127 | 444 | 628 | 960 | 949 | 1201 | 2286 | 33.33 |
| SOYBEAN OIL | 72 | 109 | 149 | 242 | 138 | 242 | 252 | 345 | 368 | 445 | 430 | 16.31 |
| GROUNDNUTS SHELLED BASIS | 33 | 13 | 6 | 13 | 55 | 40 | 9 | 17 | 13 | 14 | 14 | .59 |
| GROUNDNUT OIL | 11 | 16 | 33 | 12 | 41 | 64 | 136 | 84 | 9 | 2 | 3 | -19.13 |
| COPRA | 41 | 1 | | 1 | 21 | 1 | | | | | | |
| COCONUT OIL | 6 | 19 | 33 | 26 | 40 | 88 | 26 | 39 | 14 | 25 | 23 | - 2.63 |
| PALM NUTS KERNELS | | | | 2 | 2 | 2 | 1 | | 2 | 1 | | |
| PALM OIL | 5 | 9 | 23 | 9 | 3 | 16 | 16 | 8 | 14 | 13 | 6 | - 1.23 |
| OILSEED CAKE AND MEAL | 95 | 224 | 257 | 398 | 339 | 413 | 593 | 635 | 684 | 939 | 1045 | 18.39 |
| BANANAS | 271 | 242 | 237 | 286 | 233 | 184 | 228 | 287 | | 496 | 417 | 7.85 |
| ORANGES+TANGER+CLEMEN | 17 | 14 | 19 | 18 | 17 | 19 | 26 | 25 | 4 | 58 | 47 | 16.58 |
| LEMONS AND LIMES | 3 | 2 | 1 | 2 | 1 | 1 | 2 | 2 | 2 | 2 | 2 | 5.22 |
| COFFEE GREEN+ROASTED | 46 | 67 | 75 | 96 | 82 | 86 | 54 | 58 | 103 | 59 | 62 | - 2.18 |
| COCOA BEANS | 22 | 20 | 16 | 20 | 15 | 7 | 3 | 1 | 2 | 3 | 1 | -29.03 |
| TEA | 11 | 12 | 12 | 18 | 10 | 13 | 14 | 15 | 20 | 16 | 15 | 3.62 |
| COTTON LINT | 74 | 83 | 87 | 67 | 69 | 56 | 85 | 71 | 93 | 75 | 88 | .92 |
| JUTE AND SIMILAR FIBRES | 15 | 14 | 34 | 55 | 45 | 30 | 15 | 12 | 18 | 36 | 39 | - .45 |
| TOBACCO UNMANUFACTURED | 14 | 11 | 14 | 23 | 16 | 18 | 19 | 17 | 18 | 29 | 24 | 6.99 |
| NATURAL RUBBER | 80 | 138 | 139 | 168 | 144 | 166 | 171 | 186 | 181 | 187 | 181 | 3.51 |
| WOOL GREASY | 17 | 14 | 5 | 4 | 6 | 8 | 6 | 7 | 9 | 13 | 13 | 6.15 |
| BOVINE CATTLE 1/ | 611 | 664 | 590 | 633 | 578 | 626 | 604 | 695 | 971 | 557 | 537 | .21 |
| SHEEP AND GOATS 1/ | 114 | 137 | 65 | 226 | 316 | 41 | 55 | 54 | 122 | 124 | 220 | - .47 |
| PIGS 1/ | 37 | 48 | 38 | 42 | 48 | 59 | 36 | 34 | 25 | 9 | 28 | -10.83 |
| TOTAL MEAT | 95 | 151 | 126 | 232 | 160 | 182 | 197 | 373 | 364 | 337 | 379 | 12.90 |
| MILK DRY | 34 | 32 | 50 | 49 | 50 | 71 | 175 | 124 | 109 | 143 | 123 | 17.90 |
| TOTAL EGGS IN SHELL | 6 | 7 | 6 | 6 | 6 | 9 | 14 | 11 | 17 | 19 | 26 | 17.95 |

1/ THOUSAND HEAD
2/ EXCEPT FOR PULP FOR PAPER AND PAPER AND PAPERBOARD, ALL FOREST PRODUCTS ARE EXPRESSED IN THOUSAND CUBIC METRES

ANNEX TABLE 6. VOLUME OF IMPORTS OF MAJOR AGRICULTURAL, FISHERY AND FOREST PRODUCTS

| | 1967 | 1972 | 1973 | 1974 | 1975 | 1976 | 1977 | 1978 | 1979 | 1980 | 1981 | ANNUAL RATE OF CHANGE 1972-81 PERCENT |
|---|---|---|---|---|---|---|---|---|---|---|---|---|
| | | | | | ............THOUSAND METRIC TONS............ | | | | | | | |
| **FISHERY PRODUCTS** | | | | | | | | | | | | |
| FISH FRESH FROZEN | 23 | 40 | 58 | 69 | 126 | 97 | 92 | 94 | 130 | 135 | 74 | 8.74 |
| FISH CURED | 92 | 73 | 75 | 59 | 67 | 56 | 44 | 44 | 45 | 43 | 41 | - 7.00 |
| SHELLFISH | 4 | 4 | 7 | 9 | 5 | 3 | 4 | 4 | 7 | 7 | 4 | - .61 |
| FISH CANNED AND PREPARED | 24 | 42 | 35 | 39 | 41 | 44 | 49 | 61 | 70 | 66 | 64 | 7.83 |
| SHELLFISH CANNED+PREPAR | 1 | 1 | 1 | 2 | 1 | 1 | 1 | 1 | 2 | 1 | | |
| FISH BODY AND LIVER OIL | 20 | 29 | 19 | 23 | 20 | 44 | 27 | 36 | 36 | 78 | 33 | 9.24 |
| FISH MEAL | 105 | 187 | 44 | 61 | 143 | 75 | 71 | 106 | 115 | 99 | 100 | 1.31 |
| **FOREST PRODUCTS 2/** | | | | | | | | | | | | |
| SAWLOGS CONIFEROUS | 4 | 16 | 25 | 27 | 7 | 43 | 26 | 34 | 54 | 120 | 121 | 25.03 |
| SAWLOGS NONCONIFEROUS | 308 | 179 | 134 | 128 | 134 | 73 | 69 | 105 | 65 | 57 | 41 | -13.23 |
| FUELWOOD | 7 | 9 | 8 | 8 | 3 | 2 | 2 | 1 | 1 | 1 | 3 | -20.78 |
| SAWNWOOD CONIFEROUS | 1355 | 1497 | 1458 | 1235 | 1235 | 1639 | 1613 | 1710 | 1505 | 2000 | 2056 | 4.34 |
| SAWNWOOD NONCONIFEROUS | 88 | 187 | 202 | 685 | 742 | 427 | 520 | 679 | 684 | 910 | 729 | 14.77 |
| WOOD-BASED PANELS | 83 | 148 | 142 | 181 | 165 | 180 | 229 | 293 | 380 | 448 | 464 | 15.68 |
| PULP FOR PAPER | 419 | 636 | 649 | 807 | 543 | 534 | 461 | 576 | 643 | 726 | 700 | .33 |
| PAPER AND PAPERBOARD | 1283 | 1805 | 1746 | 2061 | 1630 | 1719 | 2066 | 1809 | 1775 | 2343 | 2391 | 2.66 |
| **NEAR EAST DEVELOPING** | | | | | | | | | | | | |
| **AGRICULTURAL PRODUCTS** | | | | | | | | | | | | |
| WHEAT+FLOUR,WHEAT EQUIV. | 4076 | 4387 | 5044 | 8294 | 8180 | 6983 | 8530 | 9558 | 10658 | 11481 | 13151 | 11.23 |
| RICE MILLED | 343 | 575 | 501 | 946 | 941 | 1111 | 1455 | 1550 | 1958 | 1805 | 1976 | 16.71 |
| BARLEY | 205 | 297 | 595 | 530 | 473 | 465 | 990 | 892 | 1570 | 2554 | 3086 | 26.94 |
| MAIZE | 335 | 460 | 423 | 803 | 807 | 1025 | 1506 | 1866 | 2286 | 3111 | 3428 | 27.57 |
| MILLET | | 2 | 3 | 30 | 3 | 10 | 6 | 4 | 3 | 2 | 2 | - 8.14 |
| SORGHUM | 10 | 3 | 5 | 4 | 77 | 197 | 189 | 254 | 102 | 202 | 207 | 63.75 |
| POTATOES | 127 | 123 | 123 | 178 | 171 | 160 | 233 | 234 | 298 | 379 | 396 | 14.45 |
| SUGAR,TOTAL (RAW EQUIV.) | 1291 | 1151 | 1601 | 1693 | 1975 | 1590 | 2124 | 2176 | 2654 | 3465 | 3386 | 11.49 |
| PULSES | 147 | 151 | 109 | 128 | 243 | 234 | 200 | 205 | 228 | 251 | 379 | 10.45 |
| SOYBEANS | 6 | 14 | 28 | 62 | 28 | 29 | 63 | 138 | 180 | 94 | 118 | 26.62 |
| SOYBEAN OIL | 63 | 181 | 108 | 232 | 270 | 332 | 230 | 280 | 379 | 442 | 574 | 14.60 |
| GROUNDNUTS SHELLED BASIS | 12 | 10 | 7 | 8 | 10 | 9 | 15 | 7 | 7 | 12 | 9 | .71 |
| GROUNDNUT OIL | 3 | 2 | 2 | 1 | 1 | 2 | 2 | 1 | 1 | 3 | | |
| COPRA | 2 | 1 | | | 8 | 7 | | 1 | | | | |
| COCONUT OIL | 5 | 8 | 5 | 8 | 22 | 31 | 8 | 11 | 9 | 17 | 12 | 5.35 |
| PALM NUTS KERNELS | | | | | 1 | 5 | | | | | | |
| PALM OIL | 59 | 91 | 89 | 78 | 137 | 76 | 148 | 164 | 187 | 232 | 158 | 10.99 |
| OILSEED CAKE AND MEAL | 42 | 136 | 88 | 117 | 100 | 237 | 379 | 459 | 441 | 417 | 640 | 24.79 |
| BANANAS | 44 | 108 | 135 | 167 | 255 | 308 | 272 | 276 | 317 | 298 | 297 | 11.48 |
| ORANGES+TANGER+CLEMEN | 98 | 225 | 284 | 408 | 532 | 634 | 543 | 462 | 555 | 570 | 569 | 8.98 |
| LEMONS AND LIMES | 23 | 13 | 14 | 27 | 32 | 54 | 52 | 46 | 79 | 81 | 79 | 23.53 |
| COFFEE GREEN+ROASTED | 55 | 59 | 55 | 56 | 49 | 51 | 53 | 42 | 40 | 45 | 54 | - 2.57 |
| COCOA BEANS | 2 | 3 | 2 | 2 | 4 | 4 | 2 | 4 | 1 | 1 | 3 | - 5.08 |
| TEA | 98 | 122 | 114 | 144 | 132 | 157 | 148 | 202 | 183 | 173 | 186 | 5.73 |
| COTTON LINT | 9 | 8 | 9 | 12 | 26 | 7 | 37 | 21 | 37 | 20 | 14 | 11.27 |
| JUTE AND SIMILAR FIBRES | 33 | 18 | 27 | 31 | 31 | 40 | 33 | 24 | 45 | 31 | 35 | 4.89 |
| TOBACCO UNMANUFACTURED | 22 | 28 | 29 | 32 | 44 | 45 | 45 | 52 | 56 | 50 | 61 | 9.01 |
| NATURAL RUBBER | 32 | 52 | 49 | 57 | 51 | 50 | 49 | 46 | 35 | 50 | 46 | - 2.23 |
| WOOL GREASY | 21 | 29 | 20 | 23 | 26 | 27 | 32 | 17 | 19 | 19 | 19 | - 3.68 |
| BOVINE CATTLE 1/ | 154 | 178 | 154 | 153 | 160 | 184 | 389 | 389 | 383 | 504 | 636 | 18.30 |
| SHEEP AND GOATS 1/ | 2386 | 5022 | 4695 | 4317 | 4921 | 5135 | 7856 | 8641 | 10379 | 12031 | 14051 | 14.50 |
| PIGS 1/ | | | 1 | | 2 | | 5 | | | | | |
| TOTAL MEAT | 30 | 75 | 90 | 142 | 251 | 331 | 483 | 586 | 678 | 942 | 1241 | 37.46 |
| MILK DRY | | | 1 | 2 | 1 | 2 | 5 | 6 | 6 | 2 | 8 | |
| TOTAL EGGS IN SHELL | 21 | 54 | 44 | 56 | 81 | 77 | 84 | 85 | 76 | 107 | 133 | 10.20 |
| **FISHERY PRODUCTS** | | | | | | | | | | | | |
| FISH FRESH FROZEN | 21 | 22 | 23 | 30 | 41 | 60 | 54 | 71 | 89 | 90 | 78 | 18.52 |
| FISH CURED | 4 | 5 | 3 | 4 | 3 | 3 | 3 | 2 | 3 | 2 | | |
| SHELLFISH | | 1 | 1 | 1 | 1 | 1 | 1 | 1 | 1 | 1 | 1 | 4.27 |
| FISH CANNED AND PREPARED | 9 | 16 | 23 | 27 | 33 | 44 | 43 | 44 | 45 | 49 | 46 | 11.62 |
| SHELLFISH CANNED+PREPAR | | | | | | | | | 1 | 1 | | |
| FISH BODY AND LIVER OIL | 1 | 2 | 2 | 2 | 2 | 2 | 3 | 2 | 2 | 1 | | |
| FISH MEAL | 6 | 13 | 12 | 28 | 27 | 51 | 136 | 56 | 57 | 44 | 47 | 18.06 |
| **FOREST PRODUCTS 2/** | | | | | | | | | | | | |
| SAWLOGS CONIFEROUS | 40 | 154 | 135 | 59 | 165 | 144 | 166 | 145 | 135 | 150 | 136 | 2.18 |
| SAWLOGS NONCONIFEROUS | 48 | 43 | 40 | 37 | 68 | 132 | 112 | 94 | 34 | 76 | 113 | 8.43 |
| PULPWOOD+PARTICLE | 51 | | 29 | 26 | 8 | 9 | 13 | 36 | 40 | 14 | 4 | 16.18 |
| FUELWOOD | 53 | 29 | 62 | 34 | 35 | 37 | 38 | 39 | 31 | 24 | 26 | - 4.41 |
| SAWNWOOD CONIFEROUS | 1050 | 1638 | 1589 | 1685 | 1634 | 2088 | 2792 | 2245 | 2493 | 2951 | 3533 | 9.16 |
| SAWNWOOD NONCONIFEROUS | 117 | 103 | 80 | 350 | 381 | 445 | 827 | 816 | 664 | 813 | 732 | 27.40 |
| WOOD-BASED PANELS | 81 | 233 | 331 | 419 | 465 | 582 | 740 | 792 | 916 | 935 | 1064 | 17.56 |
| PULP FOR PAPER | 36 | 63 | 69 | 64 | 71 | 69 | 81 | 80 | 85 | 86 | 85 | 3.76 |
| PAPER AND PAPERBOARD | 457 | 591 | 539 | 572 | 696 | 724 | 866 | 889 | 848 | 977 | 1057 | 7.72 |

1/ THOUSAND HEAD
2/ EXCEPT FOR PULP FOR PAPER AND PAPER AND PAPERBOARD, ALL FOREST PRODUCTS ARE EXPRESSED IN THOUSAND CUBIC METRES

ANNEX TABLE 6. VOLUME OF IMPORTS OF MAJOR AGRICULTURAL, FISHERY AND FOREST PRODUCTS

| | 1967 | 1972 | 1973 | 1974 | 1975 | 1976 | 1977 | 1978 | 1979 | 1980 | 1981 | ANNUAL RATE OF CHANGE 1972-81 PERCENT |
|---|---|---|---|---|---|---|---|---|---|---|---|---|
| | ....................................THOUSAND METRIC TONS.................................... | | | | | | | | | | | |
| **FAR EAST DEVELOPING** | | | | | | | | | | | | |
| **AGRICULTURAL PRODUCTS** | | | | | | | | | | | | |
| WHEAT+FLOUR,WHEAT EQUIV. | 12039 | 6490 | 10713 | 11313 | 14942 | 13386 | 7241 | 7708 | 8783 | 8924 | 8660 | - 1.53 |
| RICE MILLED | 3708 | 4482 | 4730 | 3082 | 3067 | 3778 | 3986 | 3541 | 3497 | 4511 | 4440 | .43 |
| BARLEY | 5 | 349 | 494 | 497 | 539 | 8 | 327 | 107 | 106 | 206 | 275 | - 9.83 |
| MAIZE | 781 | 1174 | 1337 | 1250 | 1428 | 1971 | 2517 | 3117 | 4114 | 3873 | 4410 | 18.43 |
| MILLET | | 26 | 43 | 13 | 29 | 10 | 1 | 2 | 2 | 2 | | |
| SORGHUM | 2107 | | 1188 | 727 | 204 | 398 | 21 | 49 | 144 | 62 | 160 | 20.46 |
| POTATOES | 105 | 90 | 96 | 100 | 89 | 95 | 106 | 119 | 145 | 157 | 152 | 6.88 |
| SUGAR,TOTAL (RAW EQUIV.) | 1005 | 1086 | 1398 | 1069 | 1100 | 1087 | 1395 | 1800 | 1874 | 2387 | 2442 | 9.90 |
| PULSES | 158 | 191 | 127 | 100 | 98 | 90 | 91 | 171 | 200 | 187 | 228 | 5.90 |
| SOYBEANS | 82 | 146 | 168 | 135 | 153 | 433 | 370 | 489 | 728 | 867 | 1105 | 28.59 |
| SOYBEAN OIL | 124 | 184 | 178 | 184 | 87 | 194 | 527 | 583 | 530 | 912 | 994 | 26.36 |
| GROUNDNUTS SHELLED BASIS | 34 | 24 | 24 | 26 | 19 | 45 | 25 | 31 | 43 | 72 | 96 | 15.34 |
| GROUNDNUT OIL | 23 | 25 | 27 | 24 | 23 | 48 | 64 | 42 | 36 | 38 | 33 | 5.82 |
| COPRA | 51 | 79 | 34 | 19 | 55 | 96 | 99 | 163 | 74 | 121 | 116 | 14.62 |
| COCONUT OIL | 33 | 36 | 58 | 41 | 34 | 55 | 74 | 162 | 91 | 58 | 163 | 14.66 |
| PALM NUTS KERNELS | 13 | 20 | 19 | 4 | 4 | 5 | 5 | 6 | 10 | 15 | 6 | - 4.39 |
| PALM OIL | 88 | 240 | 315 | 358 | 277 | 372 | 842 | 847 | 1058 | 1571 | 1340 | 24.63 |
| OILSEED CAKE AND MEAL | 103 | 233 | 151 | 272 | 334 | 534 | 725 | 839 | 1002 | 1040 | 1053 | 24.90 |
| BANANAS | 44 | 46 | 55 | 50 | 56 | 45 | 48 | 57 | 69 | 59 | 51 | 1.95 |
| ORANGES+TANGER+CLEMEN | 126 | 179 | 193 | 170 | 208 | 199 | 215 | 222 | 208 | 238 | 259 | 3.74 |
| LEMONS AND LIMES | | | | | | | | 4 | 6 | 7 | 8 | |
| COFFEE GREEN+ROASTED | 26 | 25 | 45 | 34 | 31 | 42 | 32 | 19 | 27 | 19 | 36 | - 3.29 |
| COCOA BEANS | 8 | 12 | 11 | 9 | 9 | 9 | 8 | 12 | 17 | 27 | 45 | 14.93 |
| TEA | 38 | 49 | 54 | 52 | 64 | 70 | 81 | 77 | 85 | 86 | 97 | 7.92 |
| COTTON LINT | 510 | 538 | 672 | 577 | 790 | 794 | 843 | 860 | 827 | 882 | 746 | 4.31 |
| JUTE AND SIMILAR FIBRES | 43 | 96 | 112 | 71 | 80 | 123 | 57 | 64 | 78 | 108 | 122 | .52 |
| TOBACCO UNMANUFACTURED | 51 | 50 | 51 | 74 | 54 | 61 | 70 | 64 | 69 | 82 | 93 | 5.72 |
| NATURAL RUBBER | 111 | 92 | 114 | 125 | 123 | 142 | 160 | 193 | 215 | 182 | 211 | 9.44 |
| WOOL GREASY | 16 | 21 | 14 | 16 | 26 | 27 | 32 | 29 | 31 | 33 | 39 | 9.66 |
| BOVINE CATTLE 1/ | 269 | 328 | 303 | 286 | 286 | 282 | 299 | 339 | 376 | 342 | 417 | 3.03 |
| SHEEP AND GOATS 1/ | 264 | 352 | 244 | 224 | 253 | 296 | 273 | 258 | 234 | 209 | 184 | - 3.99 |
| PIGS 1/ | 1900 | 2680 | 2700 | 2629 | 2796 | 3004 | 3023 | 3123 | 3095 | 4552 | 3146 | 3.86 |
| TOTAL MEAT | 66 | 100 | 109 | 125 | 149 | 173 | 212 | 279 | 297 | 226 | 279 | 13.37 |
| MILK DRY | 34 | 53 | 53 | 60 | 62 | 78 | 84 | 118 | 141 | 138 | 107 | 12.40 |
| TOTAL EGGS IN SHELL | 47 | 52 | 56 | 54 | 58 | 57 | 64 | 68 | 75 | 75 | 75 | 4.69 |
| **FISHERY PRODUCTS** | | | | | | | | | | | | |
| FISH FRESH FROZEN | 91 | 121 | 140 | 132 | 148 | 156 | 162 | 189 | 217 | 188 | 157 | 4.73 |
| FISH CURED | 52 | 55 | 42 | 32 | 32 | 21 | 19 | 25 | 19 | 20 | 18 | -10.70 |
| SHELLFISH | 36 | 61 | 68 | 80 | 68 | 89 | 95 | 102 | 163 | 157 | 135 | 11.44 |
| FISH CANNED AND PREPARED | 71 | 86 | 91 | 97 | 114 | 112 | 83 | 84 | 76 | 65 | 65 | - 4.39 |
| SHELLFISH CANNED+PREPAR | 21 | 18 | 17 | 15 | 14 | 16 | 15 | 14 | 14 | 9 | 7 | - 8.00 |
| FISH BODY AND LIVER OIL | 5 | 5 | 6 | 2 | 2 | 7 | 3 | 4 | 4 | 2 | 1 | -10.18 |
| FISH MEAL | 55 | 86 | 53 | 60 | 99 | 84 | 90 | 95 | 119 | 103 | 106 | 6.24 |
| **FOREST PRODUCTS 2/** | | | | | | | | | | | | |
| SAWLOGS CONIFEROUS | 299 | 373 | 827 | 773 | 461 | 750 | 1200 | 2426 | 2128 | 1536 | 1187 | 16.56 |
| SAWLOGS NONCONIFEROUS | 3103 | 5854 | 6481 | 5686 | 6164 | 7491 | 8544 | 9345 | 9337 | 6507 | 5980 | 2.50 |
| FUELWOOD | 211 | 141 | 115 | 110 | 110 | 114 | 138 | 117 | 141 | 140 | 139 | 1.74 |
| SAWNWOOD CONIFEROUS | 20 | 38 | 41 | 65 | 179 | 214 | 228 | 235 | 80 | 86 | 92 | 9.64 |
| SAWNWOOD NONCONIFEROUS | 392 | 662 | 1207 | 1108 | 981 | 1463 | 1741 | 1829 | 2345 | 1850 | 1903 | 11.72 |
| WOOD-BASED PANELS | 139 | 262 | 348 | 339 | 393 | 472 | 495 | 575 | 610 | 740 | 849 | 12.88 |
| PULP FOR PAPER | 199 | 476 | 466 | 465 | 282 | 406 | 545 | 678 | 714 | 703 | 758 | 7.64 |
| PAPER AND PAPERBOARD | 885 | 1271 | 1418 | 1320 | 1133 | 1459 | 1494 | 1774 | 2141 | 2244 | 2291 | 7.74 |
| **ASIAN CENT PLANNED ECON** | | | | | | | | | | | | |
| **AGRICULTURAL PRODUCTS** | | | | | | | | | | | | |
| WHEAT+FLOUR,WHEAT EQUIV. | 4254 | 6394 | 7428 | 7621 | 4954 | 3640 | 9114 | 10004 | 11387 | 13645 | 14836 | 10.76 |
| RICE MILLED | 1282 | 948 | 963 | 1241 | 737 | 784 | 214 | 215 | 619 | 592 | 379 | -11.48 |
| BARLEY | 27 | 452 | 279 | 321 | 174 | 333 | 265 | 336 | 704 | 402 | 407 | 4.49 |
| MAIZE | 290 | 2090 | 3079 | 2797 | 1679 | 1950 | 2092 | 3064 | 5412 | 4410 | 3261 | 7.34 |
| SORGHUM | | 5 | 41 | 73 | 152 | 255 | 394 | 473 | 517 | 417 | 484 | 53.13 |
| SUGAR,TOTAL (RAW EQUIV.) | 902 | 1165 | 1259 | 660 | 691 | 929 | 1872 | 1564 | 1355 | 1159 | 1363 | 4.69 |
| PULSES | 22 | 40 | 40 | 32 | 33 | 39 | 49 | 68 | 58 | 72 | 72 | 9.37 |
| SOYBEANS | 351 | 712 | 799 | 1181 | 854 | 829 | 985 | 1172 | 1696 | 1529 | 1751 | 9.90 |
| SOYBEAN OIL | 19 | 44 | 123 | 34 | 42 | 27 | 149 | 137 | 143 | 136 | 61 | 10.32 |
| GROUNDNUTS SHELLED BASIS | | 7 | 6 | 6 | | | | 4 | 1 | | | |
| COPRA | 5 | 4 | 4 | 4 | | | | | 1 | 3 | 1 | |
| COCONUT OIL | 13 | 38 | 20 | 20 | 44 | 33 | 18 | 20 | 29 | 35 | 28 | - .24 |
| PALM OIL | 1 | 9 | 13 | 11 | 12 | 3 | 30 | 14 | 48 | 59 | 31 | 21.45 |
| OILSEED CAKE AND MEAL | | 1 | 2 | 1 | 1 | 29 | 41 | 55 | 1 | 9 | 8 | 35.17 |
| BANANAS | | | 15 | 4 | 10 | 15 | | | | | | |

1/ THOUSAND HEAD
2/ EXCEPT FOR PULP FOR PAPER AND PAPER AND PAPERBOARD, ALL FOREST PRODUCTS ARE EXPRESSED IN THOUSAND CUBIC METRES

ANNEX TABLE 6. VOLUME OF IMPORTS OF MAJOR AGRICULTURAL, FISHERY AND FOREST PRODUCTS

| | 1967 | 1972 | 1973 | 1974 | 1975 | 1976 | 1977 | 1978 | 1979 | 1980 | 1981 | ANNUAL RATE OF CHANGE 1972-81 PERCENT |
|---|---|---|---|---|---|---|---|---|---|---|---|---|
| | | | | | | THOUSAND METRIC TONS | | | | | | |
| COFFEE GREEN+ROASTED | 1 | | | | | 7 | 6 | 6 | 5 | 6 | 8 | |
| COCOA BEANS | 2 | 2 | 8 | 6 | 8 | 11 | 12 | 15 | 17 | 17 | 16 | 21.66 |
| TEA | 6 | 4 | 6 | 7 | 6 | 5 | 5 | 6 | 5 | 5 | 4 | -1.54 |
| COTTON LINT | 201 | 327 | 676 | 616 | 386 | 428 | 421 | 819 | 836 | 1210 | 991 | 11.40 |
| JUTE AND SIMILAR FIBRES | 72 | 27 | 97 | 14 | 22 | 20 | 34 | 37 | 36 | 51 | 54 | 5.25 |
| TOBACCO UNMANUFACTURED | 18 | 24 | 20 | 23 | 11 | 13 | 15 | 23 | 26 | 36 | 58 | 9.63 |
| NATURAL RUBBER | 174 | 219 | 301 | 235 | 274 | 246 | 305 | 288 | 316 | 313 | 224 | 1.39 |
| WOOL GREASY | 19 | 25 | 23 | 18 | 17 | 21 | 20 | 25 | 51 | 59 | 80 | 15.29 |
| BOVINE CATTLE 1/ | | 1 | 1 | 4 | 8 | 1 | | | | 2 | | |
| SHEEP AND GOATS 1/ | 4 | 4 | 5 | 6 | 6 | | | | 3 | 1 | 1 | |
| PIGS 1/ | | 1 | 1 | 3 | | 2 | 1 | 4 | 3 | 3 | 4 | |
| TOTAL MEAT | | 2 | 2 | 2 | 29 | 10 | 4 | 11 | 18 | 16 | 21 | 31.53 |
| FISHERY PRODUCTS | | | | | | | | | | | | |
| FISH FRESH FROZEN | 1 | | 1 | 8 | 4 | 4 | 6 | 5 | 4 | | | |
| FISH CURED | | | | 2 | 7 | 1 | 1 | 1 | 1 | | | |
| SHELLFISH | 1 | 1 | | 3 | 4 | 4 | 8 | 9 | 14 | 2 | 2 | |
| FISH CANNED AND PREPARED | 1 | 11 | 3 | 4 | 2 | 4 | 4 | 3 | 4 | 4 | 4 | -5.06 |
| FISH BODY AND LIVER OIL | | 1 | 3 | 3 | 3 | 2 | 2 | 3 | 3 | 1 | | |
| FISH MEAL | 13 | 48 | 33 | 40 | 95 | 129 | 124 | 145 | 170 | 169 | 151 | 20.19 |
| FOREST PRODUCTS 2/ | | | | | | | | | | | | |
| SAWLOGS CONIFEROUS | 15 | 122 | 492 | 610 | 614 | 618 | 400 | 370 | 403 | 611 | 1052 | 10.80 |
| SAWLOGS NONCONIFEROUS | 779 | 4000 | 3990 | 3801 | 3887 | 4437 | 6231 | 7123 | 6764 | 6463 | 4536 | 5.96 |
| PULPWOOD+PARTICLE | | 7 | 7 | 7 | 88 | 199 | 199 | 199 | 56 | 56 | 153 | 39.48 |
| SAWNWOOD CONIFEROUS | 2 | 2 | | | 21 | 29 | 29 | 29 | 29 | 31 | 31 | |
| SAWNWOOD NONCONIFEROUS | 4 | 8 | 9 | 27 | 23 | 30 | 38 | 56 | 96 | 139 | 139 | 39.50 |
| WOOD-BASED PANELS | 12 | 5 | 1 | 1 | 3 | 12 | 13 | 24 | 36 | 51 | 51 | 55.19 |
| PULP FOR PAPER | 249 | 242 | 243 | 248 | 217 | 228 | 169 | 201 | 209 | 285 | 285 | .72 |
| PAPER AND PAPERBOARD | 87 | 212 | 167 | 189 | 174 | 217 | 294 | 405 | 425 | 703 | 703 | 18.33 |

1/ THOUSAND HEAD
2/ EXCEPT FOR PULP FOR PAPER AND PAPER AND PAPERBOARD, ALL FOREST PRODUCTS ARE EXPRESSED IN THOUSAND CUBIC METRES

ANNEX TABLE 7. INDICES OF VALUE OF EXPORTS OF AGRICULTURAL, FISHERY AND FOREST PRODUCTS

| | 1967 | 1972 | 1973 | 1974 | 1975 | 1976 | 1977 | 1978 | 1979 | 1980 | 1981 | ANNUAL RATE OF CHANGE 1972-81 PERCENT |
|---|---|---|---|---|---|---|---|---|---|---|---|---|
| | | | | | | 1969-71=100 | | | | | | |
| **WORLD** | | | | | | | | | | | | |
| AGRICULTURAL PRODUCTS | 86 | 127 | 189 | 237 | 246 | 260 | 297 | 330 | 386 | 447 | 443 | 13.37 |
| FOOD | 84 | 131 | 195 | 258 | 280 | 273 | 297 | 343 | 405 | 482 | 493 | 13.72 |
| FEED | 78 | 127 | 270 | 251 | 215 | 310 | 388 | 407 | 479 | 550 | 615 | 16.01 |
| RAW MATERIALS | 95 | 113 | 170 | 200 | 166 | 197 | 228 | 242 | 277 | 302 | 290 | 9.83 |
| BEVERAGES | 82 | 125 | 165 | 167 | 175 | 270 | 389 | 372 | 421 | 438 | 342 | 15.04 |
| FISHERY PRODUCTS | 61 | 118 | 159 | 171 | 181 | 230 | 274 | 332 | 402 | 391 | 334 | 14.23 |
| FOREST PRODUCTS | 64 | 113 | 162 | 213 | 189 | 229 | 248 | 277 | 360 | 406 | 375 | 13.64 |
| **DEVELOPED COUNTRIES** | | | | | | | | | | | | |
| AGRICULTURAL PRODUCTS | 85 | 134 | 206 | 253 | 267 | 272 | 298 | 349 | 415 | 494 | 500 | 13.78 |
| FOOD | 83 | 136 | 208 | 259 | 286 | 283 | 300 | 357 | 425 | 517 | 528 | 14.09 |
| FEED | 73 | 123 | 276 | 280 | 202 | 267 | 310 | 383 | 448 | 516 | 532 | 14.24 |
| RAW MATERIALS | 107 | 116 | 179 | 221 | 181 | 204 | 257 | 266 | 308 | 338 | 330 | 10.81 |
| BEVERAGES | 69 | 159 | 219 | 229 | 252 | 289 | 373 | 428 | 545 | 559 | 514 | 15.18 |
| FISHERY PRODUCTS | 66 | 119 | 164 | 176 | 174 | 215 | 252 | 306 | 362 | 379 | 336 | 13.35 |
| FOREST PRODUCTS | 66 | 112 | 155 | 213 | 192 | 226 | 244 | 273 | 344 | 394 | 370 | 13.44 |
| **WESTERN EUROPE** | | | | | | | | | | | | |
| AGRICULTURAL PRODUCTS | 73 | 143 | 202 | 238 | 274 | 282 | 318 | 390 | 470 | 547 | 531 | 15.20 |
| FOOD | 72 | 141 | 198 | 237 | 280 | 281 | 316 | 387 | 463 | 553 | 540 | 15.45 |
| FEED | 74 | 152 | 369 | 379 | 273 | 350 | 428 | 511 | 631 | 716 | 812 | 15.87 |
| RAW MATERIALS | 112 | 123 | 176 | 218 | 204 | 236 | 232 | 297 | 353 | 310 | 269 | 9.22 |
| BEVERAGES | 67 | 165 | 230 | 231 | 257 | 294 | 362 | 440 | 568 | 578 | 531 | 15.14 |
| FISHERY PRODUCTS | 65 | 119 | 169 | 186 | 184 | 227 | 271 | 309 | 376 | 403 | 347 | 13.55 |
| FOREST PRODUCTS | 65 | 112 | 161 | 232 | 199 | 236 | 251 | 287 | 370 | 431 | 393 | 14.05 |
| **USSR AND EASTERN EUROPE** | | | | | | | | | | | | |
| AGRICULTURAL PRODUCTS | 101 | 114 | 150 | 193 | 190 | 186 | 225 | 216 | 251 | 262 | 255 | 8.22 |
| FOOD | 100 | 110 | 149 | 194 | 183 | 173 | 205 | 195 | 233 | 243 | 236 | 7.26 |
| FEED | 198 | 59 | 95 | 115 | 115 | 265 | 266 | 231 | 224 | 192 | 124 | 10.85 |
| RAW MATERIALS | 109 | 128 | 151 | 192 | 210 | 231 | 298 | 276 | 294 | 318 | 320 | 10.62 |
| BEVERAGES | 73 | 135 | 159 | 187 | 224 | 218 | 260 | 300 | 346 | 343 | 321 | 11.05 |
| FISHERY PRODUCTS | 73 | 109 | 138 | 173 | 220 | 223 | 213 | 246 | 310 | 309 | 273 | 10.97 |
| FOREST PRODUCTS | 73 | 108 | 151 | 203 | 204 | 219 | 247 | 260 | 286 | 306 | 295 | 10.52 |
| **NORTH AMERICA DEVELOPED** | | | | | | | | | | | | |
| AGRICULTURAL PRODUCTS | 92 | 134 | 248 | 316 | 313 | 321 | 327 | 398 | 467 | 567 | 603 | 14.29 |
| FOOD | 92 | 138 | 264 | 337 | 350 | 351 | 338 | 418 | 495 | 605 | 660 | 14.48 |
| FEED | 68 | 112 | 249 | 246 | 169 | 232 | 253 | 330 | 376 | 450 | 434 | 13.27 |
| RAW MATERIALS | 101 | 122 | 173 | 242 | 195 | 207 | 273 | 312 | 354 | 416 | 386 | 12.92 |
| BEVERAGES | 83 | 130 | 265 | 376 | 285 | 515 | 1168 | 790 | 992 | 1156 | 1002 | 25.44 |
| FISHERY PRODUCTS | 66 | 116 | 182 | 161 | 173 | 227 | 296 | 439 | 510 | 484 | 431 | 18.16 |
| FOREST PRODUCTS | 65 | 113 | 149 | 190 | 178 | 218 | 235 | 259 | 327 | 371 | 359 | 13.35 |
| **OCEANIA DEVELOPED** | | | | | | | | | | | | |
| AGRICULTURAL PRODUCTS | 96 | 128 | 187 | 223 | 218 | 226 | 253 | 247 | 298 | 391 | 418 | 11.37 |
| FOOD | 89 | 145 | 180 | 223 | 259 | 254 | 262 | 272 | 323 | 454 | 479 | 12.37 |
| FEED | 63 | 112 | 235 | 274 | 205 | 219 | 499 | 476 | 506 | 294 | 397 | 12.47 |
| RAW MATERIALS | 111 | 96 | 201 | 221 | 142 | 174 | 234 | 198 | 250 | 278 | 307 | 9.28 |
| BEVERAGES | 93 | 147 | 151 | 204 | 228 | 234 | 222 | 240 | 255 | 331 | 462 | 10.85 |
| FISHERY PRODUCTS | 40 | 129 | 148 | 142 | 147 | 168 | 236 | 259 | 370 | 334 | 348 | 13.90 |
| FOREST PRODUCTS | 46 | 121 | 188 | 244 | 226 | 252 | 301 | 328 | 465 | 590 | 625 | 18.02 |

ANNEX TABLE 7. INDICES OF VALUE OF EXPORTS OF AGRICULTURAL, FISHERY AND FOREST PRODUCTS

| | 1967 | 1972 | 1973 | 1974 | 1975 | 1976 | 1977 | 1978 | 1979 | 1980 | 1981 | ANNUAL RATE OF CHANGE 1972-81 PERCENT |
|---|---|---|---|---|---|---|---|---|---|---|---|---|
| | | | | | | ....1969-71=100.... | | | | | | |
| **DEVELOPING COUNTRIES** | | | | | | | | | | | | |
| AGRICULTURAL PRODUCTS | 86 | 117 | 163 | 213 | 215 | 242 | 296 | 302 | 343 | 378 | 359 | 12.60 |
| FOOD | 87 | 120 | 165 | 255 | 268 | 251 | 289 | 311 | 362 | 407 | 417 | 12.79 |
| FEED | 84 | 134 | 263 | 208 | 235 | 373 | 502 | 443 | 526 | 600 | 738 | 18.48 |
| RAW MATERIALS | 85 | 110 | 162 | 182 | 152 | 190 | 202 | 222 | 249 | 270 | 256 | 8.83 |
| BEVERAGES | 87 | 114 | 146 | 145 | 149 | 263 | 394 | 353 | 379 | 396 | 283 | 14.91 |
| FISHERY PRODUCTS | 51 | 116 | 148 | 161 | 196 | 261 | 321 | 387 | 484 | 416 | 330 | 15.95 |
| FOREST PRODUCTS | 55 | 117 | 210 | 214 | 167 | 247 | 271 | 302 | 462 | 488 | 409 | 14.86 |
| **AFRICA DEVELOPING** | | | | | | | | | | | | |
| AGRICULTURAL PRODUCTS | 83 | 112 | 145 | 185 | 172 | 207 | 265 | 259 | 282 | 281 | 226 | 9.18 |
| FOOD | 84 | 111 | 137 | 194 | 186 | 186 | 221 | 249 | 264 | 270 | 208 | 8.20 |
| FEED | 104 | 126 | 177 | 146 | 133 | 169 | 214 | 130 | 217 | 170 | 145 | 1.92 |
| RAW MATERIALS | 85 | 114 | 154 | 196 | 142 | 180 | 186 | 186 | 210 | 242 | 248 | 7.14 |
| BEVERAGES | 79 | 114 | 157 | 165 | 160 | 265 | 410 | 322 | 358 | 332 | 257 | 12.17 |
| FISHERY PRODUCTS | 62 | 123 | 157 | 214 | 209 | 220 | 232 | 261 | 332 | 376 | 265 | 9.10 |
| FOREST PRODUCTS | 72 | 114 | 206 | 214 | 153 | 207 | 217 | 236 | 271 | 315 | 270 | 8.37 |
| **LATIN AMERICA** | | | | | | | | | | | | |
| AGRICULTURAL PRODUCTS | 83 | 122 | 174 | 221 | 242 | 274 | 340 | 350 | 389 | 435 | 422 | 14.06 |
| FOOD | 82 | 127 | 181 | 271 | 303 | 277 | 323 | 341 | 397 | 450 | 477 | 13.37 |
| FEED | 74 | 146 | 325 | 247 | 329 | 543 | 790 | 738 | 820 | 989 | 1316 | 24.67 |
| RAW MATERIALS | 88 | 110 | 150 | 168 | 158 | 179 | 214 | 250 | 245 | 258 | 265 | 9.59 |
| BEVERAGES | 83 | 116 | 153 | 139 | 141 | 286 | 387 | 375 | 396 | 429 | 280 | 15.40 |
| FISHERY PRODUCTS | 59 | 101 | 87 | 119 | 120 | 159 | 172 | 249 | 316 | 347 | 290 | 17.31 |
| FOREST PRODUCTS | 59 | 110 | 163 | 217 | 190 | 191 | 235 | 286 | 474 | 650 | 625 | 20.40 |
| **NEAR EAST DEVELOPING** | | | | | | | | | | | | |
| AGRICULTURAL PRODUCTS | 83 | 124 | 163 | 179 | 161 | 198 | 201 | 213 | 222 | 246 | 271 | 7.45 |
| FOOD | 82 | 129 | 173 | 186 | 178 | 221 | 252 | 303 | 324 | 379 | 448 | 13.72 |
| FEED | 94 | 123 | 144 | 114 | 93 | 85 | 84 | 58 | 70 | 110 | 52 | - 7.87 |
| RAW MATERIALS | 84 | 120 | 158 | 178 | 155 | 189 | 173 | 161 | 160 | 164 | 166 | 1.63 |
| BEVERAGES | 58 | 133 | 179 | 182 | 121 | 159 | 226 | 274 | 345 | 283 | 259 | 9.62 |
| FISHERY PRODUCTS | 59 | 124 | 185 | 153 | 164 | 191 | 255 | 208 | 214 | 229 | 176 | 4.56 |
| FOREST PRODUCTS | 56 | 120 | 180 | 271 | 181 | 216 | 244 | 201 | 342 | 340 | 509 | 12.25 |
| **FAR EAST DEVELOPING** | | | | | | | | | | | | |
| AGRICULTURAL PRODUCTS | 91 | 107 | 155 | 229 | 217 | 246 | 304 | 306 | 382 | 435 | 429 | 15.36 |
| FOOD | 90 | 115 | 155 | 311 | 313 | 305 | 357 | 358 | 463 | 536 | 587 | 16.97 |
| FEED | 85 | 125 | 262 | 222 | 200 | 337 | 380 | 306 | 421 | 416 | 394 | 11.64 |
| RAW MATERIALS | 83 | 96 | 165 | 185 | 146 | 196 | 214 | 249 | 315 | 357 | 315 | 13.18 |
| BEVERAGES | 15 | 106 | 105 | 124 | 149 | 197 | 381 | 316 | 331 | 375 | 306 | 17.30 |
| FISHERY PRODUCTS | 47 | 132 | 218 | 230 | 322 | 416 | 584 | 644 | 824 | 606 | 541 | 18.96 |
| FOREST PRODUCTS | 50 | 116 | 232 | 227 | 173 | 287 | 312 | 338 | 554 | 544 | 423 | 15.76 |
| **ASIAN CENT PLANNED ECON** | | | | | | | | | | | | |
| AGRICULTURAL PRODUCTS | 108 | 127 | 193 | 257 | 258 | 222 | 214 | 252 | 284 | 315 | 292 | 7.11 |
| FOOD | 117 | 119 | 184 | 278 | 283 | 221 | 193 | 234 | 263 | 313 | 293 | 6.80 |
| FEED | 108 | 95 | 192 | 151 | 171 | 253 | 229 | 161 | 253 | 480 | 1182 | 20.93 |
| RAW MATERIALS | 81 | 153 | 242 | 196 | 181 | 224 | 243 | 266 | 300 | 255 | 211 | 4.10 |
| BEVERAGES | 82 | 138 | 155 | 192 | 193 | 225 | 401 | 444 | 512 | 534 | 480 | 18.41 |
| FISHERY PRODUCTS | 7 | 140 | 224 | 146 | 280 | 498 | 573 | 674 | 804 | 427 | 138 | 9.99 |
| FOREST PRODUCTS | 44 | 138 | 163 | 132 | 134 | 175 | 194 | 256 | 313 | 296 | 296 | 11.11 |

ANNEX TABLE 8. INDICES OF VOLUME OF EXPORTS OF AGRICULTURAL, FISHERY AND FOREST PRODUCTS

| | 1967 | 1972 | 1973 | 1974 | 1975 | 1976 | 1977 | 1978 | 1979 | 1980 | 1981 | ANNUAL RATE CF CHANGE 1972-81 PERCENT |
|---|---|---|---|---|---|---|---|---|---|---|---|---|
| | | | | | | ...1969-71=100... | | | | | | |
| **WORLD** | | | | | | | | | | | | |
| AGRICULTURAL PRODUCTS | 90 | 113 | 122 | 116 | 118 | 128 | 131 | 140 | 147 | 156 | 162 | 4.13 |
| FOOD | 89 | 114 | 125 | 121 | 123 | 134 | 140 | 150 | 158 | 169 | 177 | 4.97 |
| FEED | 78 | 112 | 126 | 127 | 122 | 156 | 156 | 179 | 187 | 207 | 220 | 7.99 |
| RAW MATERIALS | 96 | 106 | 112 | 100 | 96 | 104 | 104 | 108 | 108 | 109 | 108 | .40 |
| BEVERAGES | 90 | 113 | 120 | 113 | 120 | 124 | 114 | 123 | 139 | 137 | 141 | 2.43 |
| FISHERY PRODUCTS | 81 | 107 | 108 | 101 | 104 | 111 | 117 | 125 | 132 | 131 | 123 | 2.75 |
| FOREST PRODUCTS | 76 | 106 | 120 | 118 | 97 | 116 | 120 | 128 | 136 | 137 | 134 | 2.83 |
| **DEVELOPED COUNTRIES** | | | | | | | | | | | | |
| AGRICULTURAL PRODUCTS | 88 | 116 | 130 | 126 | 128 | 138 | 144 | 157 | 168 | 183 | 187 | 5.45 |
| FOOD | 87 | 117 | 132 | 127 | 132 | 141 | 147 | 162 | 172 | 190 | 196 | 5.88 |
| FEED | 73 | 107 | 133 | 138 | 116 | 141 | 133 | 174 | 185 | 205 | 203 | 7.17 |
| RAW MATERIALS | 103 | 109 | 116 | 109 | 101 | 109 | 118 | 120 | 123 | 128 | 122 | 1.73 |
| BEVERAGES | 76 | 135 | 145 | 149 | 159 | 172 | 183 | 180 | 214 | 209 | 224 | 5.83 |
| FISHERY PRODUCTS | 88 | 107 | 111 | 103 | 105 | 110 | 112 | 123 | 129 | 132 | 123 | 2.50 |
| FOREST PRODUCTS | 78 | 105 | 118 | 120 | 97 | 115 | 119 | 128 | 136 | 139 | 136 | 3.02 |
| **WESTERN EUROPE** | | | | | | | | | | | | |
| AGRICULTURAL PRODUCTS | 79 | 117 | 129 | 133 | 138 | 146 | 149 | 162 | 180 | 193 | 205 | 6.14 |
| FOOD | 78 | 115 | 127 | 132 | 136 | 143 | 147 | 161 | 178 | 193 | 205 | 6.36 |
| FEED | 74 | 137 | 175 | 191 | 159 | 184 | 180 | 233 | 262 | 285 | 320 | 8.67 |
| RAW MATERIALS | 108 | 110 | 109 | 117 | 114 | 121 | 107 | 127 | 132 | 123 | 123 | 1.57 |
| BEVERAGES | 74 | 140 | 148 | 148 | 161 | 176 | 180 | 178 | 216 | 205 | 223 | 5.38 |
| FISHERY PRODUCTS | 86 | 108 | 109 | 101 | 105 | 113 | 111 | 116 | 126 | 129 | 116 | 2.01 |
| FOREST PRODUCTS | 76 | 106 | 125 | 127 | 94 | 115 | 117 | 130 | 142 | 142 | 141 | 3.06 |
| **USSR AND EASTERN EUROPE** | | | | | | | | | | | | |
| AGRICULTURAL PRODUCTS | 105 | 96 | 100 | 110 | 103 | 99 | 110 | 99 | 104 | 103 | 103 | .37 |
| FOOD | 105 | 90 | 93 | 105 | 93 | 85 | 96 | 85 | 92 | 88 | 88 | - .81 |
| FEED | 208 | 57 | 66 | 81 | 85 | 143 | 128 | 124 | 103 | 100 | 65 | 3.88 |
| RAW MATERIALS | 109 | 115 | 124 | 124 | 133 | 142 | 153 | 137 | 132 | 139 | 144 | 2.01 |
| BEVERAGES | 78 | 114 | 114 | 132 | 137 | 137 | 159 | 157 | 170 | 172 | 178 | 5.47 |
| FISHERY PRODUCTS | 97 | 101 | 101 | 114 | 141 | 140 | 122 | 116 | 120 | 124 | 120 | 1.59 |
| FOREST PRODUCTS | 86 | 102 | 113 | 109 | 107 | 117 | 121 | 126 | 116 | 115 | 113 | 1.16 |
| **NORTH AMERICA DEVELOPED** | | | | | | | | | | | | |
| AGRICULTURAL PRODUCTS | 94 | 124 | 153 | 138 | 140 | 156 | 162 | 192 | 197 | 224 | 225 | 6.78 |
| FOOD | 92 | 129 | 160 | 140 | 150 | 169 | 172 | 203 | 210 | 240 | 247 | 7.34 |
| FEED | 68 | 95 | 118 | 119 | 94 | 122 | 109 | 151 | 153 | 179 | 163 | 6.50 |
| RAW MATERIALS | 111 | 111 | 132 | 133 | 107 | 105 | 124 | 146 | 146 | 161 | 138 | 3.02 |
| BEVERAGES | 94 | 121 | 216 | 258 | 213 | 252 | 376 | 321 | 397 | 475 | 451 | 13.68 |
| FISHERY PRODUCTS | 86 | 103 | 124 | 96 | 101 | 114 | 149 | 189 | 181 | 185 | 181 | 8.33 |
| FOREST PRODUCTS | 78 | 106 | 113 | 114 | 96 | 114 | 119 | 124 | 132 | 139 | 133 | 3.09 |
| **OCEANIA DEVELOPED** | | | | | | | | | | | | |
| AGRICULTURAL PRODUCTS | 88 | 114 | 112 | 92 | 97 | 116 | 128 | 124 | 125 | 135 | 126 | 2.81 |
| FOOD | 88 | 119 | 119 | 103 | 110 | 129 | 142 | 147 | 142 | 161 | 143 | 3.93 |
| FEED | 65 | 113 | 144 | 94 | 116 | 177 | 208 | 200 | 221 | 96 | 121 | 2.43 |
| RAW MATERIALS | 87 | 104 | 99 | 73 | 73 | 92 | 101 | 81 | 93 | 89 | 94 | - .04 |
| BEVERAGES | 103 | 128 | 111 | 129 | 135 | 131 | 109 | 120 | 121 | 145 | 171 | 2.24 |
| FISHERY PRODUCTS | 61 | 111 | 106 | 98 | 97 | 92 | 110 | 116 | 142 | 142 | 146 | 4.38 |
| FOREST PRODUCTS | 57 | 113 | 149 | 162 | 159 | 195 | 245 | 247 | 281 | 340 | 325 | 12.61 |

ANNEX TABLE 8.    INDICES OF VOLUME OF EXPORTS OF AGRICULTURAL, FISHERY AND FOREST PRODUCTS

| | 1967 | 1972 | 1973 | 1974 | 1975 | 1976 | 1977 | 1978 | 1979 | 1980 | 1981 | ANNUAL RATE OF CHANGE 1972-81 PERCENT |
|---|---|---|---|---|---|---|---|---|---|---|---|---|
| | | | | | |  ·········1969-71=100········· | | | | | | |
| **DEVELOPING COUNTRIES** | | | | | | | | | | | | |
| AGRICULTURAL PRODUCTS | 93 | 108 | 111 | 102 | 102 | 113 | 112 | 115 | 118 | 116 | 124 | 1.62 |
| FOOD | 94 | 110 | 112 | 106 | 104 | 117 | 126 | 124 | 126 | 124 | 135 | 2.44 |
| FEED | 84 | 118 | 116 | 110 | 130 | 179 | 191 | 185 | 190 | 209 | 245 | 9.24 |
| RAW MATERIALS | 90 | 103 | 109 | 93 | 92 | 99 | 92 | 98 | 94 | 93 | 96 | - .95 |
| BEVERAGES | 95 | 105 | 112 | 100 | 106 | 107 | 91 | 104 | 113 | 112 | 113 | .61 |
| FISHERY PRODUCTS | 68 | 108 | 100 | 99 | 104 | 112 | 127 | 129 | 139 | 128 | 123 | 3.27 |
| FOREST PRODUCTS | 63 | 110 | 129 | 106 | 96 | 118 | 121 | 128 | 131 | 128 | 119 | 1.59 |
| **AFRICA DEVELOPING** | | | | | | | | | | | | |
| AGRICULTURAL PRODUCTS | 93 | 109 | 110 | 102 | 93 | 98 | 85 | 85 | 85 | 83 | 82 | - 3.46 |
| FOOD | 97 | 111 | 105 | 99 | 89 | 93 | 82 | 80 | 77 | 77 | 75 | - 4.37 |
| FEED | 105 | 114 | 94 | 74 | 80 | 91 | 78 | 47 | 67 | 46 | 32 | -10.69 |
| RAW MATERIALS | 90 | 105 | 111 | 99 | 85 | 98 | 87 | 91 | 90 | 100 | 99 | - .98 |
| BEVERAGES | 87 | 105 | 120 | 113 | 106 | 109 | 90 | 95 | 101 | 89 | 91 | - 2.62 |
| FISHERY PRODUCTS | 65 | 112 | 134 | 126 | 117 | 117 | 114 | 114 | 122 | 121 | 104 | - 1.01 |
| FOREST PRODUCTS | 81 | 105 | 121 | 103 | 81 | 101 | 99 | 99 | 100 | 99 | 88 | - 1.49 |
| **LATIN AMERICA** | | | | | | | | | | | | |
| AGRICULTURAL PRODUCTS | 91 | 104 | 107 | 99 | 103 | 112 | 119 | 124 | 127 | 122 | 136 | 3.17 |
| FOOD | 90 | 105 | 109 | 105 | 102 | 116 | 135 | 129 | 132 | 121 | 141 | 3.35 |
| FEED | 75 | 123 | 128 | 139 | 183 | 253 | 314 | 324 | 311 | 372 | 455 | 16.52 |
| RAW MATERIALS | 91 | 90 | 87 | 79 | 88 | 78 | 83 | 101 | 87 | 83 | 85 | .08 |
| BEVERAGES | 95 | 107 | 110 | 92 | 104 | 102 | 80 | 102 | 114 | 114 | 114 | .95 |
| FISHERY PRODUCTS | 83 | 100 | 54 | 64 | 69 | 65 | 70 | 75 | 91 | 97 | 91 | 3.35 |
| FOREST PRODUCTS | 79 | 108 | 127 | 107 | 89 | 97 | 116 | 136 | 170 | 199 | 199 | 7.82 |
| **NEAR EAST DEVELOPING** | | | | | | | | | | | | |
| AGRICULTURAL PRODUCTS | 90 | 113 | 115 | 86 | 83 | 98 | 93 | 108 | 90 | 86 | 97 | - 1.47 |
| FOOD | 85 | 119 | 128 | 101 | 91 | 112 | 134 | 169 | 132 | 124 | 154 | 3.45 |
| FEED | 89 | 109 | 78 | 58 | 63 | 49 | 33 | 30 | 27 | 34 | 18 | -15.83 |
| RAW MATERIALS | 93 | 109 | 109 | 78 | 80 | 91 | 69 | 72 | 67 | 63 | 64 | - 5.84 |
| BEVERAGES | 57 | 110 | 127 | 95 | 56 | 73 | 75 | 63 | 70 | 53 | 58 | - 7.58 |
| FISHERY PRODUCTS | 78 | 110 | 137 | 161 | 93 | 86 | 105 | 83 | 85 | 84 | 60 | - 7.14 |
| FOREST PRODUCTS | 57 | 106 | 113 | 101 | 95 | 99 | 104 | 91 | 133 | 126 | 177 | 4.09 |
| **FAR EAST DEVELOPING** | | | | | | | | | | | | |
| AGRICULTURAL PRODUCTS | 91 | 110 | 114 | 109 | 114 | 135 | 136 | 131 | 142 | 150 | 157 | 4.22 |
| FOOD | 90 | 122 | 117 | 116 | 130 | 164 | 174 | 161 | 183 | 196 | 207 | 7.17 |
| FEED | 84 | 118 | 125 | 108 | 101 | 166 | 127 | 105 | 135 | 111 | 112 | - .19 |
| RAW MATERIALS | 86 | 102 | 116 | 107 | 100 | 111 | 106 | 108 | 110 | 114 | 118 | .88 |
| BEVERAGES | 111 | 99 | 100 | 98 | 110 | 114 | 113 | 114 | 117 | 129 | 133 | 3.39 |
| FISHERY PRODUCTS | 60 | 119 | 162 | 147 | 177 | 209 | 257 | 264 | 261 | 219 | 234 | 7.88 |
| FOREST PRODUCTS | 56 | 109 | 137 | 112 | 102 | 132 | 133 | 136 | 137 | 126 | 113 | .99 |
| **ASIAN CENT PLANNED ECON** | | | | | | | | | | | | |
| AGRICULTURAL PRODUCTS | 112 | 113 | 129 | 120 | 114 | 111 | 107 | 114 | 120 | 118 | 108 | - .62 |
| FOOD | 118 | 105 | 127 | 120 | 112 | 99 | 92 | 99 | 106 | 110 | 97 | - 1.66 |
| FEED | 96 | 71 | 82 | 64 | 64 | 56 | 44 | 42 | 64 | 118 | 311 | 9.06 |
| RAW MATERIALS | 100 | 141 | 143 | 113 | 114 | 148 | 148 | 155 | 150 | 117 | 117 | - .51 |
| BEVERAGES | 80 | 112 | 118 | 134 | 135 | 148 | 176 | 181 | 208 | 218 | 206 | 8.22 |
| FISHERY PRODUCTS | 10 | 116 | 141 | 107 | 81 | 95 | 95 | 83 | 103 | 69 | 46 | - 7.76 |
| FOREST PRODUCTS | 52 | 125 | 105 | 78 | 96 | 100 | 103 | 129 | 112 | 98 | 98 | .03 |

ANNEX TABLE 9. INDICES OF VALUE OF IMPORTS OF AGRICULTURAL, FISHERY AND FOREST PRODUCTS

| | 1967 | 1972 | 1973 | 1974 | 1975 | 1976 | 1977 | 1978 | 1979 | 1980 | 1981 | ANNUAL RATE OF CHANGE 1972-81 PERCENT |
|---|---|---|---|---|---|---|---|---|---|---|---|---|
| | | | | | | ....1969-71=100.... | | | | | | |
| **WORLD** | | | | | | | | | | | | |
| AGRICULTURAL PRODUCTS | 85 | 126 | 183 | 234 | 251 | 260 | 297 | 331 | 389 | 449 | 445 | 13.68 |
| FOOD | 84 | 130 | 187 | 254 | 285 | 274 | 295 | 343 | 408 | 484 | 496 | 14.07 |
| FEED | 76 | 132 | 264 | 250 | 221 | 296 | 379 | 386 | 463 | 524 | 590 | 15.15 |
| RAW MATERIALS | 94 | 114 | 166 | 198 | 171 | 200 | 226 | 246 | 281 | 308 | 285 | 9.86 |
| BEVERAGES | 81 | 122 | 159 | 167 | 184 | 259 | 396 | 379 | 422 | 445 | 358 | 15.75 |
| FISHERY PRODUCTS | 62 | 118 | 156 | 176 | 178 | 222 | 259 | 312 | 386 | 373 | 362 | 14.23 |
| FOREST PRODUCTS | 65 | 111 | 162 | 214 | 187 | 224 | 251 | 281 | 358 | 398 | 363 | 13.45 |
| **DEVELOPED COUNTRIES** | | | | | | | | | | | | |
| AGRICULTURAL PRODUCTS | 84 | 127 | 181 | 218 | 235 | 250 | 283 | 311 | 364 | 401 | 384 | 12.23 |
| FOOD | 81 | 132 | 186 | 234 | 267 | 263 | 278 | 321 | 380 | 425 | 422 | 12.41 |
| FEED | 78 | 132 | 268 | 246 | 216 | 289 | 359 | 364 | 439 | 492 | 550 | 14.11 |
| RAW MATERIALS | 96 | 113 | 163 | 189 | 161 | 188 | 206 | 222 | 253 | 266 | 242 | 8.06 |
| BEVERAGES | 80 | 123 | 162 | 168 | 183 | 261 | 401 | 379 | 424 | 450 | 355 | 15.58 |
| FISHERY PRODUCTS | 61 | 119 | 158 | 177 | 176 | 222 | 260 | 311 | 388 | 375 | 371 | 14.29 |
| FOREST PRODUCTS | 66 | 112 | 163 | 211 | 184 | 220 | 241 | 270 | 347 | 381 | 341 | 12.66 |
| **WESTERN EUROPE** | | | | | | | | | | | | |
| AGRICULTURAL PRODUCTS | 85 | 129 | 180 | 210 | 223 | 235 | 277 | 309 | 356 | 383 | 340 | 11.42 |
| FOOD | 83 | 133 | 182 | 222 | 248 | 241 | 270 | 314 | 362 | 392 | 353 | 11.14 |
| FEED | 82 | 127 | 248 | 219 | 197 | 272 | 331 | 349 | 426 | 477 | 506 | 14.47 |
| RAW MATERIALS | 98 | 112 | 157 | 180 | 151 | 184 | 199 | 221 | 246 | 257 | 221 | 7.77 |
| BEVERAGES | 80 | 126 | 171 | 175 | 189 | 263 | 413 | 389 | 448 | 471 | 371 | 15.72 |
| FISHERY PRODUCTS | 68 | 112 | 154 | 175 | 171 | 196 | 229 | 279 | 348 | 372 | 327 | 13.49 |
| FOREST PRODUCTS | 65 | 111 | 162 | 225 | 188 | 231 | 249 | 269 | 353 | 412 | 373 | 13.46 |
| **USSR AND EASTERN EUROPE** | | | | | | | | | | | | |
| AGRICULTURAL PRODUCTS | 82 | 132 | 195 | 234 | 324 | 350 | 352 | 385 | 485 | 595 | 666 | 17.45 |
| FOOD | 85 | 144 | 217 | 253 | 424 | 463 | 419 | 492 | 640 | 810 | 947 | 20.76 |
| FEED | 63 | 170 | 369 | 395 | 349 | 390 | 501 | 466 | 548 | 635 | 869 | 13.72 |
| RAW MATERIALS | 85 | 106 | 150 | 200 | 180 | 175 | 204 | 199 | 240 | 262 | 242 | 8.03 |
| BEVERAGES | 63 | 131 | 140 | 176 | 215 | 258 | 377 | 340 | 366 | 428 | 358 | 14.48 |
| FISHERY PRODUCTS | 64 | 104 | 133 | 179 | 182 | 203 | 205 | 210 | 222 | 252 | 204 | 7.63 |
| FOREST PRODUCTS | 65 | 106 | 133 | 181 | 242 | 219 | 228 | 241 | 247 | 302 | 282 | 10.28 |
| **NORTH AMERICA DEVELOPED** | | | | | | | | | | | | |
| AGRICULTURAL PRODUCTS | 82 | 117 | 156 | 195 | 181 | 208 | 243 | 263 | 297 | 311 | 299 | 10.64 |
| FOOD | 75 | 120 | 158 | 215 | 193 | 189 | 196 | 221 | 259 | 278 | 294 | 8.48 |
| FEED | 73 | 118 | 216 | 202 | 200 | 271 | 309 | 338 | 400 | 353 | 381 | 12.27 |
| RAW MATERIALS | 113 | 100 | 146 | 188 | 166 | 220 | 230 | 252 | 308 | 299 | 301 | 12.01 |
| BEVERAGES | 86 | 116 | 153 | 149 | 158 | 248 | 363 | 368 | 383 | 395 | 308 | 15.01 |
| FISHERY PRODUCTS | 59 | 126 | 141 | 153 | 142 | 194 | 215 | 229 | 276 | 275 | 282 | 10.47 |
| FOREST PRODUCTS | 70 | 120 | 148 | 160 | 153 | 191 | 220 | 277 | 297 | 278 | 287 | 11.04 |
| **OCEANIA DEVELOPED** | | | | | | | | | | | | |
| AGRICULTURAL PRODUCTS | 91 | 112 | 129 | 223 | 241 | 216 | 274 | 315 | 309 | 368 | 354 | 13.13 |
| FOOD | 84 | 119 | 137 | 263 | 343 | 273 | 313 | 373 | 381 | 430 | 440 | 14.29 |
| FEED | 84 | 88 | 58 | 186 | 111 | 29 | 52 | 225 | 70 | 121 | 228 | 7.21 |
| RAW MATERIALS | 96 | 99 | 124 | 223 | 155 | 174 | 179 | 202 | 205 | 255 | 244 | 8.55 |
| BEVERAGES | 95 | 118 | 129 | 154 | 188 | 184 | 355 | 378 | 341 | 433 | 364 | 16.59 |
| FISHERY PRODUCTS | 69 | 109 | 145 | 217 | 197 | 185 | 253 | 269 | 298 | 303 | 317 | 11.25 |
| FOREST PRODUCTS | 76 | 97 | 139 | 218 | 220 | 196 | 248 | 238 | 288 | 353 | 386 | 13.40 |

ANNEX TABLE 9. INDICES OF VALUE OF IMPORTS OF AGRICULTURAL, FISHERY AND FOREST PRODUCTS

| | 1967 | 1972 | 1973 | 1974 | 1975 | 1976 | 1977 | 1978 | 1979 | 1980 | 1981 | ANNUAL RATE OF CHANGE 1972-81 PERCENT |
|---|---|---|---|---|---|---|---|---|---|---|---|---|
| | | | | | | 1969-71=100 | | | | | | |
| **DEVELOPING COUNTRIES** | | | | | | | | | | | | |
| AGRICULTURAL PRODUCTS | 91 | 121 | 188 | 302 | 318 | 301 | 352 | 412 | 492 | 650 | 699 | 18.35 |
| FOOD | 92 | 122 | 194 | 323 | 346 | 312 | 353 | 420 | 508 | 688 | 752 | 18.61 |
| FEED | 55 | 130 | 204 | 314 | 294 | 408 | 686 | 723 | 828 | 1023 | 1200 | 26.94 |
| RAW MATERIALS | 85 | 121 | 181 | 243 | 221 | 261 | 329 | 370 | 425 | 524 | 506 | 16.28 |
| BEVERAGES | 90 | 107 | 125 | 161 | 189 | 243 | 348 | 376 | 405 | 397 | 389 | 17.40 |
| FISHERY PRODUCTS | 65 | 109 | 136 | 168 | 192 | 222 | 250 | 317 | 375 | 356 | 291 | 13.70 |
| FOREST PRODUCTS | 61 | 108 | 151 | 229 | 212 | 254 | 322 | 356 | 434 | 513 | 517 | 18.28 |
| **AFRICA DEVELOPING** | | | | | | | | | | | | |
| AGRICULTURAL PRODUCTS | 87 | 128 | 180 | 290 | 353 | 313 | 388 | 456 | 518 | 668 | 720 | 18.92 |
| FOOD | 86 | 130 | 188 | 307 | 375 | 320 | 388 | 468 | 541 | 719 | 788 | 19.42 |
| FEED | 51 | 121 | 192 | 282 | 289 | 336 | 651 | 868 | 1107 | 1384 | 1903 | 34.89 |
| RAW MATERIALS | 86 | 142 | 181 | 302 | 307 | 293 | 367 | 392 | 458 | 461 | 447 | 12.84 |
| BEVERAGES | 94 | 102 | 123 | 154 | 218 | 277 | 398 | 390 | 360 | 394 | 342 | 16.63 |
| FISHERY PRODUCTS | 70 | 110 | 133 | 179 | 220 | 289 | 287 | 384 | 453 | 459 | 331 | 16.28 |
| FOREST PRODUCTS | 60 | 96 | 144 | 273 | 254 | 267 | 336 | 331 | 387 | 404 | 406 | 14.93 |
| **LATIN AMERICA** | | | | | | | | | | | | |
| AGRICULTURAL PRODUCTS | 87 | 125 | 192 | 308 | 284 | 289 | 314 | 382 | 469 | 661 | 667 | 17.60 |
| FOOD | 89 | 127 | 159 | 323 | 304 | 302 | 316 | 396 | 470 | 705 | 715 | 17.87 |
| FEED | 51 | 127 | 281 | 387 | 304 | 395 | 690 | 655 | 834 | 1064 | 1233 | 24.73 |
| RAW MATERIALS | 85 | 113 | 146 | 235 | 171 | 190 | 236 | 267 | 343 | 388 | 363 | 13.40 |
| BEVERAGES | 75 | 127 | 165 | 204 | 201 | 273 | 339 | 333 | 634 | 436 | 409 | 16.17 |
| FISHERY PRODUCTS | 66 | 99 | 112 | 135 | 162 | 147 | 163 | 204 | 249 | 262 | 200 | 10.19 |
| FOREST PRODUCTS | 65 | 104 | 120 | 205 | 175 | 192 | 217 | 222 | 258 | 377 | 390 | 14.21 |
| **NEAR EAST DEVELOPING** | | | | | | | | | | | | |
| AGRICULTURAL PRODUCTS | 80 | 130 | 179 | 408 | 503 | 446 | 536 | 640 | 755 | 1055 | 1210 | 24.74 |
| FOOD | 77 | 130 | 188 | 450 | 561 | 479 | 560 | 671 | 824 | 1182 | 1355 | 25.65 |
| FEED | 48 | 149 | 183 | 329 | 241 | 525 | 909 | 1027 | 1020 | 1072 | 1681 | 31.15 |
| RAW MATERIALS | 91 | 130 | 150 | 253 | 321 | 335 | 425 | 404 | 410 | 448 | 530 | 15.39 |
| BEVERAGES | 97 | 123 | 136 | 191 | 205 | 252 | 396 | 537 | 441 | 504 | 521 | 19.72 |
| FISHERY PRODUCTS | 66 | 115 | 163 | 293 | 319 | 446 | 671 | 764 | 864 | 851 | 572 | 23.21 |
| FOREST PRODUCTS | 65 | 120 | 153 | 252 | 328 | 372 | 542 | 531 | 549 | 676 | 751 | 21.90 |
| **FAR EAST DEVELOPING** | | | | | | | | | | | | |
| AGRICULTURAL PRODUCTS | 102 | 105 | 172 | 231 | 262 | 261 | 274 | 303 | 346 | 425 | 470 | 14.46 |
| FOOD | 108 | 105 | 184 | 249 | 284 | 265 | 259 | 299 | 345 | 434 | 489 | 14.00 |
| FEED | 57 | 124 | 158 | 266 | 297 | 360 | 574 | 587 | 727 | 901 | 871 | 25.32 |
| RAW MATERIALS | 84 | 111 | 145 | 183 | 204 | 257 | 323 | 320 | 348 | 399 | 409 | 15.37 |
| BEVERAGES | 88 | 73 | 94 | 101 | 127 | 170 | 230 | 209 | 238 | 242 | 272 | 16.06 |
| FISHERY PRODUCTS | 67 | 114 | 151 | 169 | 184 | 213 | 240 | 290 | 346 | 318 | 297 | 12.16 |
| FOREST PRODUCTS | 58 | 104 | 179 | 226 | 188 | 254 | 299 | 377 | 542 | 553 | 532 | 19.38 |
| **ASIAN CENT PLANNED ECON** | | | | | | | | | | | | |
| AGRICULTURAL PRODUCTS | 85 | 137 | 247 | 375 | 262 | 245 | 363 | 434 | 575 | 731 | 732 | 17.60 |
| FOOD | 86 | 138 | 231 | 387 | 275 | 229 | 359 | 398 | 560 | 663 | 701 | 16.65 |
| FEED | 122 | 149 | 169 | 188 | 477 | 831 | 1200 | 1640 | 564 | 1278 | 1495 | 30.95 |
| RAW MATERIALS | 82 | 136 | 289 | 345 | 226 | 284 | 361 | 520 | 628 | 913 | 810 | 19.82 |
| BEVERAGES | 156 | 116 | 149 | 190 | 126 | 375 | 836 | 560 | 697 | 696 | 752 | 26.98 |
| FISHERY PRODUCTS | 30 | 140 | 185 | 197 | 343 | 426 | 508 | 817 | 1030 | 614 | 634 | 22.07 |
| FOREST PRODUCTS | 49 | 131 | 152 | 247 | 185 | 282 | 431 | 590 | 671 | 841 | 761 | 23.66 |

ANNEX TABLE 10. INDICES OF VOLUME OF IMPORTS OF AGRICULTURAL, FISHERY AND FOREST PRODUCTS

| | 1967 | 1972 | 1973 | 1974 | 1975 | 1976 | 1977 | 1978 | 1979 | 1980 | 1981 | ANNUAL RATE OF CHANGE 1972-81 PERCENT |
|---|---|---|---|---|---|---|---|---|---|---|---|---|
| | | | | | | ......1969-71=100...... | | | | | | |
| **WORLD** | | | | | | | | | | | | |
| AGRICULTURAL PRODUCTS | 89 | 112 | 121 | 116 | 119 | 128 | 129 | 139 | 147 | 154 | 157 | 3.99 |
| FOOD | 89 | 114 | 124 | 120 | 123 | 133 | 137 | 147 | 157 | 166 | 171 | 4.74 |
| FEED | 76 | 119 | 128 | 122 | 126 | 156 | 160 | 182 | 192 | 201 | 212 | 7.40 |
| RAW MATERIALS | 94 | 106 | 109 | 101 | 100 | 104 | 102 | 109 | 110 | 111 | 107 | -.61 |
| BEVERAGES | 87 | 110 | 119 | 114 | 121 | 125 | 118 | 124 | 138 | 137 | 141 | 2.57 |
| FISHERY PRODUCTS | 82 | 109 | 107 | 108 | 108 | 116 | 118 | 125 | 135 | 134 | 132 | 3.00 |
| FOREST PRODUCTS | 75 | 107 | 120 | 117 | 96 | 113 | 118 | 127 | 136 | 135 | 127 | 2.49 |
| **DEVELOPED COUNTRIES** | | | | | | | | | | | | |
| AGRICULTURAL PRODUCTS | 89 | 113 | 120 | 112 | 115 | 125 | 121 | 128 | 134 | 135 | 137 | 2.32 |
| FOOD | 88 | 115 | 123 | 116 | 119 | 131 | 129 | 135 | 142 | 143 | 146 | 2.77 |
| FEED | 77 | 119 | 129 | 121 | 122 | 152 | 153 | 173 | 185 | 191 | 199 | 6.60 |
| RAW MATERIALS | 95 | 105 | 105 | 96 | 95 | 99 | 94 | 99 | 99 | 96 | 93 | - .85 |
| BEVERAGES | 86 | 111 | 121 | 113 | 120 | 122 | 113 | 121 | 136 | 136 | 138 | 2.29 |
| FISHERY PRODUCTS | 82 | 110 | 109 | 108 | 108 | 116 | 118 | 125 | 136 | 134 | 134 | 2.99 |
| FOREST PRODUCTS | 76 | 107 | 121 | 117 | 94 | 111 | 115 | 124 | 132 | 128 | 120 | 1.82 |
| **WESTERN EUROPE** | | | | | | | | | | | | |
| AGRICULTURAL PRODUCTS | 90 | 111 | 115 | 110 | 112 | 121 | 119 | 126 | 131 | 130 | 128 | 2.02 |
| FOOD | 90 | 113 | 116 | 115 | 117 | 124 | 125 | 131 | 134 | 135 | 132 | 2.18 |
| FEED | 82 | 114 | 121 | 109 | 112 | 143 | 143 | 167 | 180 | 185 | 192 | 7.12 |
| RAW MATERIALS | 97 | 101 | 101 | 90 | 88 | 98 | 92 | 98 | 96 | 91 | 84 | - 1.09 |
| BEVERAGES | 86 | 111 | 125 | 115 | 122 | 123 | 115 | 119 | 140 | 134 | 139 | 2.08 |
| FISHERY PRODUCTS | 88 | 107 | 98 | 97 | 101 | 104 | 102 | 109 | 122 | 129 | 119 | 2.62 |
| FOREST PRODUCTS | 77 | 106 | 122 | 118 | 90 | 113 | 113 | 121 | 135 | 133 | 126 | 2.27 |
| **USSR AND EASTERN EUROPE** | | | | | | | | | | | | |
| AGRICULTURAL PRODUCTS | 84 | 124 | 139 | 119 | 140 | 150 | 137 | 146 | 166 | 183 | 201 | 4.95 |
| FOOD | 88 | 137 | 166 | 125 | 156 | 180 | 158 | 175 | 204 | 229 | 260 | 6.73 |
| FEED | 63 | 151 | 164 | 189 | 196 | 207 | 208 | 212 | 227 | 244 | 270 | 5.71 |
| RAW MATERIALS | 89 | 102 | 99 | 103 | 105 | 96 | 96 | 98 | 104 | 109 | 106 | .54 |
| BEVERAGES | 57 | 114 | 103 | 114 | 132 | 127 | 122 | 112 | 121 | 137 | 139 | 2.20 |
| FISHERY PRODUCTS | 82 | 94 | 72 | 88 | 99 | 102 | 88 | 104 | 114 | 137 | 129 | 5.43 |
| FOREST PRODUCTS | 72 | 100 | 103 | 109 | 123 | 118 | 119 | 117 | 113 | 128 | 122 | 2.10 |
| **NORTH AMERICA DEVELOPED** | | | | | | | | | | | | |
| AGRICULTURAL PRODUCTS | 92 | 109 | 114 | 108 | 103 | 115 | 110 | 116 | 120 | 114 | 119 | .57 |
| FOOD | 87 | 110 | 114 | 109 | 99 | 116 | 112 | 112 | 114 | 107 | 114 | .28 |
| FEED | 76 | 104 | 103 | 107 | 116 | 139 | 136 | 161 | 165 | 148 | 147 | 5.53 |
| RAW MATERIALS | 107 | 107 | 106 | 105 | 107 | 112 | 110 | 113 | 117 | 107 | 111 | .64 |
| BEVERAGES | 97 | 108 | 117 | 107 | 111 | 115 | 103 | 126 | 132 | 133 | 133 | 2.52 |
| FISHERY PRODUCTS | 82 | 113 | 110 | 108 | 96 | 112 | 111 | 111 | 114 | 105 | 108 | - .01 |
| FOREST PRODUCTS | 80 | 113 | 116 | 105 | 89 | 107 | 114 | 130 | 128 | 116 | 114 | 1.39 |
| **OCEANIA DEVELOPED** | | | | | | | | | | | | |
| AGRICULTURAL PRODUCTS | 94 | 106 | 103 | 126 | 123 | 115 | 116 | 112 | 109 | 114 | 113 | .15 |
| FOOD | 101 | 106 | 108 | 138 | 151 | 126 | 136 | 131 | 129 | 128 | 130 | 1.42 |
| FEED | 80 | 88 | 40 | 75 | 45 | 5 | 20 | 100 | 20 | 38 | 55 | - 4.42 |
| RAW MATERIALS | 90 | 106 | 97 | 124 | 95 | 107 | 89 | 95 | 83 | 89 | 89 | - 2.62 |
| BEVERAGES | 89 | 107 | 107 | 112 | 120 | 114 | 124 | 104 | 117 | 127 | 121 | 1.36 |
| FISHERY PRODUCTS | 84 | 99 | 94 | 119 | 113 | 113 | 134 | 127 | 119 | 124 | 128 | 2.92 |
| FOREST PRODUCTS | 86 | 98 | 115 | 143 | 125 | 104 | 127 | 110 | 125 | 130 | 136 | 1.83 |

ANNEX TABLE 10. INDICES OF VOLUME OF IMPORTS OF AGRICULTURAL, FISHERY AND FOREST PRODUCTS

| | 1967 | 1972 | 1973 | 1974 | 1975 | 1976 | 1977 | 1978 | 1979 | 1980 | 1981 | ANNUAL RATE CF CHANGE 1972-81 PERCENT |
|---|---|---|---|---|---|---|---|---|---|---|---|---|
| | | | | | | | ···1969-71=100··· | | | | | |
| **DEVELOPING COUNTRIES** | | | | | | | | | | | | |
| AGRICULTURAL PRODUCTS | 91 | 109 | 124 | 132 | 134 | 141 | 164 | 184 | 201 | 234 | 242 | 9.39 |
| FOOD | 93 | 109 | 124 | 134 | 135 | 141 | 166 | 189 | 210 | 247 | 257 | 10.14 |
| FEED | 52 | 122 | 105 | 148 | 181 | 211 | 275 | 329 | 302 | 365 | 419 | 16.66 |
| RAW MATERIALS | 89 | 110 | 131 | 127 | 126 | 132 | 144 | 160 | 169 | 189 | 183 | 5.86 |
| BEVERAGES | 90 | 104 | 108 | 117 | 131 | 152 | 168 | 147 | 153 | 148 | 167 | 5.12 |
| FISHERY PRODUCTS · | 80 | 100 | 95 | 103 | 111 | 116 | 116 | 123 | 131 | 130 | 116 | 3.10 |
| FOREST PRODUCTS | 70 | 106 | 113 | 124 | 111 | 125 | 144 | 153 | 164 | 179 | 180 | 6.61 |
| **AFRICA DEVELOPING** | | | | | | | | | | | | |
| AGRICULTURAL PRODUCTS | 91 | 111 | 115 | 128 | 136 | 145 | 182 | 195 | 202 | 228 | 247 | 9.88 |
| FOOD | 89 | 112 | 118 | 130 | 132 | 140 | 177 | 207 | 216 | 248 | 269 | 10.98 |
| FEED | 55 | 116 | 98 | 124 | 118 | 147 | 229 | 253 | 292 | 298 | 406 | 17.08 |
| RAW MATERIALS | 98 | 123 | 128 | 145 | 150 | 147 | 149 | 156 | 165 | 159 | 151 | 2.56 |
| BEVERAGES | 106 | 93 | 90 | 100 | 155 | 185 | 241 | 126 | 116 | 117 | 138 | 3.56 |
| FISHERY PRODUCTS | 73 | 97 | 98 | 110 | 102 | 143 | 140 | 142 | 156 | 162 | 121 | 5.12 |
| FOREST PRODUCTS | 64 | 90 | 104 | 132 | 109 | 111 | 145 | 134 | 147 | 146 | 145 | 5.04 |
| **LATIN AMERICA** | | | | | | | | | | | | |
| AGRICULTURAL PRODUCTS | 88 | 111 | 125 | 146 | 135 | 142 | 166 | 200 | 216 | 269 | 268 | 10.57 |
| FOOD | 90 | 111 | 127 | 148 | 140 | 147 | 174 | 213 | 227 | 291 | 289 | 11.53 |
| FEED | 50 | 109 | 110 | 166 | 141 | 171 | 223 | 240 | 273 | 323 | 364 | 14.79 |
| RAW MATERIALS | 83 | 109 | 110 | 125 | 103 | 105 | 118 | 122 | 135 | 144 | 145 | 3.37 |
| BEVERAGES | 83 | 122 | 130 | 147 | 133 | 148 | 134 | 149 | 191 | 169 | 180 | 4.28 |
| FISHERY PRODUCTS | 83 | 93 | 77 | 77 | 96 | 79 | 79 | 93 | 110 | 108 | 90 | 2.29 |
| FOREST PRODUCTS | 76 | 101 | 101 | 127 | 99 | 101 | 105 | 107 | 116 | 156 | 155 | 4.22 |
| **NEAR EAST DEVELOPING** | | | | | | | | | | | | |
| AGRICULTURAL PRODUCTS | 80 | 111 | 113 | 156 | 174 | 185 | 223 | 239 | 276 | 324 | 364 | 14.33 |
| FOOD | 78 | 109 | 115 | 162 | 183 | 193 | 238 | 255 | 301 | 360 | 401 | 15.69 |
| FEED | 43 | 139 | 107 | 152 | 121 | 223 | 323 | 380 | 377 | 335 | 533 | 18.81 |
| RAW MATERIALS | 91 | 127 | 103 | 130 | 164 | 166 | 163 | 143 | 151 | 163 | 198 | 4.67 |
| BEVERAGES | 90 | 108 | 105 | 124 | 114 | 136 | 134 | 172 | 157 | 154 | 173 | 5.82 |
| FISHERY PRODUCTS | 76 | 111 | 143 | 174 | 209 | 272 | 335 | 284 | 296 | 309 | 284 | 11.29 |
| FOREST PRODUCTS | 75 | 113 | 112 | 123 | 135 | 154 | 192 | 184 | 189 | 209 | 234 | 9.02 |
| **FAR EAST DEVELOPING** | | | | | | | | | | | | |
| AGRICULTURAL PRODUCTS | 103 | 100 | 122 | 110 | 122 | 130 | 136 | 144 | 151 | 172 | 173 | 5.91 |
| FOOD | 108 | 99 | 126 | 112 | 121 | 129 | 132 | 143 | 151 | 178 | 178 | 6.05 |
| FEED | 53 | 122 | 94 | 132 | 147 | 140 | 179 | 205 | 219 | 251 | 234 | 10.58 |
| RAW MATERIALS | 93 | 101 | 112 | 99 | 122 | 130 | 147 | 145 | 146 | 145 | 147 | 4.79 |
| BEVERAGES | 74 | 96 | 113 | 105 | 125 | 138 | 152 | 143 | 158 | 158 | 185 | 6.76 |
| FISHERY PRODUCTS | 86 | 103 | 104 | 102 | 111 | 109 | 101 | 109 | 110 | 106 | 107 | .44 |
| FOREST PRODUCTS | 67 | 107 | 127 | 116 | 108 | 137 | 155 | 181 | 200 | 184 | 184 | 7.50 |
| **ASIAN CENT PLANNED ECON** | | | | | | | | | | | | |
| AGRICULTURAL PRODUCTS | 82 | 123 | 156 | 147 | 114 | 112 | 145 | 186 | 222 | 246 | 237 | 8.14 |
| FOOD | 82 | 125 | 140 | 137 | 105 | 98 | 139 | 164 | 209 | 208 | 211 | 7.10 |
| FEED | 119 | 210 | 243 | 252 | 1810 | 2000 | 2381 | 3419 | 1652 | 3186 | 3571 | 39.58 |
| RAW MATERIALS | 83 | 118 | 157 | 175 | 126 | 135 | 146 | 226 | 246 | 326 | 284 | 9.53 |
| BEVERAGES | 127 | 116 | 159 | 170 | 130 | 200 | 209 | 211 | 355 | 289 | 305 | 11.55 |
| FISHERY PRODUCTS | 41 | 122 | 79 | 235 | 230 | 233 | 294 | 290 | 274 | 245 | 254 | 10.34 |
| FOREST PRODUCTS | 53 | 135 | 135 | 139 | 134 | 152 | 187 | 227 | 226 | 268 | 236 | 8.87 |

ANNEX TABLE 11. THE IMPORTANCE OF AGRICULTURE IN THE ECONOMY

| COUNTRY | AGRICULTURAL GDP AS % TOTAL GDP 1979 | AGRIC.POPULATION AS % TOTAL POPULATION 1981 | AGRIC.EXPORTS AS % TOTAL EXPORTS 1981 | AGRIC.IMPORTS AS % TOTAL IMPORTS 1981 | SHARE OF TOTAL IMPORTS FINANCED BY AGR.EXPORTS % 1981 |
|---|---|---|---|---|---|
| ALGERIA | 6 | 48 | 1 | 17 | 1 |
| ANGOLA | | 57 | 10 | 23 | 13 |
| BENIN | 47 | 45 | 98 | 32 | 14 |
| BOTSWANA | 12 | 79 | 21 | 11 | 11 |
| BRIT.INDIAN OCEAN TERRIT | | 50 | | | |
| BURUNDI | 57 | 83 | 94 | 16 | 40 |
| CAMEROON | 32 | 80 | 33 | 7 | 28 |
| CAPE VERDE | | 56 | 35 | 42 | 3 |
| CENTRAL AFRICAN REPUBLIC | 34 | 87 | 35 | 30 | 50 |
| CHAD | | 83 | 78 | 9 | 79 |
| COMOROS | | 63 | 82 | 44 | 49 |
| CONGO | 14 | 33 | 3 | 23 | 5 |
| DJIBOUTI | | 48 | | 31 | |
| EGYPT | 23 | 50 | 22 | 36 | 8 |
| EQUATORIAL GUINEA | | 74 | | | |
| ETHIOPIA | 52 | 79 | 86 | 10 | 44 |
| GABON | 6 | 76 | 1 | 14 | 1 |
| GAMBIA | 38 | 78 | 62 | 27 | 13 |
| GHANA | | 50 | 45 | 15 | 37 |
| GUINEA | 40 | 80 | 7 | 17 | 7 |
| GUINEA-BISSAU | | 82 | 54 | 34 | 15 |
| IVORY COAST | 25 | 79 | 58 | 17 | 52 |
| KENYA | 56 | 77 | 49 | 11 | 28 |
| LESOTHO | 31 | 83 | 30 | 25 | 4 |
| LIBERIA | 34 | 69 | 23 | 18 | 21 |
| LIBYA | 2 | 14 | | 12 | |
| MADAGASCAR | 36 | 82 | 85 | 17 | 46 |
| MALAWI | 43 | 83 | 86 | 13 | 68 |
| MALI | 42 | 86 | 91 | 19 | 49 |
| MAURITANIA | 23 | 82 | 17 | 37 | 16 |
| MAURITIUS | 15 | 28 | 64 | 30 | 37 |
| MOROCCO | 18 | 51 | 18 | 25 | 10 |
| MOZAMBIQUE | 44 | 63 | 33 | 16 | 14 |
| NAMIBIA | | 48 | | | |
| NIGER | 33 | 87 | 24 | 18 | 22 |
| NIGERIA | 22 | 52 | 2 | 15 | 2 |
| REUNION | | 27 | 84 | 24 | 11 |
| RWANDA | 41 | 89 | 78 | 9 | 25 |
| ST. HELENA | | | | 31 | |
| SAO TOME AND PRINCIPE | | 52 | 50 | 23 | 61 |
| SENEGAL | 24 | 74 | 14 | 34 | 7 |
| SEYCHELLES | | 48 | 18 | 19 | 3 |
| SIERRA LEONE | 33 | 64 | 15 | 21 | 8 |
| SOMALIA | 60 | 79 | 83 | 92 | 83 |
| SOUTH AFRICA | 7 | 28 | 11 | 4 | 10 |
| SPANISH NORTH AFRICA | | 16 | | | |
| SUDAN | 39 | 76 | 76 | 20 | 32 |
| SWAZILAND | | 72 | 56 | 4 | 26 |
| TANZANIA | 53 | 80 | 73 | 9 | 31 |
| TOGO | 27 | 67 | 18 | 16 | 11 |
| TUNISIA | 16 | 40 | 8 | 15 | 5 |
| UGANDA | 8 | 80 | 87 | 8 | 40 |
| UPPER VOLTA | 40 | 81 | 79 | 18 | 20 |
| WESTERN SAHARA | | 39 | | | |
| ZAIRE | 31 | 74 | 14 | 33 | 25 |
| ZAMBIA | 14 | 66 | 1 | 7 | 1 |
| ZIMBABWE | 12 | 58 | 35 | 3 | 45 |
| | | | | | |
| ANTIGUA AND BARBUDA | | 9 | 6 | 25 | 1 |
| BAHAMAS | | 9 | | 2 | |
| BARBADOS | 9 | 16 | 18 | 16 | 7 |
| BELIZE | | 28 | 65 | 26 | 52 |
| BERMUDA | | 7 | | 20 | |
| BRITISH VIRGIN ISLANDS | | 7 | | 23 | |
| CANADA | 4 | 5 | 11 | 7 | 12 |
| CAYMAN ISLANDS | | 11 | | | |
| COSTA RICA | 19 | 34 | 66 | 10 | 56 |
| CUBA | | 23 | 82 | 14 | 61 |
| DOMINICA | | 33 | 95 | 23 | 20 |
| DOMINICAN REPUBLIC | 19 | 56 | 66 | 17 | 57 |
| EL SALVADOR | 30 | 51 | 72 | 17 | 58 |
| GREENLAND | | 6 | 2 | 18 | 1 |
| GRENADA | | 33 | 83 | 21 | 28 |
| GUADELOUPE | | 16 | 86 | 26 | 14 |
| GUATEMALA | | 54 | 56 | 9 | 46 |
| HAITI | | 66 | 27 | 42 | 16 |
| HONDURAS | 32 | 62 | 86 | 11 | 46 |
| JAMAICA | 7 | 20 | 11 | 17 | 7 |
| MARTINIQUE | | 14 | 32 | 20 | 6 |
| MEXICO | 10 | 35 | 8 | 14 | 6 |
| MONTSERRAT | | 9 | | 21 | |
| NETHERLANDS ANTILLES | | 9 | 1 | 4 | 1 |
| NICARAGUA | 29 | 41 | 80 | 27 | 99 |
| PANAMA | 14 | 34 | 51 | 8 | 10 |

ANNEX TABLE 11. THE IMPORTANCE OF AGRICULTURE IN THE ECONOMY

| COUNTRY | AGRICULTURAL GDP AS % TOTAL GDP 1979 | AGRIC.POPULATION AS % TOTAL POPULATION 1981 | AGRIC.EXPORTS AS % TOTAL EXPORTS 1981 | AGRIC.IMPORTS AS % TOTAL IMPORTS 1981 | SHARE OF TOTAL IMPORTS FINANCED BY AGR.EXPORTS % 1981 |
|---|---|---|---|---|---|
| PUERTO RICO | 6 | 3 | | | |
| ST.KITTS-NEVIS | | 9 | 60 | 26 | 43 |
| ST. LUCIA | | 33 | 71 | 20 | 16 |
| ST.PIERRE AND MIQUELON | | | | 14 | |
| ST. VINCENT | | 34 | 72 | 21 | 23 |
| TRINIDAD AND TOBAGO | 3 | 16 | 2 | 11 | 2 |
| TURKS AND CAICOS IS. | | 17 | | | |
| UNITED STATES | 3 | 2 | 20 | 7 | 16 |
| US VIRGIN ISLANDS | | 9 | | 2 | |
| | | | | | |
| ARGENTINA | 12 | 13 | 69 | 5 | 58 |
| BOLIVIA | 43 | 49 | 4 | 10 | 4 |
| BRAZIL | 13 | 37 | 42 | 9 | 41 |
| CHILE | 7 | 18 | 9 | 10 | 6 |
| COLOMBIA | 29 | 27 | 73 | 8 | 41 |
| ECUADOR | 13 | 44 | 20 | 9 | 23 |
| FRENCH GUIANA | | 21 | 3 | 19 | |
| GUYANA | 22 | 21 | 45 | 18 | 47 |
| PARAGUAY | 31 | 49 | 114 | 22 | 55 |
| PERU | 9 | 39 | 8 | 21 | 9 |
| SURINAME | 10 | 17 | 12 | 10 | 12 |
| URUGUAY | 13 | 12 | 61 | 7 | 47 |
| VENEZUELA | 6 | 17 | | 16 | |
| | | | | | |
| AFGHANISTAN | 53 | 77 | 45 | 12 | 28 |
| BAHRAIN | | 61 | | 6 | 1 |
| BANGLADESH | 54 | 83 | 21 | 16 | 6 |
| BHUTAN | | 93 | | | |
| BRUNEI | | 8 | | 14 | |
| BURMA | 45 | 51 | 64 | 12 | 79 |
| CHINA | | 59 | 12 | 28 | 11 |
| CYPRUS | 11 | 34 | 38 | 16 | 19 |
| EAST TIMOR | | 58 | | | |
| GAZA STRIP (PALESTINE) | | 3 | 25 | 8 | 15 |
| HONG KONG | 1 | 2 | 4 | 14 | 4 |
| INDIA | 36 | 62 | 36 | 12 | 21 |
| INDONESIA | 29 | 58 | 8 | 13 | 14 |
| IRAN | | 37 | 2 | 20 | 1 |
| IRAQ | 8 | 40 | 1 | 14 | |
| ISRAEL | 7 | 7 | 16 | 13 | 11 |
| JAPAN | 4 | 10 | 1 | 13 | 1 |
| JORDAN | 8 | 25 | 17 | 15 | 4 |
| KAMPUCHEA,DEMOCRATIC | | 73 | 28 | 20 | 2 |
| KOREA DPR | | 45 | 19 | 19 | 11 |
| KOREA REP | 20 | 37 | 3 | 17 | 2 |
| KUWAIT | 3 | 2 | 1 | 16 | 1 |
| LAOS | | 73 | 1 | 34 | |
| LEBANON | | 9 | 17 | 30 | 8 |
| MACAU | | 3 | 1 | 18 | 1 |
| MALAYSIA | 25 | 46 | 31 | 13 | 30 |
| MALDIVES | | 79 | | 50 | |
| MONGOLIA | | 48 | 45 | 12 | 28 |
| NEPAL | 58 | 92 | 19 | 16 | 15 |
| OMAN | 3 | 61 | 1 | 13 | 1 |
| PAKISTAN | 3 | 53 | 42 | 14 | 23 |
| PHILIPPINES | 25 | 45 | 32 | 8 | 23 |
| QATAR | | 61 | | 14 | |
| SAUDI ARABIA KINGDOM OF | 2 | 60 | | 14 | |
| SINGAPORE | 1 | 2 | 7 | 7 | 6 |
| SRI LANKA | 27 | 53 | 59 | 20 | 34 |
| SYRIA | 17 | 47 | 11 | 14 | 5 |
| THAILAND | 26 | 75 | 56 | 6 | 40 |
| TURKEY | 23 | 53 | 54 | 4 | 29 |
| UNITED ARAB EMIRATES | 1 | 61 | | 9 | 1 |
| VIET NAM | | 70 | 26 | 31 | 8 |
| YEMEN ARAB REPUBLIC | 30 | 74 | 10 | 31 | |
| YEMEN DEMOCRATIC | | 58 | 1 | 38 | 2 |
| | | | | | |
| ALBANIA | | 60 | | | |
| ANDORRA | | 22 | | | |
| AUSTRIA | 4 | 9 | 5 | 8 | 3 |
| BELGIUM-LUXEMBOURG | 6 | 3 | 11 | 12 | 10 |
| BULGARIA | 19 | 32 | 11 | 7 | 11 |
| CZECHOSLOVAKIA | 7 | 10 | 4 | 13 | 4 |
| DENMARK | 16 | 7 | 32 | 13 | 29 |
| FAEROE ISLANDS | | 5 | 4 | 13 | 3 |
| FINLAND | 8 | 13 | 6 | 7 | 6 |
| FRANCE | 47 | 8 | 18 | 11 | 15 |
| GERMAN DEMOCRATIC REP. | | 9 | 3 | 11 | 3 |
| GERMANY, FED. REP. OF | | 4 | 6 | 14 | 6 |
| GIBRALTAR | | 21 | | | |
| GREECE | 16 | 36 | 30 | 13 | 15 |

ANNEX TABLE 11. THE IMPORTANCE OF AGRICULTURE IN THE ECONOMY

| COUNTRY | AGRICULTURAL GDP AS % TOTAL GDP 1979 | AGRIC. POPULATION AS % TOTAL POPULATION 1981 | AGRIC. EXPORTS AS % TOTAL EXPORTS 1981 | AGRIC. IMPORTS AS % TOTAL IMPORTS 1981 | SHARE OF TOTAL IMPORTS FINANCED BY AGR. EXPORTS % 1981 |
|---|---|---|---|---|---|
| HUNGARY | 13 | 17 | 26 | 11 | 25 |
| ICELAND | | 11 | 3 | 10 | 3 |
| IRELAND | 7 | 20 | 33 | 14 | 25 |
| ITALY | 7 | 11 | 8 | 14 | 6 |
| LIECHTENSTEIN | | 4 | | | |
| MALTA | 4 | 5 | 6 | 19 | 3 |
| MONACO | | 4 | | | |
| NETHERLANDS | 4 | 5 | 23 | 16 | 24 |
| NORWAY | 5 | 7 | 2 | 7 | 2 |
| POLAND | 16 | 30 | 6 | 21 | 5 |
| PORTUGAL | 14 | 26 | 10 | 18 | 4 |
| ROMANIA | | 46 | 10 | 11 | 10 |
| SAN MARINO | | 24 | | | |
| SPAIN | 8 | 16 | 17 | 12 | 11 |
| SWEDEN | 3 | 5 | 3 | 7 | 3 |
| SWITZERLAND | | 5 | 3 | 10 | 3 |
| UNITED KINGDOM | 2 | 2 | 7 | 12 | 7 |
| YUGOSLAVIA | 13 | 36 | 8 | 7 | 6 |
| | | | | | |
| AMERICAN SAMOA | | 56 | 6 | 25 | 8 |
| AUSTRALIA | | 6 | 42 | 4 | 43 |
| CHRISTMAS ISLAND (AUST.) | | 50 | | | |
| COCOS (KEELING) ISLANDS | | 100 | | | |
| COOK ISLANDS | | 58 | 60 | 22 | 9 |
| FIJI | 22 | 39 | 58 | 13 | 29 |
| FRENCH POLYNESIA | | 55 | 19 | 20 | 1 |
| GUAM | | 56 | | 6 | |
| JOHNSTON ISLAND | | 100 | | | |
| KIRIBATI | | 56 | 6 | 33 | 8 |
| MIDWAY ISLANDS | | 50 | | | |
| NAURU | | 57 | | 24 | |
| NEW CALEDONIA | | 60 | 1 | 20 | 1 |
| NEW ZEALAND | 13 | 9 | 64 | 6 | 65 |
| NIUE | | 50 | 20 | 23 | 2 |
| NORFOLK ISLAND | | 50 | | | |
| PACIFIC IS. (TRUST TR.) | | 56 | 38 | 22 | 18 |
| PAPUA NEW GUINEA | 34 | 82 | 29 | 18 | 24 |
| SAMOA | | 56 | 46 | 19 | 13 |
| SOLOMON ISLANDS | | 60 | 27 | 11 | 27 |
| TOKELAU | | 50 | | | |
| TONGA | | 56 | 68 | 36 | 18 |
| TUVALU | | 50 | | 48 | |
| VANUATU | | 60 | 54 | 13 | 30 |
| WAKE ISLAND | | 100 | | | |
| WALLIS AND FUTUNA IS. | | 60 | | | |
| | | | | | |
| USSR | 16 | 16 | 4 | 29 | 4 |

ANNEX TABLE 12A. RESOURCES AND THEIR USE IN AGRICULTURE

| COUNTRY | ARABLE LAND AS % OF TOTAL LAND 1980 | IRRIGATED LAND AS % OF ARABLE LAND 1980 | FOREST LAND AS % OF TOTAL LAND 1980 | AGRIC.POPULATION PER HA OF ARABLE LAND 1980 | AGRIC.LAB.FORCE AS % OF AGRIC.POPULATION 1981 |
|---|---|---|---|---|---|
| ALGERIA | 3 | 5 | 2 | 1.2 | 22 |
| ANGOLA | 3 | | 43 | 1.2 | 26 |
| BENIN | 16 | 1 | 36 | .9 | 46 |
| BOTSWANA | 2 | | 2 | .5 | 46 |
| BURUNDI | 51 | | 2 | 2.7 | 47 |
| CAMEROON | 15 | | 55 | 1.0 | 46 |
| CAPE VERDE | 10 | 5 | | 4.6 | 32 |
| CENTRAL AFRICAN REPUBLIC | 3 | | 64 | 1.0 | 54 |
| CHAD | 3 | | 16 | 1.2 | 38 |
| COMOROS | 42 | | 16 | 2.5 | 36 |
| CONGO | 2 | | 63 | .8 | 34 |
| DJIBOUTI | | | | 152.0 | 31 |
| EGYPT | 3 | 100 | | 7.4 | 28 |
| EQUATORIAL GUINEA | 8 | | 61 | 1.2 | 29 |
| ETHIOPIA | 13 | | 24 | 1.8 | 41 |
| GABON | 2 | | 78 | .9 | 47 |
| GAMBIA | 27 | 12 | 22 | 1.7 | 49 |
| GHANA | 12 | 1 | 38 | 2.2 | 37 |
| GUINEA | 6 | 1 | 43 | 2.6 | 44 |
| GUINEA-BISSAU | 10 | | 38 | 1.7 | 30 |
| IVORY COAST | 12 | 1 | 31 | 1.6 | 50 |
| KENYA | 4 | 2 | 4 | 5.6 | 38 |
| LESOTHO | 10 | | | 3.8 | 52 |
| LIBERIA | 4 | 1 | 39 | 3.7 | 36 |
| LIBYA | 1 | 11 | | .2 | 25 |
| MADAGASCAR | 5 | 16 | 23 | 2.4 | 48 |
| MALAWI | 25 | | 48 | 2.2 | 44 |
| MALI | 2 | 5 | 7 | 2.9 | 53 |
| MAURITANIA | | 5 | 15 | 6.9 | 30 |
| MAURITIUS | 58 | 15 | 31 | 2.5 | 36 |
| MOROCCO | 17 | 7 | 12 | 1.3 | 26 |
| MOZAMBIQUE | 4 | 2 | 20 | 2.2 | 37 |
| NAMIBIA | 1 | 1 | 13 | .7 | 32 |
| NIGER | 3 | 1 | 2 | 1.4 | 31 |
| NIGERIA | 33 | | 16 | 1.4 | 37 |
| REUNION | 21 | 10 | 41 | 2.8 | 30 |
| RWANDA | 39 | | 11 | 4.4 | 52 |
| ST. HELENA | 6 | | 3 | | |
| SAO TOME AND PRINCIPE | 38 | | | 1.3 | 24 |
| SENEGAL | 27 | 3 | 28 | .8 | 41 |
| SEYCHELLES | 19 | | 19 | 6.4 | 31 |
| SIERRA LEONE | 25 | | 29 | 1.3 | 37 |
| SOMALIA | 2 | 15 | 14 | 3.5 | 38 |
| SOUTH AFRICA | 11 | 8 | 4 | .6 | 36 |
| SPANISH NORTH AFRICA | | | | | 34 |
| SUDAN | 5 | 14 | 21 | 1.1 | 31 |
| SWAZILAND | 12 | 15 | 6 | 2.0 | 45 |
| TANZANIA | 6 | 1 | 48 | 2.8 | 41 |
| TOGO | 26 | 1 | 31 | 1.3 | 41 |
| TUNISIA | 30 | 3 | 3 | .5 | 24 |
| UGANDA | 28 | | 30 | 1.9 | 41 |
| UPPER VOLTA | 9 | | 26 | 2.2 | 53 |
| WESTERN SAHARA | | | | 27.0 | 24 |
| ZAIRE | 3 | | 78 | 3.3 | 42 |
| ZAMBIA | 7 | | 28 | .8 | 36 |
| ZIMBABWE | 7 | 4 | 62 | 1.7 | 33 |
| | | | | | |
| ANTIGUA AND BARBUDA | 18 | | 16 | .9 | 43 |
| BAHAMAS | 2 | | 32 | 1.4 | 36 |
| BARBADOS | 77 | | | 1.3 | 42 |
| BELIZE | 2 | 2 | 44 | .9 | 30 |
| BERMUDA | | | 20 | | 50 |
| BRITISH VIRGIN ISLANDS | 20 | | 7 | .3 | |
| CANADA | 5 | 1 | 35 | | 43 |
| CAYMAN ISLANDS | | | 23 | | 50 |
| COSTA RICA | 10 | 5 | 36 | 1.6 | 34 |
| CUBA | 28 | 30 | 17 | .7 | 31 |
| DOMINICA | 23 | | 41 | 1.6 | 32 |
| DOMINICAN REPUBLIC | 25 | 12 | 13 | 2.7 | 26 |
| EL SALVADOR | 35 | 15 | 7 | 3.4 | 31 |
| GREENLAND | | | | | 67 |
| GRENADA | 41 | | 9 | 2.7 | 32 |
| GUADELOUPE | 28 | 4 | 40 | 1.1 | 37 |
| GUATEMALA | 17 | 4 | 42 | 2.2 | 30 |
| HAITI | 32 | 8 | 4 | 4.3 | 50 |
| HONDURAS | 16 | 5 | 36 | 1.3 | 29 |
| JAMAICA | 24 | 12 | 28 | 1.7 | 35 |
| MARTINIQUE | 25 | 19 | 26 | 1.9 | 36 |
| MEXICO | 12 | 22 | 25 | 1.1 | 29 |
| MONTSERRAT | 10 | | 40 | 1.0 | |
| NETHERLANDS ANTILLES | 8 | | | 2.9 | 39 |
| NICARAGUA | 13 | | 38 | .8 | 30 |
| PANAMA | 8 | 5 | 55 | 1.2 | 34 |
| PUERTO RICO | 16 | 28 | 20 | .9 | 33 |

ANNEX TABLE 12A. RESOURCES AND THEIR USE IN AGRICULTURE

| COUNTRY | ARABLE LAND AS % OF TOTAL LAND 1980 | IRRIGATED LAND AS % OF ARABLE LAND 1980 | FOREST LAND AS % OF TOTAL LAND 1980 | AGRIC.POPULATION PER HA OF ARABLE LAND 1980 | AGRIC.LAB.FORCE AS % OF AGRIC.POPULATION 1981 |
|---|---|---|---|---|---|
| ST.KITTS-NEVIS | 39 | | 17 | .5 | 29 |
| ST. LUCIA | 28 | 6 | 18 | 2.4 | 33 |
| ST.PIERRE AND MIQUELON | 13 | | 4 | | |
| ST. VINCENT | 50 | 6 | 41 | 1.9 | 30 |
| TRINIDAD AND TOBAGO | 31 | 13 | 45 | 1.2 | 39 |
| TURKS AND CAICOS IS. | 2 | | | 1.0 | |
| UNITED STATES | 21 | 11 | 31 | | 46 |
| US VIRGIN ISLANDS | 21 | | 6 | 1.4 | 40 |
| | | | | | |
| ARGENTINA | 13 | 4 | 22 | .1 | 38 |
| BOLIVIA | 3 | 4 | 52 | .8 | 33 |
| BRAZIL | 7 | 3 | 68 | .8 | 31 |
| CHILE | 7 | 23 | 21 | .4 | 33 |
| COLOMBIA | 5 | 5 | 51 | 1.2 | 30 |
| ECUADOR | 9 | 20 | 53 | 1.4 | 32 |
| FRENCH GUIANA | | | 82 | 3.3 | 38 |
| GUYANA | 2 | 33 | 92 | .5 | 33 |
| PARAGUAY | 5 | 3 | 52 | .8 | 32 |
| PERU | 3 | 35 | 55 | 2.1 | 28 |
| SURINAME | | 65 | 96 | 1.3 | 25 |
| URUGUAY | 11 | 4 | 3 | .2 | 39 |
| VENEZUELA | 4 | 8 | 40 | .7 | 31 |
| | | | | | |
| AFGHANISTAN | 12 | 33 | 3 | 1.5 | 33 |
| BAHRAIN | 3 | 50 | | 96.5 | 25 |
| BANGLADESH | 68 | 18 | 16 | 8.1 | 34 |
| BHUTAN | 2 | | 69 | 13.0 | 48 |
| BRUNEI | 2 | | 79 | 2.1 | 26 |
| BURMA | 15 | 10 | 49 | 1.8 | 40 |
| CHINA | 11 | 46 | 13 | 5.9 | 46 |
| CYPRUS | 47 | 22 | 19 | .5 | 44 |
| EAST TIMOR | 5 | | 74 | 5.6 | 30 |
| GAZA STRIP (PALESTINE) | | | | | 29 |
| HONG KONG | 7 | 57 | 13 | 18.4 | 47 |
| INDIA | 57 | 23 | 23 | 2.6 | 38 |
| INDONESIA | 11 | 28 | 67 | 4.5 | 34 |
| IRAN | 10 | 37 | 11 | .9 | 28 |
| IRAQ | 13 | 32 | 3 | 1.0 | 25 |
| ISRAEL | 20 | 49 | 6 | .6 | 36 |
| JAPAN | 13 | 67 | 67 | 2.6 | 52 |
| JORDAN | 14 | 6 | 1 | .6 | 24 |
| KAMPUCHEA,DEMOCRATIC | 17 | 3 | 76 | 1.6 | 38 |
| KOREA DPR | 19 | 47 | 74 | 3.7 | 45 |
| KOREA REP | 22 | 52 | 67 | 6.8 | 38 |
| KUWAIT | | 100 | | 23.0 | 25 |
| LAOS | 4 | 13 | 56 | 3.1 | 47 |
| LEBANON | 34 | 24 | 7 | .8 | 26 |
| MACAU | | | | | 33 |
| MALAYSIA | 13 | 9 | 68 | 1.5 | 35 |
| MALDIVES | 10 | | 3 | 41.0 | 43 |
| MONGOLIA | 1 | 3 | 10 | .7 | 37 |
| NEPAL | 17 | 10 | 33 | 5.7 | 47 |
| OMAN | | 93 | | 13.4 | 26 |
| PAKISTAN | 26 | 70 | 4 | 2.3 | 27 |
| PHILIPPINES | 33 | 13 | 41 | 2.3 | 35 |
| QATAR | | | | 73.0 | 26 |
| SAUDI ARABIA KINGDOM OF | 1 | 36 | 1 | 4.9 | 26 |
| SINGAPORE | 14 | | 5 | 6.5 | 39 |
| SRI LANKA | 33 | 24 | 37 | 3.7 | 35 |
| SYRIA | 31 | 9 | 3 | .8 | 26 |
| THAILAND | 35 | 15 | 31 | 2.0 | 45 |
| TURKEY | 37 | 7 | 26 | .9 | 41 |
| UNITED ARAB EMIRATES | | 38 | | 49.5 | 26 |
| VIET NAM | 19 | 28 | 32 | 6.3 | 45 |
| YEMEN ARAB REPUBLIC | 14 | 9 | 8 | 1.6 | 28 |
| YEMEN DEMOCRATIC | 1 | 34 | 7 | 5.3 | 26 |
| | | | | | |
| ALBANIA | 27 | 51 | 45 | 2.2 | 43 |
| ANDORRA | 2 | | 22 | 7.0 | 43 |
| AUSTRIA | 20 | | 40 | .4 | 45 |
| BELGIUM-LUXEMBOURG | 27 | | 21 | .4 | 39 |
| BULGARIA | 38 | 29 | 35 | .7 | 52 |
| CZECHOSLOVAKIA | 41 | 2 | 36 | .3 | 50 |
| DENMARK | 63 | 15 | 12 | .1 | 48 |
| FAEROE ISLANDS | 2 | | | .7 | 50 |
| FINLAND | 8 | 3 | 76 | .3 | 46 |
| FRANCE | 34 | 6 | 27 | .2 | 43 |
| GERMAN DEMOCRATIC REP. | 47 | 3 | 28 | .3 | 53 |
| GERMANY, FED. REP. OF | 31 | 4 | 30 | .3 | 47 |
| GIBRALTAR | | | | | 33 |
| GREECE | 30 | 24 | 20 | .9 | 42 |
| HUNGARY | 58 | 5 | 17 | .4 | 44 |

ANNEX TABLE 12A. RESOURCES AND THEIR USE IN AGRICULTURE

| COUNTRY | ARABLE LAND AS % OF TOTAL LAND 1980 | IRRIGATED LAND AS % OF ARABLE LAND 1980 | FOREST LAND AS % OF TOTAL LAND 1980 | AGRIC. POPULATION PER HA OF ARABLE LAND 1980 | AGRIC. LAB. FORCE AS % OF AGRIC. POPULATION 1981 |
|---|---|---|---|---|---|
| ICELAND | | | 1 | 3.4 | 42 |
| IRELAND | 14 | | 5 | .7 | 38 |
| ITALY | 42 | 23 | 22 | .5 | 37 |
| LIECHTENSTEIN | 25 | | 19 | .3 | |
| MALTA | 44 | 7 | | 1.2 | 35 |
| NETHERLANDS | 25 | 32 | 9 | .9 | 39 |
| NORWAY | 3 | 9 | 27 | .4 | 38 |
| POLAND | 49 | 1 | 29 | .7 | 56 |
| PORTUGAL | 39 | 18 | 40 | .7 | 39 |
| ROMANIA | 46 | 22 | 28 | 1.0 | 55 |
| SAN MARINO | 17 | | | 5.0 | 40 |
| SPAIN | 41 | 15 | 31 | .3 | 36 |
| SWEDEN | 7 | 2 | 64 | .2 | 39 |
| SWITZERLAND | 10 | 6 | 26 | .8 | 50 |
| UNITED KINGDOM | 29 | 2 | 9 | .2 | 46 |
| YUGOSLAVIA | 31 | 2 | 36 | 1.1 | 46 |
| | | | | | |
| AMERICAN SAMOA | 40 | | 50 | 2.3 | 33 |
| AUSTRALIA | 6 | 3 | 14 | | 43 |
| CHRISTMAS ISLAND (AUST.) | | | | | 50 |
| COOK ISLANDS | 26 | | | 1.8 | 27 |
| FIJI | 13 | | 65 | 1.1 | 34 |
| FRENCH POLYNESIA | 20 | | 31 | 1.1 | 33 |
| GUAM | 22 | | 18 | 4.8 | 36 |
| KIRIBATI | 51 | | 3 | .9 | 36 |
| NAURU | | | | | 25 |
| NEW CALEDONIA | 1 | | 51 | 8.6 | 38 |
| NEW ZEALAND | 2 | 37 | 26 | .6 | 40 |
| NIUE | 65 | | 23 | .1 | 50 |
| PACIFIC IS. (TRUST TR.) | 33 | | 22 | 1.3 | 36 |
| PAPUA NEW GUINEA | 1 | | 71 | 7.1 | 49 |
| SAMOA | 43 | | 47 | .7 | 33 |
| SOLOMON ISLANDS | 2 | | 93 | 2.7 | 38 |
| TONGA | 79 | | 12 | 1.0 | 33 |
| TUVALU | | | | | 50 |
| VANUATU | 6 | | 1 | .8 | 38 |
| WALLIS AND FUTUNA IS. | 25 | | | 1.2 | 33 |
| | | | | | |
| USSR | 10 | 8 | 41 | .2 | 50 |

ANNEX TABLE 12B. RESOURCES AND THEIR USE IN AGRICULTURE

| COUNTRY | AGRICULTURAL GFCF $ PER HA ARABLE LAND 1979 | AGRICULTURAL GFCF $ PER CAPUT OF AGRIC.LAB.FORCE 1979 | FERTILIZER USE PER HA ARAB.LAND KG/HA 1980 | NOS. OF TRACTORS PER 000 HA ARABLE LAND 1980 | OFFICIAL COMMITM. TO AGRICULTURE $ PER CAPUT 1981 |
|---|---|---|---|---|---|
| ALGERIA | | | 32 | 6 | |
| ANGOLA | | | 5 | 3 | 1.9 |
| BENIN | | | 2 | | 12.8 |
| BOTSWANA | | | 1 | 2 | 18.4 |
| BURUNDI | | | 1 | | 15.3 |
| CAMEROON | | | 5 | | 9.7 |
| CAPE VERDE | | | 3 | 1 | 37.7 |
| CENTRAL AFRICAN REPUBLIC | | | | | 3.0 |
| CHAD | | | | | 2.9 |
| CONGO | | | 1 | 1 | |
| DJIBOUTI | | | 1900 | 48 | .6 |
| EGYPT | 134.1 | 65.5 | 232 | 9 | 5.8 |
| ETHIOPIA | | | 4 | | 2.4 |
| GABON | | | | 3 | 34.6 |
| GAMBIA | | | 12 | | 11.3 |
| GHANA | | | 4 | 1 | 1.4 |
| GUINEA | | | | | 2.8 |
| GUINEA-BISSAU | | | 1 | | 25.9 |
| IVORY COAST | | | 14 | 1 | 11.5 |
| KENYA | 49.6 | 24.1 | 26 | 3 | 6.7 |
| LESOTHO | | | 15 | 2 | 8.3 |
| LIBERIA | | | 9 | 1 | 5.8 |
| LIBYA | | | 37 | 7 | |
| MADAGASCAR | | | 3 | 1 | 8.9 |
| MALAWI | | | 11 | 1 | 3.2 |
| MALI | | | 6 | | 9.9 |
| MAURITANIA | | | 11 | 1 | 22.7 |
| MAURITIUS | 230.8 | 257.3 | 249 | 3 | 3.7 |
| MOROCCO | | | 34 | 3 | 2.5 |
| MOZAMBIQUE | | | 9 | 2 | 7.8 |
| NAMIBIA | | | | 4 | |
| NIGER | | | 1 | | 6.4 |
| NIGERIA | | | 6 | | 5.1 |
| REUNION | | | 206 | 23 | |
| RWANDA | | | | | 14.4 |
| ST. HELENA | | | | 3 | |
| SAO TOME AND PRINCIPE | | | | 3 | 36.0 |
| SENEGAL | | | 4 | | 28.4 |
| SEYCHELLES | | | | 6 | |
| SIERRA LEONE | | | 1 | | 11.4 |
| SOMALIA | | | | 2 | 16.9 |
| SOUTH AFRICA | 60.6 | 275.2 | 78 | 13 | |
| SUDAN | | | 6 | 1 | 8.1 |
| SWAZILAND | | | 71 | 13 | 15.3 |
| TANZANIA | | | 7 | 4 | 12.1 |
| TOGO | | | 3 | | 8.9 |
| TUNISIA | | | 13 | 7 | 29.3 |
| UGANDA | | | | | 4.2 |
| UPPER VOLTA | | | 4 | | 8.5 |
| WESTERN SAHARA | | | | 6 | |
| ZAIRE | | | 1 | | 2.3 |
| ZAMBIA | | | 16 | 1 | 14.4 |
| ZIMBABWE | 24.3 | 44.2 | 65 | 8 | 2.9 |
| | | | | | |
| ANTIGUA AND BARBUDA | | | | 29 | |
| BAHAMAS | | | 75 | 5 | 2.0 |
| BARBADOS | | | 176 | 17 | 25.2 |
| BELIZE | | | 31 | 25 | 1.8 |
| BRITISH VIRGIN ISLANDS | | | | 1 | |
| CANADA | 89.0 | 7336.2 | 43 | 15 | |
| COSTA RICA | 158.4 | 300.8 | 150 | 12 | 1.0 |
| CUBA | | | 165 | 21 | |
| DOMINICA | | | 176 | 5 | 39.3 |
| DOMINICAN REPUBLIC | | | 42 | 3 | 7.3 |
| EL SALVADOR | | | 89 | 5 | 8.2 |
| GRENADA | | | | 2 | 68.8 |
| GUADELOUPE | | | 73 | 19 | |
| GUATEMALA | 41.7 | 64.1 | 51 | 2 | 5.0 |
| HAITI | | | | 1 | 3.6 |
| HONDURAS | | | 14 | 2 | 15.7 |
| JAMAICA | | | 66 | 11 | 8.3 |
| MARTINIQUE | | | 335 | 33 | |
| MEXICO | | | 52 | 5 | 10.3 |
| MONTSERRAT | | | | 13 | |
| NETHERLANDS ANTILLES | | | | 15 | |
| NICARAGUA | | | 36 | 1 | 6.2 |
| PANAMA | | | 53 | 7 | 29.8 |
| PUERTO RICO | | | | 26 | |
| ST.KITTS-NEVIS | | | 150 | 15 | |
| ST. LUCIA | | | 282 | 2 | |
| ST. VINCENT | | | 229 | 4 | |
| TRINIDAD AND TOBAGO | | | 51 | 15 | |
| UNITED STATES | 99.5 | 8254.1 | 112 | 25 | |
| US VIRGIN ISLANDS | | | 157 | 46 | |

ANNEX TABLE 12B. RESOURCES AND THEIR USE IN AGRICULTURE

| COUNTRY | AGRICULTURAL GFCF $ PER HA ARABLE LAND 1979 | AGRICULTURAL GFCF $ PER CAPUT OF AGRIC.LAB.FORCE 1979 | FERTILIZER USE PER HA ARAB.LAND KG/HA 1980 | NOS. OF TRACTORS PER 000 HA ARABLE LAND 1980 | OFFICIAL COMMITM. TO AGRICULTURE $ PER CAPUT 1981 |
|---|---|---|---|---|---|
| ARGENTINA | | | 3 | 5 | 8.0 |
| BOLIVIA | | | 2 | | .9 |
| BRAZIL | | | 68 | 5 | 3.3 |
| CHILE | | | 21 | 6 | 1.8 |
| COLOMBIA | | | 54 | 5 | 3.9 |
| ECUADOR | | | 28 | 2 | 10.0 |
| FRENCH GUIANA | | | 25 | 20 | |
| GUYANA | | | 41 | 9 | 42.7 |
| PARAGUAY | | | 3 | 2 | 26.9 |
| PERU | | | 32 | 4 | 8.9 |
| SURINAME | | | 31 | 27 | 130.2 |
| URUGUAY | | | 42 | 15 | .6 |
| VENEZUELA | 98.0 | 428.8 | 64 | 10 | |
| | | | | | |
| AFGHANISTAN | | | 6 | | |
| BANGLADESH | | | 46 | | 5.1 |
| BHUTAN | | | 1 | | 2.7 |
| BRUNEI | | | | 3 | |
| BURMA | | | 10 | 1 | 3.8 |
| CHINA | | | 150 | 7 | |
| CYPRUS | 107.2 | 497.8 | 34 | 25 | 22.5 |
| EAST TIMOR | | | | 1 | |
| HONG KONG | | | | 1 | |
| INDIA | | | 31 | 2 | 1.9 |
| INDONESIA | | | 63 | 1 | 3.9 |
| IRAN | | | 36 | 4 | |
| IRAQ | | | 17 | 4 | |
| ISRAEL | 375.5 | 1598.8 | 199 | 65 | |
| JAPAN | | | 372 | 224 | |
| JORDAN | | | 10 | 3 | 20.7 |
| KAMPUCHEA,DEMOCRATIC | | | 3 | | |
| KOREA DPR | | | 326 | 13 | |
| KOREA REP | 617.5 | 241.6 | 376 | 1 | 1.3 |
| KUWAIT | | | 440 | 35 | |
| LAOS | | | 8 | 1 | 4.4 |
| LEBANON | | | 76 | 9 | .7 |
| MALAYSIA | | | 105 | 2 | 11.8 |
| MONGOLIA | | | 9 | 8 | |
| NEPAL | | | 10 | | 7.6 |
| OMAN | | | 79 | 2 | |
| PAKISTAN | | | 50 | 2 | 2.7 |
| PHILIPPINES | | | 34 | 2 | 4.8 |
| QATAR | | | 400 | | |
| SAUDI ARABIA KINGDOM OF | | | 35 | 1 | |
| SINGAPORE | | | 550 | 6 | |
| SRI LANKA | | | 77 | 11 | 20.6 |
| SYRIA | 36.2 | 194.2 | 22 | 5 | |
| THAILAND | | | 16 | 2 | 6.0 |
| TURKEY | | | 41 | 15 | 3.6 |
| UNITED ARAB EMIRATES | | | 269 | | .7 |
| VIET NAM | | | 41 | 4 | .9 |
| YEMEN ARAB REPUBLIC | | | 4 | 1 | 5.6 |
| YEMEN DEMOCRATIC | | | 10 | 6 | 7.0 |
| | | | | | |
| ALBANIA | | | 125 | 14 | |
| AUSTRIA | | | 249 | 191 | |
| BELGIUM-LUXEMBOURG | 646.6 | 4400.8 | 499 | 132 | |
| BULGARIA | | | 198 | 15 | |
| CZECHOSLOVAKIA | | | 335 | 26 | |
| DENMARK | | | 236 | 71 | |
| FINLAND | 384.5 | 2864.6 | 204 | 88 | |
| FRANCE | | | 301 | 81 | |
| GERMAN DEMOCRATIC REP. | | | 325 | 29 | |
| GERMANY, FED. REP. OF | 827.9 | 4991.6 | 471 | 195 | |
| GREECE | 127.1 | 330.4 | 134 | 36 | |
| HUNGARY | | | 262 | 10 | |
| ICELAND | | | 3648 | 1650 | |
| IRELAND | | | 618 | 144 | |
| ITALY | | | 170 | 86 | |
| LIECHTENSTEIN | | | | 102 | |
| MALTA | | | 115 | 29 | 1.2 |
| NETHERLANDS | | | 789 | 207 | |
| NORWAY | 1228.8 | 7982.4 | 299 | 160 | |
| POLAND | | | 236 | 42 | |
| PORTUGAL | | | 73 | 20 | 2.1 |
| ROMANIA | | | 117 | 14 | 10.5 |
| SPAIN | | | 81 | 26 | |
| SWEDEN | 362.6 | 5568.6 | 162 | 61 | |
| SWITZERLAND | | | 441 | 230 | |
| UNITED KINGDOM | 337.6 | 4357.7 | 294 | 73 | |
| YUGOSLAVIA | | | 105 | 53 | 11.4 |
| | | | | | |
| AMERICAN SAMOA | | | | 4 | |

ANNEX TABLE 12B. RESOURCES AND THEIR USE IN AGRICULTURE

| COUNTRY | AGRICULTURAL GFCF $ PER HA ARABLE LAND 1979 | AGRICULTURAL GFCF $ PER CAPUT OF AGRIC.LAB.FORCE 1979 | FERTILIZER USE PER HA ARAB.LAND KG/HA 1980 | NOS. OF TRACTORS PER 000 HA ARABLE LAND 1980 | OFFICIAL COMMITM. TO AGRICULTURE $ PER CAPUT 1981 |
|---|---|---|---|---|---|
| AUSTRALIA | | | 28 | 7 | |
| COOK ISLANDS | | | | 22 | |
| FIJI | | | 61 | 7 | 15.1 |
| FRENCH POLYNESIA | | | 10 | 2 | 20.0 |
| GUAM | | | | 7 | |
| NEW CALEDONIA | | | 160 | 100 | 42.4 |
| NEW ZEALAND | | | 1018 | 204 | |
| NIUE | | | | 1 | |
| PACIFIC IS. (TRUST TR.) | | | | 1 | |
| PAPUA NEW GUINEA | | | 15 | 4 | 5.5 |
| SAMOA | | | | | 108.9 |
| TONGA | | | | 1 | 96.0 |
| VANUATU | | | | 1 | |
| | | | | | |
| USSR | | | 81 | 11 | |

ANNEX TABLE 13. MEASURES OF OUTPUT AND PRODUCTIVITY IN AGRICULTURE

| COUNTRY | AGRICULTURAL GDP $ PER CAPUT AGRIC. POPULATION 1979 | AGRICULTURAL GDP GROWTH RATE 1970-78 % | INDEX OF FOOD PRODUC. PER CAPUT 1969-71=100 1979-81 | INDEX OF TOT. AGR. PRODUC. PER CAPUT 1969-71=100 1979-81 | PER CAPUT DIETARY ENERGY SUPPLIES AS % OF REQUIREM. 1980 | INDEX OF VALUE OF AGRIC. EXPORTS 1969-71=100 1979-81 |
|---|---|---|---|---|---|---|
| ALGERIA | 221 | 20.8 | 82 | 82 | 101 | 66 |
| ANGOLA | | 15.9 | 80 | 58 | 89 | 98 |
| BENIN | 247 | 13.4 | 96 | 95 | 101 | 143 |
| BOTSWANA | 155 | 18.4 | 65 | 65 | 101 | 429 |
| BURUNDI | 115 | 11.9 | 100 | 101 | 94 | 435 |
| CAMEROON | 244 | 20.9 | 101 | 100 | 105 | 373 |
| CAPE VERDE | | 32.5 | 88 | 88 | 121 | 212 |
| CENTRAL AFRICAN REPUBLIC | 123 | 17.8 | 102 | 99 | 96 | 202 |
| CHAD | | 18.3 | 96 | 93 | 74 | 317 |
| COMOROS | | 18.0 | 93 | 92 | 99 | 253 |
| CONGO | 328 | 10.0 | 82 | 82 | 98 | 133 |
| DJIBOUTI | | | | | | 210 |
| EGYPT | 185 | 18.4 | 90 | 88 | 118 | 115 |
| EQUATORIAL GUINEA | | 17.4 | | | | 118 |
| ETHIOPIA | 72 | 6.4 | 85 | 85 | 75 | 306 |
| GABON | 406 | 19.5 | 94 | 94 | 122 | 523 |
| GAMBIA | 154 | 30.9 | 67 | 67 | 95 | 169 |
| GHANA | | 24.8 | 74 | 74 | 87 | 245 |
| GUINEA | 158 | 18.3 | 87 | 87 | 83 | 155 |
| GUINEA-BISSAU | | 16.8 | 89 | 89 | 99 | 292 |
| IVORY COAST | 372 | 23.9 | 110 | 105 | 116 | 560 |
| KENYA | 74 | 18.4 | 84 | 93 | 89 | 387 |
| LESOTHO | 70 | 25.4 | 86 | 81 | 107 | 152 |
| LIBERIA | 245 | 1.0 | 95 | 90 | 109 | 342 |
| LIBYA | 940 | 21.6 | 141 | 139 | 147 | |
| MADAGASCAR | 140 | 17.1 | 94 | 94 | 109 | 307 |
| MALAWI | 102 | 6.9 | 96 | 103 | 92 | 444 |
| MALI | 87 | 2.3 | 88 | 92 | 83 | 510 |
| MAURITANIA | 97 | 2400.0 | 77 | 77 | 90 | 239 |
| MAURITIUS | 672 | 24.5 | 90 | 92 | 121 | 399 |
| MOROCCO | 213 | 11.8 | 81 | 81 | 109 | 217 |
| MOZAMBIQUE | 155 | 21.9 | 73 | 70 | 80 | 92 |
| NAMIBIA | | 27.2 | 83 | 83 | 96 | 173 |
| NIGER | 117 | 8.6 | 93 | 93 | 95 | 146 |
| NIGERIA | 369 | 21.1 | 91 | 91 | 100 | 151 |
| REUNION | | 30.4 | 106 | 104 | 130 | 252 |
| RWANDA | 115 | 17.8 | 104 | 107 | 95 | 587 |
| SAO TOME AND PRINCIPE | | 14.9 | 79 | 78 | 101 | 273 |
| SENEGAL | 157 | 27.9 | 76 | 76 | 100 | 185 |
| SEYCHELLES | | 17.8 | | | | 316 |
| SIERRA LEONE | 128 | 15.1 | 81 | 82 | 89 | 343 |
| SOMALIA | 194 | 9.2 | 64 | 64 | 92 | 486 |
| SOUTH AFRICA | 452 | 10.5 | 104 | 102 | 116 | 401 |
| SUDAN | 190 | 20.4 | 103 | 88 | 102 | 186 |
| SWAZILAND | | 19.8 | 105 | 111 | 108 | 584 |
| TANZANIA | 149 | 22.9 | 91 | 87 | 86 | 221 |
| TOGO | 159 | 8.2 | 91 | 90 | 93 | 217 |
| TUNISIA | 379 | 14.7 | 124 | 124 | 116 | 313 |
| UGANDA | 1106 | 25.6 | 86 | 71 | 79 | 147 |
| UPPER VOLTA | 81 | 8.1 | 94 | 96 | 85 | 367 |
| ZAIRE | 97 | 22.5 | 87 | 86 | 96 | 201 |
| ZAMBIA | 126 | 10.8 | 92 | 92 | 91 | 109 |
| ZIMBABWE | 110 | 11.3 | 92 | 98 | 81 | 353 |
| | | | | | | |
| ANTIGUA AND BARBUDA | | | 136 | 136 | 88 | |
| BAHAMAS | | | 85 | 85 | 98 | |
| BARBADOS | 1227 | 14.5 | 93 | 93 | 129 | 250 |
| BELIZE | | 7.2 | 110 | 110 | 119 | 633 |
| BRITISH VIRGIN ISLANDS | | 17.1 | | | | |
| CANADA | 7230 | 12.3 | 109 | 108 | 127 | 411 |
| COSTA RICA | 965 | 19.9 | 110 | 109 | 120 | 407 |
| CUBA | | | 106 | 105 | 120 | 677 |
| DOMINICA | | | 91 | 91 | 90 | 124 |
| DOMINICAN REPUBLIC | 312 | 14.6 | 99 | 101 | 96 | 322 |
| EL SALVADOR | 428 | 19.5 | 104 | 97 | 94 | 479 |
| GREENLAND | | | | | | 64 |
| GRENADA | | 14.4 | 99 | 99 | 87 | 323 |
| GUADELOUPE | | 19.3 | 83 | 82 | 115 | 241 |
| GUATEMALA | | 9.6 | 116 | 115 | 93 | 439 |
| HAITI | | 2.0 | 89 | 88 | 83 | 297 |
| HONDURAS | 266 | 11.3 | 80 | 88 | 96 | 423 |
| JAMAICA | 390 | 16.8 | 91 | 91 | 118 | 140 |
| MARTINIQUE | | 21.7 | 87 | 88 | 117 | 170 |
| MEXICO | 487 | 14.0 | 106 | 103 | 120 | 229 |
| NETHERLANDS ANTILLES | | | 46 | 46 | 108 | 8930 |
| NICARAGUA | 393 | 15.5 | 87 | 85 | 97 | 333 |
| PANAMA | 611 | 10.0 | 102 | 102 | 98 | 196 |
| PUERTO RICO | 2776 | 8.9 | 80 | 79 | | |
| ST. KITTS-NEVIS | | | | | | 413 |
| ST. LUCIA | | 13500.0 | 91 | 91 | 99 | 297 |
| ST. VINCENT | | 20.0 | 106 | 106 | 91 | 359 |
| TRINIDAD AND TOBAGO | 656 | 12.6 | 70 | 69 | 113 | 166 |
| UNITED STATES | 14406 | 8.6 | 116 | 115 | 139 | 576 |
| US VIRGIN ISLANDS | | | | | | 3 |

ANNEX TABLE 13.   MEASURES OF OUTPUT AND PRODUCTIVITY IN AGRICULTURE

| COUNTRY | AGRICULTURAL GDP $ PER CAPUT AGRIC. POPULATION 1979 | AGRICULTURAL GDP GROWTH RATE 1970-78 % | INDEX OF FOOD PRODUC. PER CAPUT 1969-71=100 1979-81 | INDEX OF TOT. AGR. PRODUC. PER CAPUT 1969-71=100 1979-81 | PER CAPUT DIETARY ENERGY SUPPLIES AS % OF REQUIREM. 1980 | INDEX OF VALUE OF AGRIC. EXPORTS 1969-71=100 1979-81 |
|---|---|---|---|---|---|---|
| ARGENTINA | 5886 | 10.3 | 116 | 115 | 128 | 422 |
| BOLIVIA | 314 | 21.7 | 102 | 103 | 87 | 505 |
| BRAZIL | 566 | 22.9 | 125 | 118 | 106 | 433 |
| CHILE | 711 | 8.0 | 97 | 97 | 114 | 1022 |
| COLOMBIA | 1023 | 19.0 | 122 | 120 | 109 | 453 |
| ECUADOR | 361 | 17.5 | 97 | 98 | 91 | 361 |
| FALKLAND IS. (MALVINAS) | | | | | | 414 |
| GUYANA | 539 | 22.0 | 91 | 91 | 110 | 270 |
| PARAGUAY | 710 | 20.5 | 111 | 114 | 126 | 602 |
| PERU | 206 | 6.4 | 84 | 84 | 93 | 174 |
| SURINAME | 1188 | 16.7 | 187 | 186 | 108 | 646 |
| URUGUAY | 2203 | 3.8 | 104 | 100 | 109 | 329 |
| VENEZUELA | 1009 | 17.5 | 104 | 101 | 107 | 156 |
| | | | | | | |
| AFGHANISTAN | 78 | 21.4 | 97 | 95 | 73 | 534 |
| BAHRAIN | | | | | | 46 |
| BANGLADESH | 83 | 9.5 | 93 | 92 | 88 | 98 |
| BHUTAN | | | 107 | 107 | 41 | 243 |
| BRUNEI | | | 130 | 128 | 119 | 154 |
| BURMA | 118 | 15.8 | 103 | 103 | 107 | 266 |
| CHINA | | | 116 | 117 | 107 | 302 |
| CYPRUS | 873 | 2.8 | 101 | 101 | 128 | 294 |
| GAZA STRIP (PALESTINE) | | | | | | 333 |
| HONG KONG | 1528 | 13.0 | 71 | 71 | 128 | 471 |
| INDIA | 97 | 6.3 | 103 | 103 | 86 | 370 |
| INDONESIA | 166 | 22.0 | 118 | 116 | 108 | 475 |
| IRAN | | 22.9 | 112 | 107 | 124 | 130 |
| IRAQ | 454 | 15.7 | 89 | 88 | 111 | 154 |
| ISRAEL | 3896 | 15.8 | 103 | 107 | 118 | 355 |
| JAPAN | 3372 | 17.2 | 91 | 90 | 124 | 174 |
| JORDAN | 176 | 11.7 | 75 | 75 | 96 | 756 |
| KAMPUCHEA, DEMOCRATIC | | 12.9 | 45 | 45 | 90 | 23 |
| KOREA DPR | | | 134 | 132 | 129 | 512 |
| KOREA REP | 817 | 23.2 | 126 | 125 | 127 | 635 |
| KUWAIT | 2818 | 31.1 | | | | 490 |
| LAOS | | | 110 | 109 | 89 | 508 |
| LEBANON | | 32.8 | 109 | 105 | 100 | 346 |
| MACAU | | | 64 | 64 | 106 | 423 |
| MALAYSIA | 787 | | 139 | 123 | 119 | 496 |
| MALDIVES | | | 92 | 92 | 83 | 229 |
| MONGOLIA | | | 92 | 91 | 111 | 256 |
| NEPAL | 79 | 7.8 | 84 | 84 | 88 | 81 |
| OMAN | 173 | 9.5 | | | | 6469 |
| PAKISTAN | 127 | 9.9 | 104 | 103 | 100 | 406 |
| PHILIPPINES | 337 | 16.6 | 122 | 124 | 103 | 374 |
| SAUDI ARABIA KINGDOM OF | 239 | 17.8 | 29 | 30 | 120 | 3212 |
| SINGAPORE | 2464 | 12.8 | 148 | 145 | 136 | 554 |
| SRI LANKA | 111 | 7.3 | 148 | 120 | 102 | 202 |
| SYRIA | 423 | 22.3 | 163 | 143 | 118 | 180 |
| THAILAND | 206 | 17.6 | 129 | 126 | 104 | 583 |
| TURKEY | 608 | 22.4 | 112 | 111 | 120 | 385 |
| UNITED ARAB EMIRATES | 282 | 29.9 | | | | 4226 |
| VIET NAM | | | 112 | 113 | 91 | 488 |
| YEMEN ARAB REPUBLIC | 156 | 14.2 | 96 | 97 | 93 | 39 |
| YEMEN DEMOCRATIC | | | 102 | 99 | 86 | 119 |
| | | | | | | |
| ALBANIA | | | 106 | 105 | 110 | 373 |
| AUSTRIA | 4053 | 13.2 | 113 | 113 | 135 | 488 |
| BELGIUM-LUXEMBOURG | 7910 | 9.6 | 109 | 109 | 154 | 567 |
| BULGARIA | 1283 | 15.6 | 116 | 115 | 146 | 245 |
| CZECHOSLOVAKIA | 1961 | 3.6 | 114 | 113 | 141 | 340 |
| DENMARK | 27855 | 15.1 | 111 | 112 | 133 | 390 |
| FINLAND | 4931 | 13.0 | 103 | 103 | 118 | 398 |
| FRANCE | 5496 | 9.7 | 117 | 117 | 134 | 538 |
| GERMAN DEMOCRATIC REP. | | 50.6 | 129 | 130 | 144 | 505 |
| GERMANY, FED. REP. OF | | 12.3 | 110 | 110 | 133 | 821 |
| GREECE | 1500 | 14.0 | 123 | 122 | 147 | 339 |
| HUNGARY | 1875 | 11.5 | 132 | 131 | 134 | 422 |
| ICELAND | | | 108 | 106 | 109 | 556 |
| IRELAND | 1601 | 14.2 | 116 | 115 | 148 | 490 |
| ITALY | 3292 | 10.0 | 112 | 112 | 148 | 459 |
| MALTA | 1778 | 10.8 | 113 | 113 | 124 | 165 |
| NETHERLANDS | 7855 | 14.6 | 115 | 116 | 131 | 478 |
| NORWAY | 7079 | 16.4 | 117 | 117 | 124 | 385 |
| POLAND | 898 | 1.6 | 96 | 96 | 134 | 193 |
| PORTUGAL | 980 | 14.9 | 74 | 74 | 128 | 302 |
| ROMANIA | | | 146 | 145 | 126 | 397 |
| SPAIN | 2277 | 14.0 | 125 | 125 | 136 | 479 |
| SWEDEN | 7117 | 13.5 | 117 | 117 | 119 | 331 |
| SWITZERLAND | | | 119 | 119 | 132 | 295 |
| UNITED KINGDOM | 6853 | 8.8 | 122 | 122 | 132 | 840 |
| YUGOSLAVIA | 930 | 15.6 | 117 | 116 | 140 | 258 |
| | | | | | | |
| AUSTRALIA | | 8.3 | 117 | 107 | 118 | 384 |

ANNEX TABLE 13. MEASURES OF OUTPUT AND PRODUCTIVITY IN AGRICULTURE

| COUNTRY | AGRICULTURAL GDP $ PER CAPUT AGRIC. POPULATION 1979 | AGRICULTURAL GDP GROWTH RATE 1970-78 ● % | INDEX OF FOOD PRODUC. PER CAPUT 1969-71=100 1979-81 | INDEX OF TOT. AGR. PRODUC. PER CAPUT 1969-71=100 1979-81 | PER CAPUT DIETARY ENERGY SUPPLIES AS % OF REQUIREM. 1980 | INDEX OF VALUE OF AGRIC. EXPORTS 1969-71=100 1979-81 |
|---|---|---|---|---|---|---|
| COCOS (KEELING) ISLANDS | | | | | | 250 |
| COOK ISLANDS | | | | | | 179 |
| FIJI | 787 | 28.6 | 104 | 105 | 109 | 391 |
| FRENCH POLYNESIA | | 16.8 | 87 | 87 | 100 | 208 |
| KIRIBATI | | 58.1 | | | | 202 |
| NEW CALEDONIA | | 3.0 | 83 | 80 | 94 | 115 |
| NEW ZEALAND | 9116 | 5.8 | 107 | 105 | 132 | 335 |
| NIUE | | | | | | 229 |
| PACIFIC IS. (TRUST TR.) | | | | | | 572 |
| PAPUA NEW GUINEA | 301 | 20.7 | 97 | 100 | 85 | 487 |
| SAMOA | | | 97 | 97 | 86 | 232 |
| SOLOMON ISLANDS | | | 125 | 125 | 81 | 574 |
| TONGA | | | 114 | 114 | 120 | 209 |
| VANUATU | | | 92 | 92 | 94 | 282 |
| | | | | | | |
| USSR | 2367 | 5.3 | 102 | 102 | 132 | 170 |

ANNEX TABLE 14.  CARRY-OVER STOCKS OF SELECTED AGRICULTURAL PRODUCTS

| Product | | | Crop year ending in | | | | | | | |
|---|---|---|---|---|---|---|---|---|---|---|
| Country | Date | 1976 | 1977 | 1978 | 1979 | 1980 | 1981 | 1982[a] | 1983[b] |
| | | ............... million metric tons ................ | | | | | | | |
| **CEREALS** | | | | | | | | | |
| Developed countries | | 100.8 | 146.6 | 146.2 | 176.8 | 156.2 | 133.9 | 177.3 | 227.2 |
| Canada | | 12.4 | 18.3 | 19.5 | 22.0 | 14.3 | 12.9 | 14.9 | 18.3 |
| United States | | 36.6 | 61.6 | 74.2 | 72.6 | 78.1 | 62.2 | 104.4 | 152.5 |
| Australia | | 3.4 | 2.8 | 1.6 | 5.7 | 5.0 | 2.7 | 3.1 | 1.0 |
| EEC | | 14.5 | 14.6 | 13.8 | 17.7 | 15.8 | 15.7 | 14.7 | 19.2 |
| Japan | | 5.8 | 7.2 | 8.8 | 9.9 | 10.6 | 8.8 | 7.4 | 6.0 |
| USSR | | 13.0 | 24.0 | 10.0 | 30.0 | 16.0 | 14.0 | 14.0 | 14.0 |
| Developing countries | | 88.6 | 101.3 | 94.7 | 99.2 | 101.2 | 101.6 | 100.7 | 104.3 |
| Far East | | 70.9 | 77.5 | 73.4 | 81.1 | 82.0 | 75.6 | 75.3 | 79.5 |
| Bangladesh | | 0.6 | 0.4 | 0.6 | 0.2 | 0.8 | 1.3 | 0.7 | 0.5 |
| China | | 39.3 | 43.0 | 39.0 | 46.0 | 53.0 | 45.5 | 43.0 | 44.0 |
| India | | 10.0 | 15.5 | 14.7 | 14.9 | 10.9 | 7.4 | 7.5 | 10.2 |
| Pakistan | | 1.0 | 0.6 | 0.6 | 0.7 | 1.1 | 1.5 | 2.3 | 2.5 |
| Near East | | 7.8 | 10.0 | 8.7 | 6.7 | 9.4 | 10.6 | 10.6 | 9.4 |
| Turkey | | 2.0 | 3.6 | 3.5 | 1.4 | 0.8 | 0.6 | 0.6 | 0.6 |
| Africa | | 3.2 | 4.4 | 4.9 | 3.9 | 2.9 | 3.6 | 4.8 | 4.4 |
| Latin America | | 6.7 | 9.4 | 7.7 | 7.5 | 6.8 | 11.8 | 10.0 | 11.0 |
| Argentina | | 2.2 | 3.2 | 1.7 | 2.3 | 1.5 | 1.0 | 1.3 | 2.3 |
| Brazil | | 1.4 | 2.1 | 2.1 | 0.7 | 1.3 | 3.8 | 2.6 | 3.5 |
| World Total of which: | | 189.4 | 247.9 | 240.0 | 276.0 | 257.4 | 235.5 | 277.9 | 331.6 |
| Wheat | | 77.3 | 116.2 | 97.8 | 117.8 | 105.0 | 97.6 | 102.8 | 121.7 |
| Rice (milled basis) | | 37.4 | 37.7 | 40.1 | 44.1 | 41.9 | 43.0 | 42.7 | 41.8 |
| Coarse grains | | 74.7 | 94.1 | 103.0 | 114.1 | 109.4 | 94.8 | 132.4 | 168.0 |
| **SUGAR (raw value)** | | | | | | | | | |
| World total | 1 Sept. | 20.5 | 24.8 | 30.3 | 31.4 | 26.3 | 24.5 | 32.0 | 38.0 |
| **COFFEE** | | | | | | | | | |
| Exporting countries[c] | | 1.58 | 1.85 | 1.93 | 1.76 | 1.86 | 1.86 | 2.55 | ... |
| | | ............... thousand metric tons ................. | | | | | | | |
| **DRIED SKIM MILK** | | | | | | | | | |
| United states | 31 Dec. | 220 | 308 | 265 | 220 | 266 | 420 | 606 | ... |
| EEC | 31 Dec. | 1243 | 1066 | 824 | 322 | 276 | 354 | 668 | ... |
| Total of above | | 1463 | 1374 | 1089 | 542 | 542 | 774 | 1274 | ... |

a/  Estimate. - b/ Forecast.  - c/ Excludes privately held stocks in Brazil.

ANNEX TABLE 15.   ANNUAL CHANGES IN CONSUMER PRICES:   ALL ITEMS AND FOOD

| Region and country | All items | | | | | | Food | | | | | |
|---|---|---|---|---|---|---|---|---|---|---|---|---|
| | 1960 to 1965 | 1965 to 1970 | 1970 to 1975 | 1978 to 1979 | 1979 to 1980 | 1980 to 1981 | 1960 to 1965 | 1965 to 1970 | 1970 to 1975 | 1978 to 1979 | 1979 to 1980 | 1980 to 1981 |
| | ...................... Percent per year............................ | | | | | | | | | | | |
| **Developed countries** | | | | | | | | | | | | |
| **WESTERN COUNTRIES** | | | | | | | | | | | | |
| Austria | 3.9 | 3.3[a/] | 7.4 | 3.6 | 6.3 | 6.8 | 4.4 | 2.1[a/] | 6.7 | 2.6 | 4.5 | 5.8 |
| Belgium | 2.5 | 3.5 | 8.3 | 4.5 | 6.7 | 7.6 | 2.9 | 3.5 | 7.5 | 0.5 | 3.6 | 6.0 |
| Denmark | 5.5 | 7.5 | 9.5 | 9.6 | 12.3 | 11.7 | 4.2 | 7.5 | 10.7 | ... | 10.1 | 11.6 |
| Finland | 5.3 | 4.6[b/] | 2.0 | 7.3 | 11.5 | 12.0 | 5.9 | 5.2[b/] | 12.4 | 3.3 | 12.9 | 13.1 |
| France | 3.8 | 4.3 | 8.8 | 10.5 | 13.3 | 13.1 | 4.3 | 3.8 | 9.6 | 8.3 | 8.8 | 12.7 |
| Germany, Fed. Rep. of | 2.8 | 2.4 | 6.2 | 4.1 | 5.5 | 5.9 | 2.6 | 1.3 | 5.6 | 1.7 | 4.7 | 4.9 |
| Greece | 1.6 | 2.5 | 13.1 | 19.0 | 24.9 | 24.4 | 2.5 | 2.6 | 14.7 | 18.8 | 27.5 | 30.1 |
| Iceland | 11.0 | 12.8 | 24.8 | 44.1 | 58.5 | 50.8 | 15.2 | 13.3 | 28.3 | 33.0 | 65.2 | 55.3 |
| Ireland | 4.2 | 5.3 | 13.0 | 13.2 | 18.2 | 20.4 | 3.9 | 4.3 | 14.3 | 14.8 | 10.7 | 15.0 |
| Italy | 4.9 | 3.0 | 11.4 | 14.8 | 21.2 | 19.5 | 4.6 | 2.2 | 11.6 | 13.2 | 15.6 | 18.1 |
| Netherlands | 3.5 | 4.8 | 8.6 | 4.3 | 6.4 | 6.7 | 4.0 | 4.3 | 6.9 | 2.1 | 4.4 | 5.6 |
| Norway | 4.1 | 5.0 | 8.3 | 4.8 | 10.9 | 13.6 | 4.5 | 5.3 | 8.3 | 4.3 | 8.8 | 16.6 |
| Portugal | 2.6 | 6.4 | 15.3 | 24.2 | 16.5 | 20.0 | 2.8 | 5.2 | 16.3 | 28.0 | 11.1 | 19.5 |
| Spain | 7.0 | 5.1 | 12.0 | 15.7 | 15.5 | 14.6 | 7.7 | 3.7 | 12.1 | 10.2 | 9.0 | 13.6 |
| Sweden | 3.6 | 4.5 | 7.8 | 7.2 | 13.7 | 12.5 | 5.3 | 4.5 | 7.9 | 5.3 | 11.5 | 15.0 |
| Switzerland | 3.2 | 3.4 | 7.9 | 3.6 | 4.0 | 6.5 | 2.9 | 0.9 | 7.3 | 3.7 | 7.0 | 10.4 |
| United Kingdom | 3.6 | 4.6 | 12.3 | 13.4 | 18.0 | 11.9 | 3.6 | 4.6 | 15.1 | 12.0 | 12.1 | 8.4 |
| Yugoslavia | 13.6 | 10.5 | 19.3 | 19.4 | 31.6 | 40.9 | 17.3 | 9.0 | 19.1 | 17.4 | 30.3 | 42.8 |
| **NORTH AMERICA** | | | | | | | | | | | | |
| Canada | 1.6 | 3.8 | 7.4 | 9.2 | 10.2 | 12.4 | 2.2 | 3.4 | 11.1 | 13.2 | 10.7 | 11.4 |
| United States | 1.3 | 4.2 | 6.7 | 11.5 | 13.5 | 10.2 | 1.4 | 4.0 | 9.5 | 10.9 | 8.7 | 7.7 |
| **OCEANIA** | | | | | | | | | | | | |
| Australia | 1.8 | 3.1 | 10.2 | 9.1 | 10.2 | 9.7 | 2.0 | 2.1 | 9.8 | 14.0 | 12.6 | 9.2 |
| New Zealand | 2.7 | 4.1 | 9.8 | 13.7 | 17.1 | 15.4 | 2.4 | 4.1 | 9.4 | 17.3 | 20.5 | 16.7 |
| **OTHER DEVELOPED COUNTRIES** | | | | | | | | | | | | |
| Israel | 7.1 | 4.0 | 23.9 | 83.4 | 131.0 | 117.0 | 5.6 | 3.1 | 25.1 | 78.3 | 154.0 | 199.0 |
| Japan | 6.0 | 5.4 | 12.0 | 3.6 | 8.0 | 4.9 | 7.2 | 6.1 | 13.0 | 2.2 | 6.0 | 5.3 |
| South Africa | 2.1 | 3.4 | 9.3 | 13.2 | 13.8 | 15.1 | 2.6 | 3.0 | 11.7 | 15.7 | 18.9 | 22.1 |

See notes at end of table

ANNEX TABLE 15.  ANNUAL CHANGES IN CONSUMER PRICES:  ALL ITEMS AND FOOD (continued)

| Region and country | All items | | | | | | Food | | | | | |
|---|---|---|---|---|---|---|---|---|---|---|---|---|
| | 1960 to 1965 | 1965 to 1970 | 1970 to 1975 | 1978 to 1979 | 1979 to 1980 | 1980 to 1981 | 1960 to 1965 | 1965 to 1970 | 1970 to 1975 | 1978 to 1979 | 1979 to 1980 | 1980 to 1981 |
| ...Percent per year... | | | | | | | | | | | | |

Developing countries

LATIN AMERICA

| | | | | | | | | | | | | |
|---|---|---|---|---|---|---|---|---|---|---|---|---|
| Argentina | 23.0 | 19.4 | 59.5 | 159.5 | 101.0 | 104.0 | 23.0 | 18.3 | 58.0 | 169.0 | 95.0 | 99.0 |
| Barbados | ... | ... | 18.6 | 13.2 | 14.2 | 14.6 | ... | ... | 21.0 | 11.1 | 12.0 | 14.9 |
| Bolivia | 5.1 | 5.9 | 23.7 | 19.7 | 47.2 | 32.1 | 2.1 | 7.8 | 27.2 c/ | 18.6 | 47.6 | 35.2 |
| Brazil | 60.0 | 28.0 | 23.5 c/ | 50.2 | 78.0 | 95.7 | 60.0 | 26.0 | 25.9 c/ | 56.9 | 83.2 | 92.5 |
| Chile | 27.0 | 26.0 | 225.4 | 33.4 | 35.1 | 19.7 | 30.0 | 26.0 | 245.5 | 31.0 | 36.1 | 14.2 |
| Colombia | 12.4 | 10.1 | 19.5 | 24.2 | 27.9 | 29.4 | 13.4 | 9.2 | 24.0 | 23.5 | 36.6 | 25.1 |
| Costa Rica | 2.3 | 2.5 | 13.7 | 9.2 | 18.1 | 37.0 | 2.2 | 3.8 | 3.7 | 12.6 | 21.7 | 36.7 |
| Dominican Republic | 2.7 | 1.0 | 11.1 | 9.2 | 16.7 | 7.5 | 2.5 | 0.1 | 13.3 | 14.5 | 15.4 | 0.4 |
| Ecuador | 4.0 | 4.6 | 13.7 | 10.3 | 13.0 | 16.4 | 4.9 | 6.0 | 18.4 | 10.0 | 11.0 | 14.2 |
| El Salvador | 0.2 | 1.1 | 8.4 | ... | 17.4 | 14.7 | 1.1 | 2.2 | 8.8 | ... | 19.3 | 17.6 |
| Guatemala | 0.1 | 1.5 | 2.9 | 11.4 | 10.7 | 11.4 | 0.1 | 1.7 | 3.3 | 10.2 | 11.2 | 11.2 |
| Guyana | 1.9 | 1.5 | 8.2 | 17.8 | 14.1 | 22.2 | 2.3 | 2.8 | 12.2 | 18.9 | 12.1 | 27.6 |
| Haiti | 3.7 | 1.7 | 13.7 | 13.0 | 17.8 | 13.8 | 4.1 | 1.8 | 15.5 | 15.6 | 26.6 | 14.2 |
| Honduras | 2.7 | 1.6 | 6.5 | 9.0 | 18.1 | 9.4 | 3.2 | 1.8 | 8.0 | 7.6 | 17.1 | 7.3 |
| Jamaica | 2.9 | 4.3 | 14.9 | 29.1 | 26.9 | ... | 2.4 | 4.7 | 17.2 | 33.2 | 33.7 | ... |
| Mexico | 1.9 | 3.5 | 12.4 | 18.1 | 26.3 | 28.0 | 1.6 | 3.8 | 13.9 | 18.2 | 25.0 | 26.1 |
| Panama | 1.1 d/ | 1.6 | 7.8 | 7.9 | 13.8 | 7.3 | 1.4 d/ | 1.7 | 9.9 | 10.2 | 12.6 | 9.1 |
| Paraguay | ... | 1.2 | 12.6 | 28.2 | 22.4 | 13.0 | ... | 0.3 | 15.4 | 29.4 | 19.3 | 6.4 |
| Peru | 9.4 | 7.8 e/ | 12.1 | 67.6 | 59.2 | 75.4 | 10.5 | 7.1 e/ | 13.9 | 74.2 | 58.8 | 76.4 |
| Puerto Rico | 2.2 | 3.2 | 8.8 | 6.5 | 10.3 | 9.8 | 3.0 | 4.1 | 12.6 | 7.2 | 9.9 | 9.2 |
| Suriname | ... | ... | 8.2 | 14.9 | 14.0 | 9.0 | ... | ... | 9.5 | 12.8 | 12.2 | 14.9 |
| Trinidad & Tobago | 2.2 f/ | 3.8 | 13.7 | 14.7 | 17.5 | 14.4 | 2.1 f/ | 3.7 | 17.1 | 13.8 | 19.4 | 16.5 |
| Uruguay | 16.2 f/ | 60.0 | 73.4 | 66.8 | 63.4 | 34.0 | 13.1 f/ | 60.0 | 76.0 | 70.9 | 57.9 | 25.6 |
| Venezuela | 1.7 | 1.6 | 5.5 | 12.3 | 23.1 | 14.7 | 1.7 | 0.9 | 8.5 | 16.7 | 33.0 | 18.6 |

FAR EAST

| | | | | | | | | | | | | |
|---|---|---|---|---|---|---|---|---|---|---|---|---|
| Afghanistan | ... | ... | ... | ... | 2.5 | 4.3 | ... | ... | ... | ... | 8.8 | ... |
| Bangladesh | ... | 4.0 b/ | 39.0 g/ | 12.7 | 13.2 | 13.2 | ... | 3.2 b/ | 42.0 g/ | 12.7 | 12.6 | 13.6 |
| Burma | ... | 6.4 b/ | 17.8 | 5.7 | 0.6 | 0.3 | ... | 2.9 b/ | 21.0 | 5.6 | 1.8 | -4.6 |
| Dem. Kampuchea | 4.3 | 4.5 | 100.9 | ... | ... | ... | 2.7 | 6.7 | 112.8 | ... | ... | ... |
| India | 6.1 | 8.9 h/ | 13.2 | 6.4 | 11.5 | 13.1 | 6.5 | 9.8 h/ | 14.2 | 4.6 | 12.1 | 14.5 |
| Indonesia | ... | 100.0 | 21.3 | ... | 18.1 | 12.2 | ... | 100.0 | 25.2 | ... | 14.8 | 14.7 |
| Korea, Rep. of | 15.4 | 12.3 | 14.3 | 18.3 | 28.7 | 23.3 | 18.3 | 12.5 | 16.8 | 13.8 | 26.6 | 29.1 |
| Lao, People's D.R. | 38.0 | 6.0 | 35.2 | ... | ... | ... | 39.0 | 4.0 | 40.9 | ... | ... | ... |
| Malaysia (peninsular) | 0.5 | 0.4 b/ | 6.7 | 3.6 | 6.7 | 9.6 | 0.6 | 0.4 b/ | 10.4 | 2.3 | 3.6 | 10.3 |
| Nepal | ... | 6.2 | 10.3 | 4.3 | 14.6 | 12.3 | ... | 7.2 | 9.8 | 5.7 | 16.5 | 12.0 |
| Pakistan | 2.6 | 5.6 | 15.2 | 9.4 | 11.7 | 13.8 | 3.8 | 6.0 | 16.6 | 7.1 | 10.0 | 15.2 |
| Philippines | 4.8 | 3.6 a/ | 18.7 | 16.5 | 17.6 | 12.3 | 6.8 | 5.2 a/ | 20.1 | 15.1 | 15.2 | 12.2 |
| Sri Lanka | 1.7 | 4.2 | 8.0 | 10.8 | 26.1 | 18.0 | 1.3 | 4.9 | 9.1 | 10.8 | 29.0 | 17.6 |
| Thailand | 1.5 | 2.5 | 9.8 | 10.3 | 19.9 | 13.4 | 2.0 | 4.2 | 11.9 | 9.2 | 18.7 | 10.5 |

See notes at end of table

ANNEX TABLE 15.   ANNUAL CHANGES IN CONSUMER PRICES:   ALL ITEMS AND FOOD (continued)

| Region and country | All items | | | | | | Food | | | | | |
|---|---|---|---|---|---|---|---|---|---|---|---|---|
| | 1960 to 1965 | 1965 to 1970 | 1970 to 1975 | 1978 to 1979 | 1979 to 1980 | 1980 to 1981 | 1960 to 1965 | 1965 to 1970 | 1970 to 1975 | 1978 to 1979 | 1979 to 1980 | 1980 to 1981 |
| | ...................................Percent per year............................... | | | | | | | | | | | |
| **AFRICA** | | | | | | | | | | | | |
| Algeria | ... | ... | 5.1 | 11.4 | 9.6 | | ... | ... | 7.2 | 13.5 | 10.8 | ... |
| Botswana | ... | ...[k/] | ... | 11.7 | 13.9 | 16.3 | ... | ...[k/] | ... | 11.0 | 18.2 | 22.3 |
| Cameroon | ... | 3.3[k/] | 10.2 | 6.6 | 9.9 | 10.2[i/] | ... | 4.6[k/] | 11.5 | 4.8 | 9.0 | 12.9[i/] |
| Ethiopia | ...[d/] | 3.0[e/] | 3.7 | 16.0 | 4.5 | 4.3[i/] | ...[d/] | 3.5[e/] | 2.7 | 18.0 | 5.2 | 3.4[i/] |
| Gabon | 4.4[d/] | 3.0 | 11.4 | 8.0 | 12.3 | 8.7 | 3.3[d/] | 2.1 | 2.7 | 9.6[i/] | ... | ... |
| Gambia | ... | ... | 10.5 | 6.1 | 6.7 | 6.1 | ... | ... | 12.8 | 5.8 | 5.2 | 5.3 |
| Ghana | 11.8 | 3.7 | 17.4 | 62.7 | 50.1 | 116.5 | 14.0 | 2.1 | 20.3 | 73.5 | 52.2 | 111.1 |
| Ivory Coast | 2.6 | 4.9 | 8.2[g/] | 16.7 | 14.9 | 8.5 | 2.8 | 5.9 | 9.3[g/] | 22.0 | 18.8 | 5.2 |
| Kenya | 2.0 | 1.7 | 13.9 | 7.2 | 11.6 | 13.8[m/] | 1.9 | 2.0 | 14.7 | 5.6 | 14.3 | 12.9[m/] |
| Liberia | ... | 4.4 | 12.1 | 11.4 | 13.8 | 6.5[m/] | ... | 3.4 | 13.7 | 11.6 | 9.0 | 3.8[m/] |
| Madagascar | ... | 2.3[b/] | 9.7 | 14.0 | 18.2 | 30.5 | ... | 2.2[b/] | 12.0 | 14.5 | 18.7 | 32.0 |
| Malawi | ...[d/] | 2.0[b/] | 8.9 | 11.3 | 18.3 | 9.5 | ...[d/] | 3.4[b/] | 10.7 | 13.9 | 24.7 | 11.1 |
| Mauritius | 1.0[d/] | 3.0 | 13.1[e/] | 14.5 | 41.9 | 12.5 | 0.6[d/] | 3.0 | 14.7[e/] | 14.4 | 51.2 | 14.5 |
| Morocco | 4.0[n/] | 0.6 | 5.4[e/] | 8.3 | 9.4 | 12.5 | 4.6[n/] | 0.1 | 7.2[e/] | 6.4 | 7.3 | 14.9 |
| Mozambique | 1.9[n/] | 3.7 | 10.5 | ... | ... | ... | 0.7[n/] | 4.7 | 11.1 | ... | ... | ... |
| Niger | ... | 3.8 | 7.9 | 7.3 | 10.3 | 22.9 | ... | 4.4 | 10.6 | 5.5 | 11.0 | 28.5 |
| Nigeria | 3.2 | 5.6 | 11.5 | 11.6 | 9.9 | 20.8 | 2.0 | 8.8 | 13.1 | 8.4 | 7.1 | 24.3 |
| Senegal | ...[p/] | ... | 13.0 | 9.5 | 8.7 | 5.8 | ...[p/] | ... | 16.5 | 8.3 | 9.8 | 0.8 |
| Sierra Leone | 3.9[p/] | 4.3[k/] | 8.4 | 21.3 | 11.0 | 23.2 | 0.6[p/] | 4.8[k/] | 11.0 | 23.5 | 9.1 | 23.6 |
| Somalia | 7.4 | 2.5[k/] | 7.5 | 24.0 | 58.7 | ... | 7.5 | 2.8[k/] | 9.1 | 22.4 | 76.6 | ... |
| Swaziland | ... | 2.7[b/] | 9.3 | 14.3 | 19.8 | 19.8 | ... | 2.5[b/] | 9.8 | 12.3 | 24.7 | 24.5 |
| Tanzania | 1.2 | 3.7[e/] | 13.1 | 13.6 | 30.2 | 25.6[i/] | 1.2 | 2.5[e/] | 17.7 | 12.3 | 27.2 | 23.5[i/] |
| Togo | ... | 2.1[e/] | 8.9 | 7.7 | 7.8 | 12.8[i/] | ... | 2.6[e/] | 9.7 | 6.9 | 6.9 | 13.1[i/] |
| Tunisia | 4.5 | 2.9 | 4.8 | 7.7 | 10.0 | 9.0 | 4.8 | 3.1 | 5.2 | 9.3 | 13.6 | 8.9 |
| Uganda | 5.4[n/] | 4.0 | 23.4 | ... | ... | ... | 7.3[n/] | 3.5 | 24.3 | ... | ... | ... |
| Zaire | 15.6[n/] | 23.0[h/] | 18.6 | ... | 41.4 | 35.4 | 19.0[n/] | 22.0[h/] | 21.2 | ... | 21.2 | 39.2 |
| Zambia | 2.4 | 8.7[h/] | 7.1 | 9.7 | 11.7 | 14.0 | 2.4 | 8.8[h/] | 7.4 | 8.9 | 14.4 | 15.0 |
| Zimbabwe | ... | ... | ... | 13.2 | 5.4 | 13.1 | ... | ... | ... | 12.1 | 3.7 | 12.0 |
| **NEAR EAST** | | | | | | | | | | | | |
| Cyprus | 0.3 | 2.9[a/] | 8.0 | 9.5 | 13.5 | 10.7 | 0.2 | 3.2[a/] | 10.2 | 6.7 | 14.5 | 11.4 |
| Egypt | 3.2 | 3.2[a/] | 5.8 | 9.9 | 20.7 | 10.4 | 6.5 | 6.2[a/] | 8.6 | 7.5 | 26.7 | 14.1 |
| Iran | 2.0 | 1.4 | 9.6 | 10.4[i/] | 20.7 | 24.2 | 3.1 | 0.9 | 10.0 | 22.4[i/] | 28.5 | 29.6 |
| Iraq | ... | 3.5[b/] | 11.3 | 8.6[i/] | ... | ... | ... | 3.1[b/] | 18.1 | 11.0[i/] | ... | ... |
| Jordan | ... | 2.8[b/] | 6.0 | 14.2 | 11.1 | 11.1 | ... | 3.1[b/] | 9.2 | 19.4 | 10.9 | 7.5 |
| Lebanon | ... | 1.8[e/] | 4.5 | ... | ... | ... | ... | 2.0[e/] | -3.5 | ... | ... | ... |
| Libya | ... | 6.1[a/] | 16.4 | ... | ... | ... | ... | 8.3[a/] | 15.9 | ... | ... | ... |
| Saudi Arabia | ... | ...[a/] | ... | 1.8 | 3.1[j/] | ... | ... | ...[a/] | ... | 1.8 | 6.1[j/] | ... |
| Sudan | 3.3[d/] | 3.4[a/] | 11.6 | 30.8 | 36.9[j/] | ... | 4.2[d/] | 2.8[a/] | 12.0 | 31.8 | 38.7[j/] | ... |
| Syria | 1.3[d/] | 4.2[k/] | 16.7 | 4.4 | 19.2 | 18.2 | 1.3[d/] | 4.7[k/] | 18.2 | 5.7 | 19.2 | 19.3 |
| Turkey | 3.6 | 7.1[k/] | 6.2 | 56.5 | 116.5 | 35.9 | 4.8 | 8.7[k/] | 7.7 | 51.3 | 106.5 | 40.7 |

a/1965-69.   b/1967-70.   c/1972-75.   d/1962-65.   e/1966-70.   f/1960-62.   g/1973-75.
h/1965-68.   i/January-September.   j/January-May.   k/1968-70.   m/January-June.   n/1963-65.
p/1961-65.

Source:   International Labour Office.   Bulletin of Labour Statistics.   1982-84.

ANNEX TABLE 16. PER CAPUT DIETARY ENERGY SUPPLIES IN RELATION TO NUTRITIONAL REQUIREMENTS
IN SELECTED DEVELOPED AND DEVELOPING COUNTRIES

| COUNTRY | 1967-69 | 1970-72 | 1975-77 | 1978-80 | REQUIREMENTS |
|---|---|---|---|---|---|
| | | % OF REQUIREMENTS | | | KILOCAL/CAPUT /DAY |
| ALGERIA | 77 | 80 | 94 | 100 | 2400 |
| ANGOLA | 83 | 88 | 91 | 90 | 2350 |
| BENIN | 95 | 97 | 92 | 100 | 2300 |
| BOTSWANA | 85 | 87 | 88 | 94 | 2320 |
| BURUNDI | 95 | 91 | 92 | 92 | 2330 |
| CAMEROON | 90 | 95 | 105 | 106 | 2320 |
| CAPE VERDE | 79 | 88 | 95 | 117 | 2350 |
| CENTRAL AFRICAN REPUBLIC | 93 | 98 | 96 | 96 | 2260 |
| CHAD | 97 | 86 | 75 | 76 | 2380 |
| COMOROS | 94 | 96 | 94 | 99 | 2340 |
| CONGO | 94 | 96 | 100 | 99 | 2220 |
| EGYPT | 101 | 101 | 114 | 118 | 2510 |
| ETHIOPIA | 87 | 85 | 77 | 74 | 2330 |
| GABON | 93 | 94 | 113 | 122 | 2340 |
| GAMBIA | 95 | 95 | 91 | 95 | 2380 |
| GHANA | 96 | 98 | 93 | 88 | 2300 |
| GUINEA | 88 | 87 | 87 | 84 | 2310 |
| GUINEA-BISSAU | 88 | 90 | 99 | 102 | 2310 |
| IVORY COAST | 111 | 111 | 107 | 114 | 2310 |
| KENYA | 97 | 98 | 93 | 89 | 2320 |
| LESOTHO | 90 | 89 | 94 | 107 | 2280 |
| LIBERIA | 98 | 99 | 102 | 107 | 2310 |
| LIBYA | 101 | 103 | 135 | 145 | 2360 |
| MADAGASCAR | 105 | 107 | 109 | 107 | 2270 |
| MALAWI | 92 | 101 | 97 | 96 | 2320 |
| MALI | 88 | 83 | 84 | 85 | 2350 |
| MAURITANIA | 89 | 81 | 81 | 89 | 2310 |
| MAURITIUS | 104 | 109 | 115 | 119 | 2270 |
| MOROCCO | 98 | 106 | 109 | 110 | 2420 |
| MOZAMBIQUE | 89 | 88 | 84 | 81 | 2340 |
| NAMIBIA | 100 | 101 | 98 | 98 | 2280 |
| NIGER | 90 | 89 | 86 | 94 | 2350 |
| NIGERIA | 92 | 94 | 95 | 99 | 2360 |
| REUNION | 108 | 108 | 119 | 128 | 2270 |
| RWANDA | 84 | 88 | 92 | 95 | 2320 |
| SAO TOME AND PRINCIPE | 93 | 93 | 83 | 99 | 2350 |
| SENEGAL | 99 | 97 | 97 | 100 | 2380 |
| SIERRA LEONE | 97 | 95 | 91 | 92 | 2300 |
| SOMALIA | 96 | 98 | 96 | 92 | 2310 |
| SOUTH AFRICA | 111 | 114 | 119 | 115 | 2450 |
| SUDAN | 84 | 90 | 95 | 101 | 2350 |
| SWAZILAND | 92 | 95 | 100 | 108 | 2320 |
| TANZANIA | 88 | 87 | 91 | 87 | 2320 |
| TOGO | 96 | 95 | 88 | 92 | 2300 |
| TUNISIA | 93 | 99 | 111 | 115 | 2390 |
| UGANDA | 95 | 97 | 84 | 80 | 2330 |
| UPPER VOLTA | 85 | 81 | 85 | 85 | 2370 |
| ZAIRE | 99 | 101 | 102 | 96 | 2220 |
| ZAMBIA | 93 | 94 | 95 | 86 | 2310 |
| ZIMBABWE | 87 | 91 | 88 | 80 | 2390 |
| | | | | | |
| ANTIGUA AND BARBUDA | 85 | 87 | 86 | 88 | 2420 |
| BAHAMAS | 102 | 102 | 93 | 96 | 2420 |
| BARBADOS | 113 | 122 | 121 | 126 | 2420 |
| BELIZE | 109 | 112 | 113 | 118 | 2260 |
| CANADA | 124 | 125 | 126 | 126 | 2660 |
| COSTA RICA | 104 | 109 | 111 | 118 | 2240 |
| CUBA | 105 | 114 | 116 | 118 | 2310 |
| DOMINICA | 89 | 90 | 89 | 91 | 2420 |
| DOMINICAN REPUBLIC | 85 | 86 | 94 | 94 | 2260 |
| EL SALVADOR | 80 | 81 | 91 | 94 | 2290 |
| GRENADA | 91 | 97 | 85 | 87 | 2420 |
| GUADELOUPE | 94 | 99 | 108 | 113 | 2420 |
| GUATEMALA | 92 | 93 | 93 | 94 | 2190 |
| HAITI | 82 | 83 | 79 | 83 | 2260 |
| HONDURAS | 93 | 92 | 92 | 96 | 2260 |
| JAMAICA | 104 | 115 | 116 | 115 | 2240 |
| MARTINIQUE | 97 | 99 | 111 | 116 | 2420 |
| MEXICO | 116 | 116 | 118 | 120 | 2330 |
| NETHERLANDS ANTILLES | 99 | 102 | 107 | 108 | 2420 |
| NICARAGUA | 113 | 108 | 109 | 102 | 2250 |
| PANAMA | 108 | 104 | 104 | 99 | 2310 |
| ST. LUCIA | 86 | 91 | 92 | 99 | 2420 |
| ST. VINCENT | 91 | 94 | 92 | 91 | 2420 |
| TRINIDAD AND TOBAGO | 96 | 99 | 104 | 112 | 2420 |
| UNITED STATES | 129 | 132 | 135 | 138 | 2640 |
| | | | | | |
| ARGENTINA | 125 | 126 | 127 | 128 | 2650 |
| BOLIVIA | 81 | 83 | 85 | 87 | 2390 |
| BRAZIL | 105 | 104 | 104 | 105 | 2390 |
| CHILE | 111 | 112 | 107 | 112 | 2440 |
| COLOMBIA | 90 | 93 | 101 | 107 | 2320 |
| ECUADOR | 85 | 87 | 91 | 91 | 2290 |
| GUYANA | 102 | 101 | 108 | 109 | 2270 |
| PARAGUAY | 116 | 119 | 120 | 126 | 2310 |
| PERU | 95 | 96 | 94 | 92 | 2350 |
| SURINAME | 106 | 106 | 109 | 109 | 2260 |
| URUGUAY | 107 | 112 | 109 | 107 | 2670 |
| VENEZUELA | 96 | 95 | 103 | 107 | 2470 |

ANNEX TABLE 16. PER CAPUT DIETARY ENERGY SUPPLIES IN RELATION TO NUTRITIONAL REQUIREMENTS
IN SELECTED DEVELOPED AND DEVELOPING COUNTRIES

| COUNTRY | 1967-69 | 1970-72 | 1975-77 | 1978-80 | REQUIREMENTS |
| --- | --- | --- | --- | --- | --- |
| | --------------- % OF REQUIREMENTS --------------- | | | | KILOCAL/CAPUT /DAY |
| AFGHANISTAN | 89 | 80 | 81 | 75 | 2440 |
| BANGLADESH | 89 | 88 | 81 | 85 | 2210 |
| BHUTAN | 40 | 40 | 41 | 41 | 2310 |
| BRUNEI | 102 | 108 | 117 | 119 | 2240 |
| BURMA | 100 | 100 | 102 | 106 | 2160 |
| CHINA | 89 | 91 | 99 | 105 | 2360 |
| CYPRUS | 116 | 126 | 124 | 129 | 2480 |
| HONG KONG | 113 | 119 | 117 | 126 | 2290 |
| INDIA | 86 | 92 | 86 | 90 | 2210 |
| INDONESIA | 89 | 90 | 96 | 106 | 2160 |
| IRAN | 89 | 94 | 122 | 121 | 2410 |
| IRAQ | 91 | 94 | 100 | 110 | 2410 |
| ISRAEL | 115 | 119 | 121 | 118 | 2570 |
| JAPAN | 115 | 119 | 120 | 123 | 2340 |
| JORDAN | 96 | 95 | 90 | 97 | 2460 |
| KAMPUCHEA, DEMOCRATIC | 100 | 100 | 84 | 81 | 2220 |
| KOREA DPR | 102 | 106 | 117 | 127 | 2340 |
| KOREA REP | 104 | 112 | 116 | 124 | 2350 |
| LAOS | 95 | 95 | 87 | 84 | 2220 |
| LEBANON | 101 | 102 | 103 | 101 | 2480 |
| MACAU | 85 | 88 | 89 | 101 | 2290 |
| MALAYSIA | 109 | 112 | 115 | 118 | 2240 |
| MALDIVES | 81 | 79 | 78 | 81 | 2210 |
| MONGOLIA | 98 | 99 | 108 | 112 | 2430 |
| NEPAL | 92 | 91 | 92 | 87 | 2200 |
| PAKISTAN | 90 | 95 | 96 | 100 | 2310 |
| PHILIPPINES | 85 | 87 | 94 | 102 | 2260 |
| SAUDI ARABIA KINGDOM OF | 86 | 84 | 88 | 119 | 2420 |
| SINGAPORE | 111 | 123 | 126 | 135 | 2300 |
| SRI LANKA | 104 | 103 | 95 | 101 | 2220 |
| SYRIA | 99 | 102 | 105 | 115 | 2480 |
| THAILAND | 101 | 101 | 101 | 104 | 2220 |
| TURKEY | 111 | 111 | 116 | 118 | 2520 |
| VIET NAM | 96 | 102 | 97 | 94 | 2160 |
| YEMEN ARAB REPUBLIC | 87 | 83 | 93 | 94 | 2420 |
| YEMEN DEMOCRATIC | 88 | 88 | 80 | 87 | 2410 |
| | | | | | |
| ALBANIA | 104 | 105 | 109 | 118 | 2410 |
| AUSTRIA | 128 | 131 | 131 | 133 | 2630 |
| BELGIUM-LUXEMBOURG | 134 | 141 | 141 | 149 | 2640 |
| BULGARIA | 139 | 141 | 144 | 146 | 2500 |
| CZECHOSLOVAKIA | 139 | 141 | 140 | 141 | 2470 |
| DENMARK | 124 | 127 | 124 | 130 | 2690 |
| FINLAND | 115 | 117 | 115 | 115 | 2710 |
| FRANCE | 134 | 134 | 133 | 134 | 2520 |
| GERMAN DEMOCRATIC REP. | 130 | 133 | 139 | 143 | 2620 |
| GERMANY, FED. REP. OF | 122 | 126 | 126 | 132 | 2670 |
| GREECE | 123 | 129 | 139 | 145 | 2500 |
| HUNGARY | 126 | 128 | 133 | 134 | 2630 |
| ICELAND | 106 | 113 | 112 | 113 | 2660 |
| IRELAND | 137 | 139 | 146 | 150 | 2510 |
| ITALY | 133 | 140 | 137 | 145 | 2520 |
| MALTA | 121 | 123 | 122 | 123 | 2480 |
| NETHERLANDS | 128 | 129 | 129 | 130 | 2690 |
| NORWAY | 115 | 118 | 118 | 123 | 2680 |
| POLAND | 128 | 130 | 136 | 135 | 2620 |
| PORTUGAL | 124 | 128 | 128 | 130 | 2450 |
| ROMANIA | 115 | 116 | 127 | 128 | 2650 |
| SPAIN | 115 | 120 | 134 | 136 | 2460 |
| SWEDEN | 112 | 113 | 117 | 117 | 2690 |
| SWITZERLAND | 126 | 130 | 125 | 131 | 2690 |
| UNITED KINGDOM | 132 | 133 | 129 | 132 | 2520 |
| YUGOSLAVIA | 131 | 131 | 139 | 139 | 2540 |
| | | | | | |
| AUSTRALIA | 122 | 126 | 124 | 120 | 2660 |
| FIJI | 92 | 92 | 98 | 108 | 2660 |
| FRENCH POLYNESIA | 106 | 106 | 99 | 100 | 2660 |
| NEW CALEDONIA | 110 | 112 | 106 | 98 | 2660 |
| NEW ZEALAND | 134 | 135 | 132 | 133 | 2640 |
| PAPUA NEW GUINEA | 80 | 83 | 83 | 86 | 2660 |
| SAMOA | 79 | 81 | 85 | 86 | 2660 |
| SOLOMON ISLANDS | 81 | 78 | 77 | 80 | 2660 |
| TONGA | 93 | 99 | 116 | 121 | 2660 |
| VANUATU | 90 | 92 | 89 | 93 | 2660 |
| | | | | | |
| USSR | 130 | 131 | 133 | 132 | 2560 |

ANNEX TABLE 17.  ANNUAL SHARES OF AGRICULTURAL "BROAD" DEFINITION IN TOTAL
OFFICIAL COMMITMENTS MADE TO ALL SECTORS BY MULTILATERAL
AND BILATERAL SOURCES, 1974-81

|  | 1974 | 1975 | 1976 | 1977 | 1978 | 1979 | 1980 | 1981[a] |
|---|---|---|---|---|---|---|---|---|
| | ..................... % ..................... | | | | | | | |
| **CONCESSIONAL & NON-CONCESSIONAL COMMITMENTS** | | | | | | | | |
| Multilateral agencies b/ | 32 | 38 | 32 | 36 | 39 | 36 | 38 | 36 |
| World Bank c/ | 33 | 40 | 31 | 39 | 41 | 37 | 33 | 33 |
| Regional Development Banks c/ | 28 | 37 | 36 | 35 | 31 | 33 | 45 | 44 |
| OPEC Multilateral c/ | 41 | 8 | 25 | 13 | 30 | 7 | 16 | 15 |
| Bilateral sources | 9 | 7 | 7 | 10 | 9 | ... | ... | ... |
| DAC/EEC | 10 | 8 | 8 | 11 | 11 | 12 | 11 | 11 |
| OPEC Bilateral | 3 | 6 | 5 | 6 | 3 | ... | ... | ... |
| All sources (multilateral + bilateral) | 15 | 14 | 14 | 17 | 17 | ... | ... | ... |
| **CONCESSIONAL COMMITMENTS ONLY (ODA)** | | | | | | | | |
| Multilateral agencies b/ | 45 | 43 | 46 | 44 | 49 | 49 | 49 | 53 |
| World Bank c/ | 46 | 43 | 44 | 54 | 52 | 52 | 45 | 58 |
| Regional Development Banks c/ | 48 | 46 | 54 | 50 | 48 | 53 | 62 | 64 |
| OPEC Multilateral c/ | 33 | 21 | 29 | 11 | 29 | 7 | 15 | 14 |
| Bilateral sources | 12 | 10 | 9 | 14 | 13 | 16 | 13 | 14 |
| DAC/EEC | 14 | 13 | 11 | 16 | 17 | 18 | 16 | 17 |
| OPEC Bilateral | 4 | 5 | 5 | 7 | 3 | 7 | 1 | 4 |
| All sources (multilateral + bilateral) | 16 | 14 | 15 | 18 | 19 | 21 | 19 | 21 |

a/  Preliminary.

b/  Including also UNDP, CGIAR, FAO/TF, FAO/TCP (from 1977) and IFAD (from 1978).

c/  Excluding commitments to CGIAR.

Source:  FAO and OECD.

ANNEX TABLE 18.   PERCENTAGE DISTRIBUTION OF OFFICIAL COMMITMENTS
TO AGRICULTURE "BROAD" DEFINITION BY MULTILATERAL
AND BILATERAL SOURCES, 1974-1981

| | 1974 | 1975 | 1976 | 1977 | 1978 | 1979 | 1980 | 1981[a] |
|---|---|---|---|---|---|---|---|---|
| | ................... % ......................... | | | | | | | |
| **CONCESSIONAL & NON-CONCESSIONAL COMMITMENTS** | | | | | | | | |
| Multilateral agencies | 52 | 58 | 57 | 57 | 58 | 52 | 59 | 58 |
| World Bank b/ | 37 | 41 | 37 | 38 | 43 | 34 | 35 | 34 |
| Regional Development Banks b/ | 11 | 13 | 14 | 14 | 10 | 12 | 15 | 17 |
| OPEC Multilateral b/ | 1 | - | 2 | 2 | 2 | - | 1 | 1 |
| Others c/ | 3 | 4 | 4 | 3 | 3 | 6 | 8 | 6 |
| Bilateral sources | 48 | 42 | 43 | 43 | 42 | 48 | 41 | 42 |
| DAC/EEC | 44 | 31 | 36 | 38 | 40 | 44 | 40 | 40 |
| OPEC Bilateral | 4 | 11 | 7 | 5 | 2 | 4 | 1 | 2 |
| All sources (multilateral + bilateral) | 100 | 100 | 100 | 100 | 100 | 100 | 100 | 100 |
| **CONCESSIONAL COMMITMENTS ONLY (ODA)** | | | | | | | | |
| Multilateral agencies | 37 | 38 | 47 | 36 | 41 | 37 | 45 | 43 |
| World Bank b/ | 22 | 21 | 23 | 19 | 26 | 18 | 21 | 21 |
| Regional Development Banks b/ | 10 | 10 | 15 | 11 | 8 | 11 | 12 | 12 |
| OPEC Multilateral b/ | 1 | 1 | 3 | 2 | 2 | - | 1 | 1 |
| Others c/ | 4 | 6 | 6 | 4 | 5 | 8 | 11 | 9 |
| Bilateral sources | 63 | 62 | 53 | 64 | 59 | 63 | 55 | 57 |
| DAC/EEC | 59 | 50 | 47 | 56 | 56 | 59 | 53 | 54 |
| OPEC Bilateral | 4 | 12 | 6 | 8 | 3 | 4 | 2 | 3 |
| All sources (multilateral + bilateral) | 100 | 100 | 100 | 100 | 100 | 100 | 100 | 100 |

a/  Preliminary.

b/  Excluding commitments to CGIAR.

c/  Including UNDP, CGIAR, FAO/TF, FAO/TCP (from 1977) and IFAD (from 1978).

ANNEX TABLE 19.   PERCENTAGE DISTRIBUTION OF OFFICIAL COMMITMENTS
TO AGRICULTURE (EXCLUDING TECHNICAL ASSISTANCE
GRANTS) BY PURPOSE, 1974-1981

| | 1974 | 1975 | 1976 | 1977 | 1978 | 1979 | 1980 | 1981[a] |
|---|---|---|---|---|---|---|---|---|
| | ..................... % ..................... | | | | | | | |
| Land and water development [b] | 21 | 21 | 19 | 25 | 26 | 18 | 25 | 17 |
| Agricultural services | 6 | 7 | 7 | 12 | 12 | 10 | 13 | 7 |
| Supply of inputs | 12 | 7 | 7 | 4 | 5 | 3 | 6 | 5 |
| Crop production | 5 | 4 | 10 | 5 | 8 | 7 | 7 | 6 |
| Livestock | 5 | 3 | 5 | 3 | 4 | 3 | 2 | 2 |
| Fisheries [c] | 3 | 2 | 2 | 3 | 3 | 3 | 3 | 3 |
| Research, extension, training | - | 3 | 3 | 4 | 4 | 3 | 5 | 5 |
| Agriculture, unallocated | 10 | 11 | 13 | 11 | 12 | 17 | 9 | 14 |
| TOTAL NARROW DEFINITION | 62 | 58 | 66 | 67 | 74 | 64 | 70 | 59 |
| Rural development/infrastructure | 13 | 16 | 16 | 16 | 15 | 16 | 19 | 22 |
| Manufacturing of inputs [d] | 16 | 23 | 7 | 5 | 4 | 11 | 2 | 10 |
| Agro-industries | 3 | 2 | 10 | 9 | 5 | 6 | 7 | 5 |
| Forestry | 5 | 1 | 1 | 2 | 2 | 3 | 2 | 2 |
| Regional development | 1 | - | - | 1 | - | - | - | 2 |
| TOTAL BROAD DEFINITION | 100 | 100 | 100 | 100 | 100 | 100 | 100 | 100 |

[a]/  Preliminary.

[b]/  Including river development.

[c]/  Including inputs such as fishing trawlers, fishing gear.

[d]/  Mostly fertilizers.

ANNEX TABLE 20.   DAC COUNTRIES:   BILATERAL ODA COMMITMENTS FROM INDIVIDUAL
COUNTRIES AND PROPORTION TO AGRICULTURE (BROAD DEFINITION)

| | Bilateral ODA to all sectors | | | | | Proportion of ODA to agriculture | | | | |
|---|---|---|---|---|---|---|---|---|---|---|
| | 1977 | 1978 | 1979 | 1980 | 1981 | 1977 | 1978 | 1979 | 1980 | 1981 |
| | ............ million $ ............ | | | | | ............ % ............ | | | | |
| Australia | 460 | 453 | 453 | 522 | 590 | 19 | 17 | 14 | 8 | 14 |
| Austria | 88 | 115 | 70 | 140 | 265 | 13 | 44 | 20 | 47 | 10 |
| Belgium | 358 | 444 | 462 | 512 | 432 | 3 | 4 | 4 | 4 | 4 |
| Canada | 902 | 1 136 | 676 | 512 | 1 011 | 15 | 23 | 21 | 31 | 39 |
| Denmark | 155 | 395 | 288 | 260 | 225 | 30 | 19 | 32 | 37 | 44 |
| Finland | 23 | 35 | 85 | 112 | 111 | 4 | 29 | 8 | 15 | 19 |
| France | 2 453 | 2 977 | 3 746 | 4 766 | 4 430 | 8 | 6 | 7 | 6 | 8 |
| Germany | 1 718 | 2 446 | 3 972 | 4 617 | 3 467 | 19 | 21 | 21 | 16 | 13 |
| Italy | 78 | 63 | 63 | 138 | 443 | 6 | 9 | 15 | 24 | 6 |
| Japan | 1 900 | 2 272 | 2 528 | 3 369 | 3 437 | 18 | 23 | 25 | 16 | 24 |
| Netherlands | 910 | 1 272 | 1 327 | 1 592 | 1 066 | 29 | 29 | 35 | 24 | 27 |
| New Zealand | 35 | 47 | 53 | 54 | 52 | 41 | 20 | 18 | 24 | 33 |
| Norway | 168 | 226 | 234 | 247 | 255 | 25 | 33 | 25 | 28 | 27 |
| Sweden | 685 | 521 | 782 | 611 | 615 | 35 | 11 | 31 | 34 | 33 |
| Switzerland | 154 | 110 | 174 | 139 | 253 | 15 | 30 | 13 | 33 | 46 |
| UK | 694 | 1 530 | 1 964 | 1 459 | 1 000 | 15 | 8 | 11 | 7 | 8 |
| USA | 4 291 | 4 757 | 5 186 | 5 378 | 5 135 | 10 | 14 | 15 | 20 | 16 |
| Total DAC countries | 15 071 | 18 797 | 22 062 | 24 426 | 22 787 | 15 | 16 | 18 | 16 | 17 |

Source:   OECD

ANNEX TABLE 21.  REGIONAL DISTRIBUTION OF OFFICIAL COMMITMENTS (EXCLUDING TECHNICAL ASSISTANCE GRANTS) TO AGRICULTURE "BROAD" DEFINITION FROM ALL SOURCES, 1974-1981

| | 1974 | 1975 | 1976 | 1977 | 1978 | 1979 | 1980 | 1981[a] |
|---|---|---|---|---|---|---|---|---|
| | ..................... % ..................... | | | | | | | |
| **CONCESSIONAL & NON-CONCESSIONAL COMMITMENTS** | | | | | | | | |
| Far East and Pacific | 42 | 50 | 36 | 39 | 49 | 46 | 46 | 42 |
| Africa | 22 | 18 | 23 | 29 | 22 | 24 | 22 | 28 |
| Latin America | 21 | 22 | 28 | 24 | 21 | 22 | 24 | 23 |
| Near East | 15 | 10 | 13 | 7 | 8 | 8 | 8 | 7 |
| Total 4 developing regions | 100 | 100 | 100 | 100 | 100 | 100 | 100 | 100 |
| **CONCESSIONAL COMMITMENTS** | | | | | | | | |
| Far East and Pacific | 50 | 53 | 36 | 43 | 53 | 55 | 50 | 49 |
| Africa | 23 | 19 | 28 | 33 | 26 | 23 | 26 | 31 |
| Latin America | 16 | 14 | 23 | 14 | 14 | 13 | 14 | 12 |
| Near East | 11 | 14 | 13 | 10 | 7 | 9 | 10 | 8 |
| Total 4 developing regions | 100 | 100 | 100 | 100 | 100 | 100 | 100 | 100 |

a/  Preliminary.

Note:  Data on bilateral (DAC and OPEC) commitments are incomplete.

Foto-Tipo-lito  SAGRAF - Napoli